HELEN RAPSON received an Honours Degree in Botany from the University of London. She went on to work in the Scientific Civil Service and then to lecture at a college of Further Education. She is now Head of Science at Greenshaw High School, a large outer London comprehensive. She has been an Examiner in Biology for the Cambridge Examinations Syndicate for some years.

D0773799

GCE A-Level Passbooks

BIOLOGY, H. Rapson, B.Sc.

CHEMISTRY, J. E. Chandler, B.Sc and
R. J. Wilkinson, Ph.D.

PHYSICS, J. Garrood, Ph.D.

PURE MATHEMATICS, R. Parsons, B.Sc and
T. Dawson, B.Sc.

PURE AND APPLIED MATHEMATICS,
R. A. Parsons, B.Sc. and A. G. Dawson, B.Sc.

APPLIED MATHEMATICS, E. M. Peet, B.A.

ECONOMICS, Roger Maile, B.A.

GEOGRAPHY, R. Bryant, B.A., Ph.D.,
R. Knowles, M.A. and J. Wareing, B.A., M.Sc.

GCE A-Level Passbook
Biology

H. Rapson, B.Sc.

Published by Intercontinental Book Productions
in conjunction with Seymour Press Ltd.
Distributed by Seymour Press Ltd.,
334 Brixton Road, London, SW9 7AG

ibp Published 1979 by Intercontinental Book Productions,
Berkshire House, Queen Street, Maidenhead, Berks., SL6 1NF
in conjunction with Seymour Press Ltd.

1st edition, 3rd impression 1.81.3
Copyright © 1979 Intercontinental Book Productions
Made and printed by Hunt Barnard Printing Ltd.,
Aylesbury, Bucks.
ISBN 0 85047 924 X

Contents

Introduction

Although there are differences in content in the G.C.E. 'A' level syllabuses of the major Examination Boards, a large proportion of the body of knowledge expected is common to them all. The aim of this book is to supply in concise form the basic information required. This common core of knowledge includes the detailed structure of a cell, the basic physiological processes of living organisms such as nutrition, respiration, transport systems, excretion and osmoregulation, co-ordination by the nervous system and hormones, and reproduction. An understanding of genetics and an appreciation of the process of evolution is also expected.

Modern scientific work, particularly in the fields of biochemistry, electron microscopy and molecular biology has led to many new discoveries and at the same time revealed the essential unity of all living organisms, it has resulted in a move away from the traditional detailed study of a small number of organisms at 'A' level in favour of a consideration of the basic similarities of cell structure and vital processes. However, while research is showing us further similarities and common biochemical pathways, it is essential to retain the concept of a complete organism and not shatter it into a set of isolated functions. Partly for this reason *Amoeba* and *Hydra* have been considered in some detail in Chapter 2.

In the first chapter a few pages are devoted to classification in order that the animals and plants studied during the course may be placed in their correct systematic position. The ability to assign an animal or plant to its group speedily is a useful one and lays the foundation for the correct identification of organisms found in the field. Many an interesting and potentially useful piece of field work or investigation in the laboratory has been spoiled by later doubt about the true identity of the organisms concerned.

Clearly, a knowledge of chemistry and physics is very useful, not only in the 'A' level course but for an increase in understanding and appreciation of the exciting scientific work being carried out today where so much is being discovered on the borders of the different disciplines where biologists, chemists, physicists and others meet. A chapter on basic biochemistry is included together with a few background topics which it is hoped will prove useful.

The last chapter is devoted to the environment. We live in a technological age and are in danger of losing sight of the fact that man is an animal species, part of the unity of living things and subject to the same natural laws; his survival in the long term depends on maintaining the stability of his environment. Man the most intelligent of all animals has a special responsibility. Increasingly it is expected that a biologist should have an informed opinion about environmental problems, this is not possible without basic facts, some of which are set out in this chapter.

The author would like to thank the Headmaster and colleagues in the Science Department of Greenshaw High School for their interest and for useful discussions.

Chapter 1
Classification

The system of classification

If we are to learn something about the vast number of different kinds of living organisms, it is necessary to sort them into groups so that within each group the animals or plants exhibit features in common. In this way by studying some members of a group we know something about the group as a whole, and are able to recognize other living organisms which belong to it. During the long process of evolution groups of organisms have diverged. A natural **classification** takes account of the relationships between groups and seeks out features which reflect them and discards superficial resemblances. Classifications based on size or colour, for example, would be of little value. At the present time classifications are based on structural features to a large extent, but physiological and biochemical data are becoming more important. The **taxonomic** position of an organism is often a matter of opinion and of disagreement among authorities. New information is likely to lead to changes, no system is perfect and no classification can be regarded as a final one. This should be borne in mind when studying the selective scheme in this book.

The system of naming organisms in use today, we owe to **Carl Linnaeus** (1707 to 1778), it is called the **binomial system**. Each organism bears two names, the **specific** name and the **generic** name. Closely related forms will share the same generic name, but the two names together constitute the organism's scientific name and will define one particular kind of species. Thus the generic name *Ranunculus* is given to the buttercups, *Ranunculus repens* is the creeping buttercup while *Ranunculus acris* is the meadow buttercup. Only the generic name takes a capital letter, and in the full form the name should be followed by the initial letter or abbreviation of the name of the person who first classified the organism. Thus, *Ranunculus repens* L., indicates that the classifier was Linnaeus. Closely related genera are collected into **families**. A number of families make up an **order**, and orders may be grouped into **classes** which are themselves part of a **phylum** (the term **division** rather than phylum is often used for plants). At the top the phyla of animals constitute the **Animalia** or **animal kingdom** and the divisions of plants the **Plantae** or **plant kingdom**.

A more detailed classification of the creeping buttercup would be

Kingdom: *Plantae*.
Division: *Spermatophyta* (seed plant).
Class: *Angiospermae* (seeds enclosed in a fruit).
Sub-class: *Dicotyledones* (seed with two seed leaves).
Order: *Ranales*.
Family: *Ranunculaceae*.
Genera: *Ranunculus*.
Species: *repens*.

From the point of view of establishing a well defined scheme of classification, organisms would need to be so arranged that each group of the same rank (i.e. class or order etc.) would differ from the others of the same rank by an approximately equal amount and differ from groups belonging to a higher or lower rank by a larger amount. However, a little reflection will show that there will be many instances where organisms will not fall naturally into such clear cut groups.

Characteristics of life

The following characteristics distinguish living organisms from non-living material:

Movement Whole or part of the organism is capable of movement. This is more obvious in animals but slower movements can be detected in plants and the movement of granules in the cytoplasm of cells can be observed under the microscope.

Nutrition All living organisms take in food substances to supply materials for growth and as a source of energy.

Respiration Energy is released during the breakdown of substrates (e.g. glucose) in the cell by the process of respiration.

Excretion Metabolic processes in the cell produce waste products which are excreted.

Growth The organism increases in size as new materials are synthesised and incorporated into the body structure.

Reproduction Living organisms have the ability to produce new individuals like themselves.

Irritability All living organisms respond to stimuli. The action may be slow as in the case of a plant bending towards the light, or rapid as in the adjustment of the size of the pupil of the eye in response to changes in light intensity.

Viruses

Viruses are composed largely of genetic material without any of the other structures normally associated with cells. They show a fundamental characteristic of living organisms in that they are capable of reproduction, but only within a living host cell, there they produce further virus particles with similar characteristics to their own, destroying the host cell in the process. Away from host cells some viruses can be crystallised – not a feature normally associated with living organisms.

Differences between plants and animals

Differences between larger animals and green plants are obvious to all, the animal is capable of locomotion and goes in search of some form of organic food which it takes inside the body to begin the digestive process. The plant remains in one place making its own food from the carbon dioxide and water around it, by the process of photosynthesis. The animal form of nutrition is holozoic, that of the green plant holophytic. Some aquatic animals, however, have no need to move to search for food, the food drifts to them in the water, some of the filter and particle feeders are in this category. On the other hand, many microscopic green algae are capable of locomotion, thus having the power to remain in the surface water where the light is strong enough for them to carry out photosynthesis.

Fungi are probably plants which have lost the ability to photosynthesize, they use a source of organic food, secreting enzymes on to it to digest it and absorbing the products. If the organic food is dead material the nutrition is saprophytic, if living material is utilized the nutrition is parasitic.

On the cellular level, the green plant has a cell wall made of cellulose, a large central vacuole full of cell sap and starch is the common storage product. In the fungi chitin is a common cell wall component while oil or glycogen is stored. Animal cells have no rigid cell walls or large central vacuole and glycogen is the usual storage product.

Animal classification

The animal kingdom is divided into about twenty phyla, the exact number depending on the views of the classifier. Here the more important phyla are shown. In the main they are well recognized and agreed upon. Within the phyla some orders and classes have been omitted for simplicity, but sufficient have been retained to give an overall picture of the animal kingdom and to include among them those organisms likely to be encountered during the 'A' level course.

Phylum Protozoa
Unicellular organisms.
Class Rhizopoda Movement by pseudopodia, e.g. *Amoeba*.
Class Mastigophora (Flagellata) Movement by flagella, e.g. *Trypanosoma. Euglena* (alternatively may be placed in algae).
Class Ciliata Movement by cilia, e.g. *Paramecium*.
Class Sporozoa Parasitic forms, e.g. *Plasmodium*.

Phylum Coelenterata
Sac-like, one opening (mouth), two layers of cells, tentacles with nematoblasts, e.g. *Hydra*, jellyfish, sea anemones, corals.

Phylum Platyhelminthes
Flatworms.
Class Turbellaria Free swimming, e.g. planarians.
Class Trematoda Parasites with suckers and forked gut, e.g. flukes.
Class Cestoda Ribbon-like parasites attached by scolex, no gut, e.g. tapeworms.

Phylum Nematoda
Roundworms, e.g. *Ascaris*, hookworms.

Phylum Annelida
Segmented worms.
Class Polychaeta Many bristles, e.g. *Nereis* (ragworm), fan worms, *Arenicola* (lugworm).
Class Oligochaeta Few bristles, e.g. earthworms.
Class Hirudinea No bristles, semi-parasites with suckers, e.g. leeches.

Phylum Mollusca
Soft bodied animals with a shell.
Class Gastropoda Usually coiled shells, well developed head, e.g. whelks, snails, slugs.
Class Lamellibranchia (bivalves). Two shells, e.g. mussels,

oysters, clams.
Class Cephalopoda Highly organised marine forms, reduced shell, e.g. squids, octopus.

Phylum Arthropoda
Jointed limbs, hard exoskeleton.
Class Crustacea Mainly aquatic, breathing by gills, often with heavier exoskeleton, diverse paired appendages.
Order *Phyllopoda*. Primitive, many similar appendages, e.g. *Chirocephalus* (fairy shrimp).
Order *Isopoda*. Dorsiventral flattening, e.g. woodlice.
Order *Amphipoda*. Side to side flattening, e.g. *Gammarus* (fresh water shrimp).
Order *Decapoda* e.g. Crabs, lobsters, crayfish.
Class Arachnida Two body sections, four pairs of legs, e.g. spiders, scorpions, mites, marine king crabs.
Class Myriapoda Terrestrial, many segments, paired appendages.
Order *Chilopoda*. Carnivores, one pair of appendages per segment. Centipedes.
Order *Diplopoda*. Herbivores, two pairs of appendages per segment. Millipedes.
Class Insecta Three body sections, three pairs of legs, two pairs of wings, no abdominal appendages.
Order *Lepidoptera*. Butterflies, moths.
Order *Coleoptera*. Beetles.
Order *Hymenoptera*. Bees, wasps, ants.
Order *Diptera*. Flies.
Order *Orthoptera*. Cockroaches, grasshoppers, locusts, stick insects.
Order *Anisoptera*. Dragonflies.

Phylum Echinodermata
Marine, spiny skinned, radially symmetrical, e.g. starfish, sea urchins, sea cucumbers.

Phylum Chordata
Possess a skeletal rod, the notochord, and pharyngeal gill slits at some stage in the development.
Sub-phylum Protochordata e.g. Sea squirts, acorn worms, *Amphioxus* (This group and all the foregoing comprise the **Invertebrata**).
Sub-phylum Vertebrata (Craniata) The notochord is replaced by the vertebral column; brain and protective skull present.
Class Pisces (fishes). Aquatic, fins, gills, scales.

Sub-class Chondrichthyes Cartilaginous fish, e.g. sharks, dogfish.

Sub-class Teleostomi Bony fish, well developed skeleton and scales, e.g. herring, salmon, stickleback, cod.

Class Amphibia Fitted for life in water or on land, typically undergoing metamorphosis, soft skins, e.g. frogs, toads, newts.

Class Reptilia Skin covered by scales, reproduction on land, shelled eggs laid, e.g. snakes, lizards, crocodiles, tortoises.

Class Aves (birds). Warm blooded, wings, feathers, lay shelled eggs, show parental care, e.g. sparrow, eagle, penguin.

Class Mammalia Warm blooded, hair, most have live young, fed with milk from mammary glands, parental care shown.

Sub-class Prototheria Primitive types, lay eggs, e.g. spiny anteater, duck-billed platypus.

Sub-class Metatheria Young born incompletely formed, development completed in pouch on body of mother. Marsupials, e.g. kangaroos, koala bears, opossums.

Sub-class Eutheria Placental mammals born at a more advanced stage of development.

Order *Insectivora*. Hedgehogs, shrews.

Order *Chiroptera*. Bats.

Order *Rodentia*. Rats, mice.

Order *Lagomorpha*. Rabbits.

Order *Cetacea*. Whales, dolphins.

Order *Carnivora*. Cats, dogs, lions.

Order *Perissodactyla*. Horses.

Order *Artiodactyla*. Sheep, goats, cows.

Order *Primates*. Man, monkeys.

Plant classification

The classification of plants is much less clearly defined than that of animals; certain groups being regarded, for example, as classes by some authorities and orders by others, while the position of bacteria is controversial. For a long time the classification of the plant kingdom into four divisions has been accepted. These divisions comprise **Thallophyta** (algae, fungi, lichens), **Bryophyta** (liverworts, mosses), **Pteridophyta** (clubmosses, horsetails, ferns), and **Spermatophyta** (gymnosperms, angiosperms). More modern work including physiology, biochemistry and electron microscopy shows that the Thallophyta are not a homogeneous group. Later systems of classification now treat fungi, bacteria and the old classes of algae as separate divisions. This system is followed here. Many groups are omitted where they are unlikely to be met in the

Division Cyanophyta (Myxophyta) Blue-green algae, e.g. *Nostoc*.

Division Chlorophyta Green algae, e.g. *Chlamydomonas, Spirogyra*.

Division Phaeophyta Brown algae. Seaweeds.

Division Rhodophyta Red algae.

Division Bacillariophyta Diatoms.

Division Euglenophyta Unicellular flagellates. (Alternatively may be placed in *Protozoa* in animal kingdom).

Division Eumycophyta
True fungi, no chlorophyll, parasites or saprophytes.
Class Phycomycetes Moulds, e.g. *Mucor, Phytophthora*.
Class Ascomycetes e.g. Yeast, *Penicillium, Peziza*.
Class Basidiomycetes. Mushrooms and toadstools.
Sub-division Lichenes (lichens). An alga-fungus complex.

Division Schizomycophyta Bacteria.

Division Bryophyta
Class Hepaticae (liverworts). Most are thalloid plants of damp situations.
Class Musci (mosses). Stem and simple leaves.

Division Pteridophyta
Vascular plants with roots, stem and leaves. Many fossil members.
Order Lycopodiales (clubmosses). Small leaves, sporangia in cones, homosporous and heterosporous species.
Order Equisetales (horsetails). Leaves in whorls, sporangia borne on sporangiophores in cones, homosporous.
Order Filicales (ferns). Large leaves (fronds), sporangia in groups (sori), homosporous.

Division Spermatophyta
Seed plants forming the dominant vegetation in the world.
Class Gymnospermae Seeds borne naked, no vessels in the xylem, e.g. yew, pine, fir.
Class Angiospermae Flowering plants, seeds enclosed in a fruit, xylem vessels present.
Sub-class Monocotyledones One cotyledon in the seed, parallel veined leaves, flower parts in threes or multiples of three.
Sub-class Dicotyledones Two cotyledons in the seed, net veined

leaves, flower parts in fours or fives or multiples of these. Secondary thickening is common.

British Angiospermae

Monocotyledones
Nine orders, twenty six families, e.g.
Order *Liliflorae*. Lilies, rushes, irises etc.
Order *Orchidales*. Orchids.
Order *Glumiflorae*. Grasses.

Dicotyledones
A. **Archichlamydeae** Petals free. Twenty eight orders, seventy six families, e.g.
Order *Ranales*. Buttercups etc.
Order *Rhoeadales*. Poppies, cabbages, etc.
Order *Centrospermae*. Pinks etc.
Order *Leguminosae*. Peas, clovers etc.
Order *Rosales*. Roses, saxifrages etc.
Order *Umbellales*. Cow parsleys etc.
B. **Metachlamydeae** Petals joined. Nine orders, thirty one families, e.g.
Order *Ericales*. Heathers etc.
Order *Tubiflorae*. Snapdragon, foxglove, mints etc.
Order *Asterales*. Thistles, dandelions etc.

Key terms

Binomial system The naming of organisms scientifically with a two part name in Latin.
Classification System of arranging groups of related organisms in a carefully graded order.
Species A group of individuals bearing a close resemblance and capable of breeding among themselves but usually incapable of breeding with organisms of other groups. The name of familiar animals and plants often denotes a species e.g. man, cat, daisy.
Taxonomy Science of the classification of living organisms.

Chapter 2
The Animal Kingdom

Phylum Protozoa

Microscopic unicellular animals make up the first of the animal phyla. The group is a large one and members of it are found in fresh and salt water, in soil and associated with other animals either living on the surface or within them.

Class Rhizopoda

Amoeba is found in freshwater ponds and puddles, in soil and several species occur in man. An *Amoeba* is a minute mass of protoplasm, the largest being just visible to the unaided eye as a greyish speck. The surface of the protoplasm forms a plasma membrane (an extremely thin 'sandwich' of lipid between two protein layers), which prevents the materials making up the body of the *Amoeba* from dispersing. The protoplasm is made up of cytoplasm and a nucleus which has no fixed position. There is a clear outer layer of cytoplasm, the **ectoplasm**, and a granular inner mass, the **endoplasm.** Food particles in stages of digestion can be seen in food vacuoles and there is a large spherical contractile vacuole. *Amoeba* is not free swimming but moves along a surface in a slow

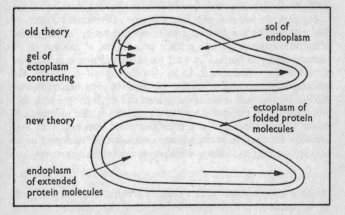

Figure 1. Locomotion in Amoeba

creeping movement by forming temporary finger-like extensions or pseudopodia. One theory is that forward movement is due to extended protein molecules of semi-solid gel forming ectoplasm, contracting at the rear and changing to folded protein molecules of endoplasm. A new theory is that movement is by a *pulling* force in front as extended protein molecules of *endoplasm* contract to folded molecules in ectoplasm. In feeding, *Amoeba* pushes out a cup-shaped pseudopodium trapping particles consisting of ciliates, diatoms and small fragments of organic matter; these are engulfed into the body with a drop of water forming a food vacuole. Enzymes are secreted into the vacuole and digestion takes place; at first there is an acid reaction in the food vacuole and later an alkaline one. The products of digestion are absorbed and assimilated, the indigestible remains being left behind as *Amoeba* moves on. Oxygen is needed for respiration and this is obtained from the water by diffusion, the continuous consumption of oxygen by the organism maintaining the diffusion gradient from the exterior to the interior. Carbon dioxide diffuses out, it is being produced continuously within the body so that the diffusion gradient is from the interior to the exterior. Nitrogenous waste diffuses out in the same way. Crystals found in older *Amoebae* are believed to be excretory products. The contractile vacuole is an osmoregulatory organ, it expels the excess water that the organism unavoidably takes in by osmosis. *Amoeba* can show irritability, it moves towards suitable prey but away from bright light and injurious chemicals or the touch of a fine needle. Reproduction is by binary fission, the nucleus divides first and this is followed by the division of the cytoplasm, the two new cells feed and grow. Division is initiated, at least in part by the surface area to volume ratio, the larger the *Amoeba* becomes the less surface area it has in relation to its volume and this surface is vital for oxygen absorption and the removal of waste products. Older *Amoebae* may form spores, the nucleus splits up into a number of portions each becoming surrounded by a small mass of cytoplasm and developing a wall, forming a cyst. In the cyst stage the protoplasm is able to withstand lower temperatures and a greater degree of desiccation so that *Amoeba* can survive severe wintery conditions or the drying up of its surroundings and emerge when favourable conditions return.

Amoeba is often regarded as a simple animal, to consider it as such is to overlook the important fact that this minute mass of protoplasm is capable of carrying out all the essential functions of higher animals.

Class Mastigophora

This is the class of flagellates. *Euglena* is an organism found in water rich in organic matter, for example, farmyard puddles. It is spindle shaped 30 to 300 μm long with a large nucleus near the posterior end, chloroplasts, and a single flagellum arising from a flask-shaped gullet. Near the gullet is a red eye spot and a contractile vacuole which discharges into the gullet. The outside of the body is covered by an elastic pellicle, fine contractile fibrils (myonemes) are spirally arranged under the pellicle. Lashing of the flagellum causes the organism to move forward proceeding in one general direction along a spiral path and rotating about the long axis, with waves of contraction passing along the body at the same time. The green species are photosynthetic but some colourless species are able to feed saprophytically by absorbing organic material from the surroundings; other colourless species take in food particles and digest them in the same manner as *Amoeba* – an essentially animal method of nutrition. *Euglena gracilis* is green when it is exposed to light and it carries out photosynthesis, but when kept in the dark it loses the green colour and survives by absorbing organic matter from the water. As the distinction between holophytic and holozoic nutrition is a fundamental difference between plants and animals, *Euglena* and its relatives appear in both plant and animal classifications. Their methods of nutrition lead some authorities to regard their ancestors as organisms which gave rise to the plant and animal kingdoms. *Euglena* reproduces by binary fission, and cysts may be formed under adverse conditions.

Class Ciliata

Paramecium is mainly a fresh water organism, favouring water where there is decaying matter. The pointed end is the posterior end and the blunt end the anterior. The species vary in size, *P. caudatum* averages about 240 μm in length. There is an oblique oral groove which narrows internally into the gullet, which itself extends into the plasmasol. An outer pellicle covers the body which is provided with paired cilia attached to granules in the plasmagel and emerging through fine pores in the pellicle. Also in the plasmagel are trichocysts capable of discharging fine threads to anchor the animal while feeding. The granules and trichocysts are joined by co-ordinating fibres and there are longitudinal myonemes. In the centre of the animal lies a large nucleus, the meganucleus, and a small nucleus, the micronucleus. There are two contractile vacuoles in fixed positions, each surrounded by radiating channels. Food vacuoles move round in the plasmasol and indigestible remains are expelled through a fixed anal pore. Cilia in the oral

19

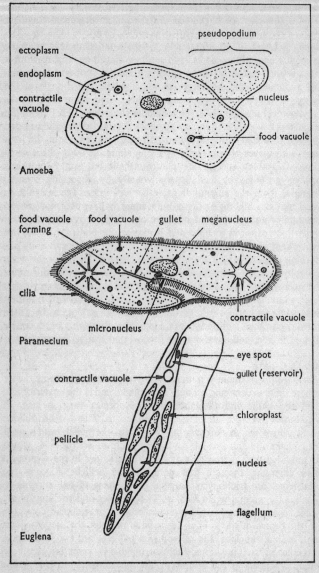

Figure 2. *Some common Protozoa*

groove draw water towards the gullet, and bacteria, which constitute the main food, reach the base of the gullet where the plasmasol closes above them trapping them in a drop of water, forming a food vacuole which circulates along a definite route. Diagonal beating of the cilia causes a spiral motion and locomotion in a forward direction. *Paramecium* reacts to obstacles or an unfavourable environment by going into reverse and setting off in a new direction; the movement of the cilia in the oral groove means that the animal is able to sample the water ahead. Binary fission is the method of reproduction, division takes place transversely; the micronucleus divides by mitosis, the meganucleus amitotically (i.e. the chromosomes are shared out in a random manner), then before the cytoplasm divides each half forms the necessary parts for a new individual. Under good conditions *Paramecium* may divide several times a day, soon building up a large colony; for this reason it has been used a good deal in population studies. Sexual reproduction is by conjugation, the ventral surfaces of two *Paramecia* come together; in each the meganucleus disintegrates and the micronucleus divides twice. Three out of four of the new nuclei disintegrate and the remaining one divides, so that each cell has two nuclei. One of each pair of nuclei behaves as a gamete and passes across to the partner cell where it fuses with the stationary one of the pair, the two cells separating at this stage. The fusion nucleus divided three times producing eight nuclei and the animal itself divides into two, so that each new cell has four nuclei. A second division of the whole body takes place so that from the original cell with the fusion nucleus, four *Paramecia* have been produced each containing two nuclei; one of these remains small, the micronucleus, the other grows becoming the meganucleus.

Phylum Coelenterata

All the members of the phylum are **diploblastic**, there are two distinct cellular layers to the body wall, an outer **ectoderm** and an inner **endoderm** separated by a non-cellular jelly, the **mesogloea**. All are aquatic organisms, the majority are marine and include jellyfish, corals and sea anemones, but *Hydra* is a fresh water organism found attached by its base to water weeds or stones in ponds or slow flowing streams. The body of *Hydra* consists of a hollow sac, the cavity being the enteron, with a single opening to it, the mouth, surrounded by six to eight tentacles. In its natural habitat the cylindrical body is stretched out and the extended tentacles wave in the water, in this stage it may measure up to 20 mm, if disturbed it contracts to a rounded mass. There are several

21

different types of cells in the ectoderm; musculo-epithelial cells which make it possible for the body to contract are the most common, then among them are sensory cells and small rounded interstitial cells which replace nematoblasts and from which gametes arise. Glandular cells secreting sticky material are found on the base of the *Hydra*. The **nematoblasts** are stinging cells found in groups on the tentacles, they are formed from interstitial cells which migrate. Each nematoblast contains a cavity (nematocyst) in which there is a coiled thread; there are a number of types of nematoblast and they are very complex. During feeding *Hydra* remains attached, when a water flea or other suitable prey touches one of the tentacles there is an instant reaction. The largest type of nematoblast has a projection, the cnidocil, which serves as a trigger, when this has been touched, the coiled hollow thread which is inside is turned inside out with explosive force, barbs at the base of the thread tear the outer tissues of the prey, and the poisoned thread paralyses the victim. Other nematoblasts discharge threads which entangle the prey. The tentacles are then wrapped round the captured organism and they contract drawing it towards the opened mouth. Inside the enteron glandular cells of the endoderm secrete enzymes which reduce the food to a soupy mass containing small fragments. This process is aided by mechanical agitation brought about by the flagellae of the endoderm cells. These fragments are engulfed by the endoderm cells forming food vacuoles which gradually digest them. Indigestible remains pass into the enteron and thence out of the mouth. Respiration and excretion take place by diffusion. In the green *Hydra*, *Chlorohydra viridissima*, cells of the green alga *Chlorella* live in the endoderm cells; photosynthetic activity means that oxygen is available for the animal which in turn contributes carbon dioxide for use by the *Chlorella* in photosynthesis. This association is an example of symbiosis. *Hydra* rarely moves from place to place, but when it does, locomotion occurs by a movement similar to that of a 'looper' caterpillar. *Hydra* places the tentacles on the surface a short distance from the base and then moves the base up near the tentacles and proceeds along in this way, or the base may be swung right over the tentacles to land on the far side, in other words *Hydra* turns somersaults. *Hydra* has a simple nervous system, it consists of a net in the mesogloea, but there is no controlling group of cells or primitive 'brain', and there are no definite pathways for nervous impulses, these may spread in all directions from any spot in the network. Narrow sensory cells are squeezed among the cells of the ectoderm and endoderm. They are sensitive to touch or injurious chemicals and from these, impulses are picked up by nerve cells in the nerve

22

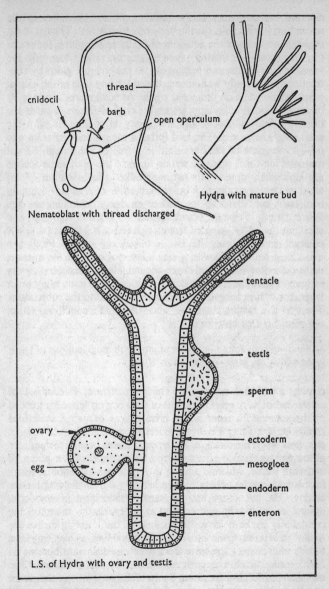

cnidocil
thread
barb
open operculum

Nematoblast with thread discharged

Hydra with mature bud

tentacle

testis

sperm

ovary

egg

ectoderm

mesogloea

endoderm

enteron

L.S. of Hydra with ovary and testis

Figure 3. Hydra

net and in some way this stimulates the muscle fibres in the musculo-epithelial cells causing the body to contract. The nerve net is able to co-ordinate the activities of *Hydra* in some way, for example, the process of catching a food organism, drawing it towards the mouth which opens, and passing it into the enteron, aided by contractions of the body wall, means that the many cells of the animal must function as a co-ordinated whole. Asexual reproduction is by budding, a small bulge appears on the wall of *Hydra* towards the base, the bud is hollow and the cavity is continuous with the enteron of the parent. The bud forms a mouth and tentacles and finally constricts at the base until it is free of the parent. Sexual reproduction takes place at certain times of the year, some species are unisexual, others are hermaphrodite. Multiplication of interstitial cells gives rise to a bulge on the side of *Hydra* which may be a testis containing sperm cells or an ovary containing an egg. When the egg is ripe the ectoderm surrounding it breaks open and sperm in the water, released from a ripe testis, collect round it, one entering and fertilizing it. The fertilized egg divides forming a blastula, a hollow ball with a single layer of cells on the outside; these cells now divide and some accumulate in the central cavity forming a gastrula. The ectoderm produces a resistant spiny outer layer, the cyst is released and becomes fastened to the substratum. The cyst is a resting stage and when favourable conditions return the young *Hydra* hatches out.

All kinds of cells found in higher animals are modifications of basic types which are already present in *Hydra*.

Obelia, a colonial member of the *Coelenterata*, is confined to marine habitats. A colony consists of a branching network attached to the substratum from which arise hollow branched structures measuring 3 to 5 cm. The living tube, the coenosarc, is enclosed in a chitinous layer, the perisarc. At the end of each branch the perisarc forms a flask-shaped structure, the hydrotheca, with a polyp or hydranth inside, which is similar to *Hydra* but has about twenty-four solid tentacles. These hydranths carry out the feeding for the colony. The coenosarc has the same arrangement of ectoderm, mesogloea, endoderm and enteron as in *Hydra*, the enteron being continuous in the colony. In the axils of the lower branches are ovoid structures, gonothecae, each containing a blastostyle, a hollow club-shaped structure from which medusae are budded off and expelled from the pore at the top of the gonotheca. The transparent medusae are about 3 mm in diameter when fully grown and shaped like a deep saucer with a fringe of many tentacles round the edge. In the centre of the concave surface there is a thick column, the manubrium, containing a terminal mouth. The gonads are formed on the concave surface of the unisexual medusae and fertilization takes place near the water surface. The fertilized egg develops into a planula, the larval stage, which eventually comes to rest and gives rise to a new colony. The phenomenon of an organism appearing in several forms is **polymorphism**. In the jellyfish the medusoid stage predominates; in the sea anemone it is absent, as in *Hydra*.

Phylum Platyhelminthes

The animals in this phylum and all higher animals are **triploblastic**, that is they have three layers of cells, ectoderm, mesoderm and endoderm. Members of the *Platyhelminthes* have no cavity in the mesoderm, they are **acoelomate**. The body is flat and there is a single opening to the gut. Gas exchange can take place by diffusion in the thin body. Characteristic 'flame cells' are concerned with excretion and osmoregulation. Most members of the group have complex sex organs and are hermaphrodite.

Class Turbellaria
The free-living planarians are very common animals in freshwater environments. These carnivores and scavengers measure 1 to 4 cm in length when extended, and may be white or grey, black or brown. Most have eyes and are sensitive to light, hiding under stones and

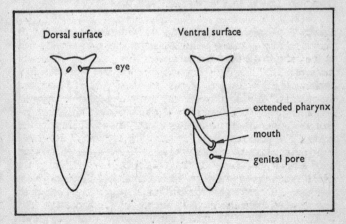

Figure 4. Crenobia, a planarian

weeds during the day and emerging at night to feed. They move by a series of muscular contractions or by extending the body and gliding by means of the cilia which cover the sides and ventral surface of the body. The planarians lay eggs in cocoons attached to water weeds or stones; they also reproduce asexually by literally tearing themselves in half. They show remarkable powers of regeneration, if damaged, each separate piece may grow into a complete new animal.

Class Trematoda

This class contains the organisms called flukes, for example, *Fasciola hepatica,* the liver fluke of sheep. The adult is oval in shape, flat, about 2·5 cm long and covered by a tough cuticle. The forked gut has one opening, the mouth, and there are oral and ventral suckers. The animal feeds in the liver on blood and cells and can cause great damage. It is hermaphrodite with complex reproductive organs, the eggs are passed from the body of the sheep in the faeces. If the eggs reach water a conical ciliated miracidium larva hatches out by pushing a lid off one end of the shell and swims in the direction of a suitable water snail, usually a species of *Limnaea*. It enters the snail's body by boring into the tissues or going through the pulmonary aperture, here it loses the cilia and becomes a sporocyst; small groups of sporocyst cells form a new type of larva, the redia. These feed on cells or fluids from the body of the secondary host and move into the digestive gland where they produce the final larvae, the cercariae which leave the snail by the

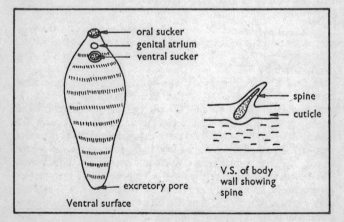

Figure 5. Fasciola hepatica, the liver fluke of sheep

26

pulmonary aperture and swim in the water, which may be drunk by a sheep. Under slightly drier conditions the cercariae form cysts on the vegetation. In the body of the sheep the cercariae penetrate the stomach wall and are attracted to the liver where they make their way to the bile duct and grow into the adult form, maintaining their position by means of the suckers. The enormous numbers of larvae produced ensure the continuation of the species. Control of the disease is brought about by draining the pasture, or where this is not practicable, introducing geese and ducks to eat the snails.

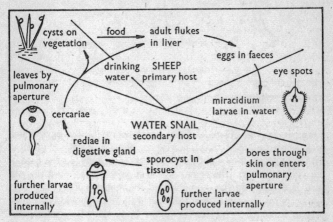

Figure 6 Life cycle of Fasciola hepatica

Another fluke causes bilharzia in man and the intermediate or secondary host is a water snail. The disease is widespread in Africa.

Class Cestoda
This class includes the parasitic tapeworms. Two of the species are parasites of man, *Taenia solium,* the pork tapeworm and *T. saginata,* the beef tapeworm. They inhabit the gut; suckers and hooks on the head preventing them being passed out with the faeces. They have a well developed cuticle which protects them, but they are able to absorb digested food through it, having no mouth or gut. They can respire anaerobically and have complex life cycles. The body is white and segmented, the production of segments or proglottides taking place just behind the head or scolex. The body may reach a length of 3·5 m, the oldest segments being furthest from the head. Each segment has a set of male and female reproductive organs, but in the mature segments all except the

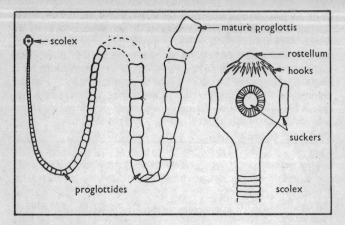

Figure 7. Taenia, a tapeworm

uterus is broken down to make more room for the eggs which may number up to 40,000. The ripe segments drop off and pass out with the faeces, the eggs being liberated eventually. In the case of the pork tapeworm the eggs may, in time, be eaten by a pig, the shell is digested in the stomach and the embryo which bears six hooks, bores its way through the gut wall into the blood or lymph system in which it travels round the body. It enters muscle and

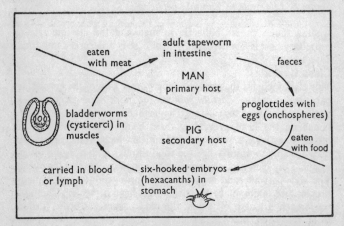

Figure 8. The life cycle of Taenia solium, the pork tapeworm

develops into the cysticercus or bladder worm stage, in which sac-like structures about 1·0 cm long, with an inverted scolex, are formed. For the life cycle to be completed the uncooked or under-cooked meat must now be eaten by man, the primary host. It resists the stomach juices, and on reaching the small intestine the scolex is everted and attached to the wall and production of proglottides commences. In communities with a good sewage disposal system, there is little risk of infection.

Phylum Nematoda

In this phylum are found the round worms which are triploblastic and acoelomate animals, some of them parasites of animals or plants, others free living. They are very similar in structure although there is great variation in size. Among the commoner parasites of man are the threadworms of children (*Oxyuris*), the two-metre long Guinea worm (*Dracunculus*) which causes elephantiasis, *Filaria* a blood parasite carried by a mosquito, hookworms (*Ancylostoma*) and *Ascaris* both intestinal parasites. *Trichinella* is parasitic in man, the pig, the rat and some other mammals. The female is about 3 mm long and the male half that size. The host becomes infected by consuming flesh containing cysts, the walls are digested in the in-testine, releasing small worms. The males fertilize the females and then die, passing out of the host's body with the faeces. The females penetrate the gut wall and produce tiny worm-like larvae in the blood and lymph vessels, later they burrow into muscles forming spindle-shaped cysts. The cysts are capable of remaining viable for ten years, and it has been shown that 1 g of meat may contain up to 3,000 cysts.

Phylum Annelida

The Annelida are triploblastic and **coelomate**. It is possible to trace the affinity between this successful group of segmented animals and other invertebrate groups.

Class Polychaeta

The worms in this class are all marine animals, some of them are free-swimming carnivores like the ragworm *Nereis*, others are burrowing such as the lugworm *Arenicola*, and a third group are filter feeding tube dwellers. They have parapodia which are paired outgrowths from the segments, bearing chaetae. There is a larval stage, a ciliated structure called a trochophore. *Nereis* is a common polychaete of the intertidal zone, the parapodia assist in getting a grip on the surface. There are well developed sense organs, eyes, sensory palps, tentacles and cirri. In the water the parapodia are used as paddles when swimming. The sexes are separate and as there are no ducts the gametes are released into the water by the bursting of the sexual segments; the adults then die. The eggs hatch into trochophores, larvae similar to those of the *Mollusca*.

Class Oligochaeta

The common earthworm, *Lumbricus terrestris,* is an animal well adapted for burrowing in the soil, it has a reduced sensory system and a means of transferring gametes. There is no trochophore stage. The earthworm feeds by extracting organic matter from the soil it swallows during burrowing, it also feeds on the surface at night. Earthworms are hermaphrodite, there are a pair of ovaries attached to the septum dividing segments 12 and 13 and the eggs are passed out through oviducts which open on segment 14. The spermathecae, structures which receive sperm, are in segments 9 and 10 and their opening is in the groove between the two segments. There are two pairs of testes attached to the septa separating segments 9

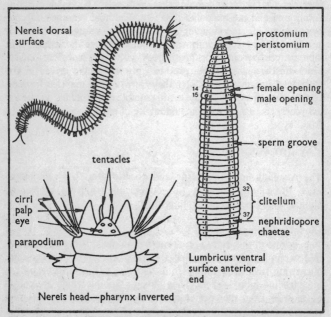

Figure 9. Nereis, the ragworm and Lumbricus, the earthworm

30

and 10, and 10 and 11; the vasa deferentia pass back and open on the ventral surface of segment 15. From these openings shallow grooves pass back to the clitellum. Copulation takes place at night, two worms lie with their ventral surfaces together in such a position that segments 9, 10, and 11 are opposite the clitellum of the other worm, the chaetae helping to keep the worms together. Each secretes a tube of mucus which surrounds its body from segments 11 to 31, these tubes prevent the mixing of sperm. In addition, the worms are tightly bound together by two separate tubes of mucus, each of which surrounds the two worms in the region of the clitellum. Seminal fluid containing sperm is forced along the seminal grooves from segment 15 to the clitellum and into the spermathecae of the other worm. The worms separate after the exchange of sperm and cocoons are formed at intervals until the stored sperm is used up. To form a cocoon the worm secretes a mucus tube and within it the cocoon itself is secreted by the clitellum. About twelve eggs are deposited in it and the cocoon is forced forward until it comes to the opening of the spermathecae, where sperm are passed into it. The cocoon is pushed along until it is free of the body, the ends closing together. Usually only one worm about 1 cm long hatches out. The activity of earthworms is beneficial to the soil in many ways, the burrows aerate the soil and provide drainage channels, the soil is mixed and the texture improved as it passes through the gut of the worm. The importance of earthworms was scarcely recognised before Darwin published his classic study of these organisms in 1881. Now there are farms for breeding earthworms and it is said that demand exceeds supply. Fertile farmland contains enormous numbers, between 120 million and 600 million/km^2.

Phylum Mollusca

The Mollusca are mainly aquatic animals but the snails and their close relatives the slugs have become adapted to land life. Many aquatic snails are air breathing and have gone back to living in water. There are some interesting features in the group, for example, the trochophore larva which is similar to that in the Polychaetae; the excellent filter feeding mechanisms of the bivalves and the advanced structures of the squid. The squid, the largest invertebrate, is an active predator with a good circulatory system and a highly developed nervous system including two large eyes, very similar structures to those of man. When similar structures such as these arise in unrelated groups, they are said to have arisen by convergence or convergent evolution.

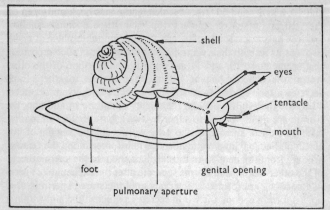

Figure 10. Helix, the snail, a gastropod mollusc

Phylum Arthropoda

About 80% of all animal species are arthropods. They have an exoskeleton of chitinous material and are basically segmented with paired appendages on the segments. The appendages show a remarkable range of adaptations as mouthparts, walking legs, paddles, respiratory, sensory and mating organs.

Class Insecta

Three quarters of all known species of animals are insects and they owe their extensive distribution to the fact that the basic body plan lends itself to a wide range of modifications enabling them to colonize new environments, and to their ability to utilize new sources of material as food. The evolution, from a primitive type, of new forms adapted to distinct modes of life is adaptive radiation. Of all animals the insects provide the best example. The ability to fly obviously confers a great advantage, but their intense activity, well developed sense organs and high reproductive rate contribute to their success. Insects compete with man attacking his food crops in the field and in storage, destroying timber and fabrics, conveying disease to him and to his domestic animals. In some of the most fertile parts of the world the insects have won.

The locust is a destructive insect, only now beginning to be controlled by man. The female lays her eggs in the sand in large numbers together with a frothy material, the whole mass hardening

32

to form a long egg pod. Eggs become larvae hatching from sand as **nymphs** like miniature adults except that they are wingless. They feed on vegetation and grow rapidly, soon the chitinous cuticle becomes a tight fit and the nymphs moult, the outer covering is cast off revealing a newer softer one beneath which soon hardens. The nymphs moult five times, each nymphal stage being an instar. At the final moult the winged adult appears. In their natural environment locusts behave like ordinary grasshoppers for a number of generations, this is the solitary phase. As the numbers build up rapidly they enter the gregarious phase, at this time they change from light green to yellow-brown, individuals become excited and restive, climbing up on to any available vegetation and finally moving off in a swarm which may fly hundreds of miles. Where they alight the insects feed voraciously leaving total destruction.

In insects which undergo complete metamorphosis, there is a division of labour among the organisms of the different stages of the life history. In butterflies, for example, the larval stage, the caterpillar, is the feeding stage, being provided with chewing jaws it eats voraciously, grows rapidly and sheds its skin at intervals to accommodate its increasing size. The pupa is a non-feeding stage in which the larva is transformed into the imago whose function is reproduction and distribution of the species, it does not grow. The sugary nectar it sucks from flowers gives it the necessary energy for flight and egg laying.

Many insects such as the honey bee, show polymorphism, that is, different members are structurally different and specialised for different functions. They are social insects, they live in a colony and co-operate. A colony is dominated by a queen, it consists of workers which are sterile females and drones which are males. The only function of the drones is to participate in the mating flight in which one will mate with the queen. The workers produce the wax and build the wax cells or honey comb, some are used for storing honey for winter food, others are set aside for the queen who lays an egg in each. Fertilized eggs develop into females, unfertilized eggs into males. Fertilized eggs laid in special cells of large size and fed by workers on royal jelly which they produce, develop into queens. Other larvae are fed mainly on honey and pollen. Workers also clean the hive, ventilate it and collect food. Eventually when the hive is over-crowded the queen will leave with a swarm of workers to set up a new colony. The remaining workers rear another queen, after mating she settles down to egg laying. Workers are able to gather food at least a mile from the hive and appear to

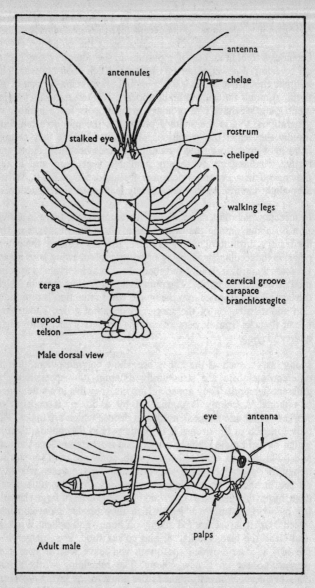

Figure 11. *Locusta*, the locust and *Astacus*, the crayfish

34

pass information about food sources to other workers in the hive.

Class Crustacea

The *Crustacea* form the second largest class in the *Arthropoda*, the most advanced members are the *Decapoda*, the crabs, lobsters and crayfish. They have massive skeletons impregnated with calcium salts. The appendages are good examples of adaptive radiation. The more primitive members provide examples of filter feeding mechanisms.

Phylum Echinodermata

Members of this group are marine organisms, they are easily recognized by their chalky exoskeleton and radial symmetry. They have tube feet which bring about movement by a water vascular system. The group includes carnivorous starfish feeding on bivalves, algae-feeding sea urchins and filter feeding sea lilies.

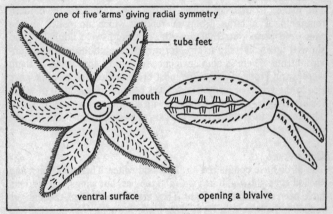

Figure 12. Asterias, the starfish, a common echinoderm

Phylum Chordata

Sub-phylum Vertebrata
(Craniata)

Class Pisces

The fish form a readily identifiable group of aquatic vertebrates with streamlined bodies, gills, fins and scales. The lateral line is sen-

35

sory and detects vibrations in the water. Modern bony fish of the order *Teleostei* have a swim bladder containing air which can be used to adjust the specific gravity of the fish in relation to the depth of the water in which it is swimming, this enables it to remain there without great expenditure of energy. The swim bladder is the relic of a lung derived from ancient ancestors which also gave rise to the groups of lung fishes and coelacanths.

Class Amphibia

The amphibians, frogs, toads, newts and salamanders are the remains of a much larger group which flourished in Carboniferous times. They are adapted for life on land and in water, but depend on water for breeding. Their eggs, protected only by jelly when laid, develop into aquatic larvae which undergo metamorphosis into the adult. The adults have lungs and a smooth skin through which gas exchange can take place.

Class Reptilia

The snakes, lizards, crocodiles, tortoises and turtles are the modern remnants of a large group of reptiles which flourished in the Mesozoic period. At that time the dinosaurs were dominant and showed great diversity in size, form and adaptation to different environments. There is some evidence to suggest that some of them were warm blooded and while most of them died out, one line gave rise to the group of birds. The reptiles became independent of water for breeding by protecting the egg with a shell to prevent drying out. The animals themselves have the skin protected by scales to prevent water loss.

Class Aves

The birds have conquered air, land and water. Their scaly legs and shelled eggs show affinites with the reptiles, but wings and feathers have been developed for flight. They are warm blooded, the feathers reducing the heat loss. Birds show elaborate behaviour patterns and considerable parental care; nest building, egg incubation, feeding and protecting the young being shared to a varying extent between the sexes.

Class Mammalia

Today the mammals are the dominant animals on land and they are represented in the air by the bats and in the sea by such animals as whales and dolphins. They are warm blooded, the characteristic covering being hair, but blubber acts as an insulating layer in marine species. Fertilization is internal, the young developing inside the body of the mother and being born at a relatively advanced stage. The young are fed on milk from mammary glands and there is a long period of parental care and protection. A diaphragm is present which contributes to efficient gas exchange. There are different types of teeth present, ear ossicles and a large cerebral cortex. In higher mammals there is intelligence and learning capacity.

Key terms

Acoelomate Having no coelom.
Coelomate Having the main body cavity situated in the mesoderm.
Diploblastic Having the body made of two layers, ectoderm and endoderm.
Ectoplasm Outer layer of cytoplasm, usually a gel (plasmagel) containing few granules; it is unlike the more fluid inner layer of cytoplasm, the endoplasm (plasmasol), which contains many granules, but the two forms grade into one another.
Endoplasm See ectoplasm.
Mesogloea Layer of jelly-like substance between ectoderm and endoderm in coelenterates.
Nymph Immature stage of insect, like adult but wingless.
Plasmagel See ectoplasm.
Plasmasol See ectoplasm.
Polymorphism Having several different forms.
Triploblastic Having the body made of three layers, ectoderm, mesoderm and endoderm.

Chapter 3
The Plant Kingdom

Algal forms

Most algae are aquatic, the smaller ones are unicellular, colonial or filamentous, the larger ones form a parenchymatous **thallus** —typically a flat dichotomously branched structure without stem, root or leaves. All are photosynthetic, but vary in colour according to the nature and relative amounts of different pigments present. They exhibit a range of forms of sexual reproduction from isogamy (fusion of similar gametes) to oogamy (fusion of egg and sperm), and different types of life cycle. The division of blue-green algae (*Cyanophyta*), contains plants capable of nitrogen fixation, for example, *Nostoc* and *Anaboena*; some are early colonizers of mud and others common components of lichens. The division of diatoms (*Bacillariophyceae*), consists of unicellular forms with a silica-impregnated cell wall like the base and lid of a box, decorated with fine sculpturings; they are important constituents of plankton. Most of the red algae (*Rhodophyta*), are beautiful small algae of rock pools.

Division Chlorophyta

The group of green algae is the most primitive. The majority are fresh water species; *Chlamydomonas* is a minute motile unicellular plant, only distinguishable from a protozoan by its chloroplast, which is cup shaped. It has a red eye spot and is light sensitive. *Spirogyra* is an unbranched filamentous form, a thread composed of long cylindrical cells each containing one or more spiral chloroplasts. Thalloid species such as sea lettuce (*Ulva*) grow high up in the intertidal zone where there is fresh water influence.

Division Phaeophyta

Most of the brown algae are the familiar seaweeds of the intertidal zone on rocky shores. The distribution is determined mainly by their relative ability to withstand desiccation, this leads to distinct zonation, the most resistant species growing near the high water mark. The brown pigment, fucoxanthin, is present in addition to chlorophyll and is responsible for the characteristic colour. *Fucus* is

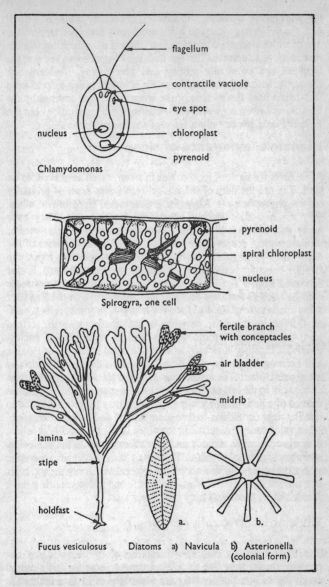

Figure 13. Some common algae

a typical brown seaweed, it is attached to rock by means of a hold-fast, the tough stipe leads to a dichotomously branched lamina, the tips of which bear conceptacles, flask-shaped pits which contain the reproductive structures. The sex cells are liberated into the sea, the fertilized egg eventually settling and germinating. Bladderwrack (*Fucus vesiculosus*) also has large air bladders which help to keep the thallus near the surface of the water when it is covered by the tide. Some brown seaweeds show alternation of generations but the diploid *Fucus* shows only a trace of the haploid phase.

Economic importance of algae

Algae form the basis of food chains in water, much as grass does on land. The productivity of the sea or fresh water depends primarily on the phytoplankton. Alginates are extracted from brown algae, they are non-toxic viscous substances forming gels. They have many uses in the food industry as thickeners and are also used in pharmaceutical preparations and cosmetics. Certain species of red algae yield carragheen which has similar properties. Agar, the familiar substance used in the culture of bacteria and fungi, is also extracted from a red alga. On farmlands near the coast seaweeds may be used as fertilizer and animal fodder, while in the Far East some species are utilized as food for humans. In some regions, such as California, there are deposits of diatomaceous earth, formed from the shells of diatoms which settled to the bottom of ancient waters; it is mined and used as a filtration aid in the sugar refining and brewing industries, also it finds use in insulating materials and as a paint filler. The extraction of minerals from seaweed was carried out in the last century but is no longer economic. Sometimes masses of algae which grew millions of years ago were subjected to just the right conditions to turn them into oil and gases which are of great value today. A new use for algae is in space vehicles where they absorb carbon dioxide and give off oxygen. On the debit side, abundant growths of algae ('blooms') may occur in reservoirs where the water contains additional mineral salts, only the top layer can absorb light and survive, the rest forms a decomposing mass which blocks filters and may taint the water.

Division Eumycophyta (Fungi)

The fungi have no chlorophyll and therefore cannot carry out photosynthesis; they live as saprophytes or parasites and store oil or glycogen. Structurally they are composed of hyphae with walls constructed of fungal cellulose, the mycelium producing spores for reproduction.

Class Phycomycetes

This is the group of moulds, they show increasing adaptation to land life, the lower members produce zoospores which need at least a film of water for swimming, the higher members have air-borne spores or **conidia**. The hyphae are **coenocytic**, that is there are no cross walls. *Phytophthora infestans* is one parasite of economic importance, it is the fungus causing potato blight. Conidia germinate on the surface of a leaf, usually in drops of dew, the germ tube entering the leaf by way of a stoma. Alternatively the conidium may behave as a zoosporangium; the contents cleave into zoospores, the tip of the sporangium dissolves and bean-shaped zoospores emerge, eventually coming to rest and producing a germ tube. Which process occurs is determined largely by the internal physiology of the conidium, chiefly its state of maturity. Inside the leaf the hyphae grow between the cells and put food-absorbing haustoria into the cells, in time hyphae bearing conidia grow through the stomata to the outside. The disease spreads rapidly in warm damp weather, the whole life cycle can be completed in five days. The spores falling on the ground are washed into the soil and affect the tubers, entering the lenticels in the corky skin, the tubers may be completely rotted. Sexual reproduction also occurs, but the spores produced have no importance in the overwintering of the fungus which survives as a resting mycelium in slightly diseased tubers. Control can be brought about by spraying the foliage just before the spores of the fungus are likely to be prevalent in the air. A well tried liquid is Bordeaux mixture, consisting of copper sulphate and lime in water. When the spores germinate they are killed off by the copper ions. Other lower moulds are *Pythium* which causes 'damping off' of seedlings and *Saprolegnia* a water mould which attacks the gills of fish.

Mucor is the common saprophytic 'pin mould' which forms a white fluffy growth with black dots which are the sporangia. Large numbers of asexual spores are produced and when dry they drift away on air currents. Resting spores, zygospores, are produced as a result of a sexual process between two different physiological strains of the mould, usually referred to as + and − strains. The two filaments put out processes the ends of which are cut off by a cross wall to form gametangia. The multinucleate contents of each mingle, the nuclei associating in pairs, one from each strain. A thick resistant wall forms round the zygospore and after a resting period it germinates and gives rise to an asexual sporangium at once, thus

41

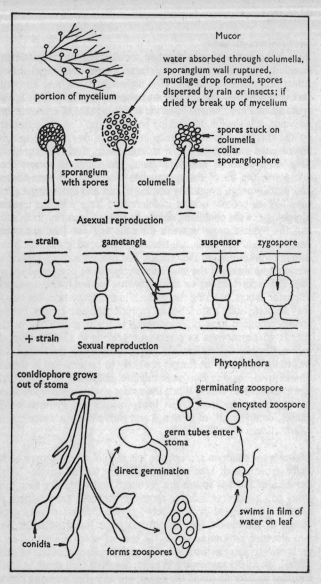

Figure 14. Mucor and Phytophthora

ensuring a rapid spread of the fungus.

Class Ascomycetes

The hyphae have cross walls and the spores are produced in elongated sporangia called asci (one **ascus** containing eight ascospores). Asci are grouped together in fruiting bodies, the form of which is used as a basis of classification. Among members of the group are the cup fungi; *Erysiphe,* a cereal parasite; *Penicillium* and Yeast.

Class Basidiomycetes

Cross walls are also present in the hyphae in this group. The fruiting bodies are large and produce basidiospores, typically four being produced externally from each special cell, the **basidium**. In the group are some prized culinary species, the field mushroom (*Agaricus campestris*), parasol mushroom (*Lepiota procera*) and chantarelle (*Cantharellus cibarius*); the highly poisonous death cap (*Amanita phalloides*); the parasitic rusts and smuts which do much harm to cereal crops; and bracket fungi of trees.

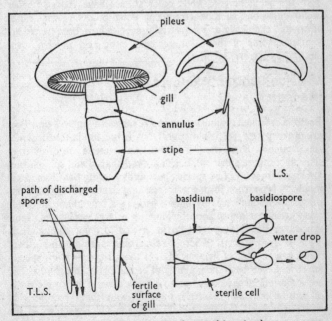

*Figure 15. Fruiting body of the mushroom (*Agaricus*)*

43

Economic importance of fungi

The fungi are important decomposers, breaking down organic matter in the soil and recycling the components. Their role as decomposers can be inconvenient to man, under damp conditions fungi may attack timber, leather and fabrics causing much damage. They also bring about food spoilage. Many fungi are pathogens of plants, causing loss of crops, others attack animals, for example, athlete's foot and ringworm are fungal diseases of man. On the credit side, man has made use of many fungi – mushrooms and a number of other species may be eaten and yeast is used in the baking of bread and in the brewing industry. In the fermentation process brought about by yeast, alcohol and carbon dioxide are formed; the gas raises the dough in bread making, while in brewing the alcohol is of importance and the carbon dioxide may be sold as 'dry ice'. Yeast is also a useful source of vitamin B. *Penicillium* is used in cheese making for soft cheeses of the Camembert and Brie types as well as the blue-veined cheeses such as Roquefort, Gorgonzola and Stilton. The first important antibiotic, penicillin comes from the same fungus, while other species have yielded further useful antibiotics, such as tetramycin. Fungi produce a wide range of organic chemicals and industrial processes have been developed to obtain some of them, for example, citric acid which is synthesized by *Aspergillus niger*.

Division Schizomycophyta (Bacteria)

Bacteria are small organisms in the size range $0 \cdot 5$ μm to 8 μm. They are prokaryotes, that is although DNA is present, in the form of a single circular fibril, there is no nucleus. Bacteria are of different shapes, cocci are spherical, bacilli are rod-shaped and spirochaetes are spiral forms. A few species have cells bearing flagella and are motile. A proportion form spores, resistant structures which aid dispersal. Reproduction is by binary fission – a bacterium can divide every twenty minutes, soon building up a large population. Some species of bacteria congregate in groups forming characteristic association patterns. There are aerobic species and others which are capable of living with or without oxygen, a few species are strict anaerobes. The majority of bacteria are saprophytes, they are important decomposers able to break down a very wide range of substances. Soil bacteria together with fungi recycle vital elements needed for the growth of plants, for example, in the nitrogen cycle. Others live symbiotically in the root nodules of leguminous plants, fixing atmospheric nitrogen. Some soil saprophytes such as tetanus bacteria, can become parasites if they enter wounds. Typhoid, diptheria and some types of pneumonia are also bacterial diseases of man; other pathogens attack his animals and crops. As with the fungi the decomposition brought about by bacteria can cause great problems to man, particularly perhaps in food spoilage where there may be additional hazards to health if the food is consumed.

Viruses

The taxonomic position of viruses is controversial, they are often studied with the bacteria and are placed here for convenience. Viruses are too small to be seen under the ordinary light microscope, the electron microscope shows them to be only about one-tenth of the size of bacteria. They pass easily through filters which retain bacteria. Virus particles appear to consist of nucleic acid with a protein coat, they do not possess enzyme systems and are unable to multiply outside a host. Inside a living cell the host cell cannot distinguish between its own nucleic acid and that belonging to the virus, so it responds to the genetic 'blueprint' introduced by the virus by making viral type materials, some of which will be enzymes. The new enzymes and the host enzymes will be utilized to make new virus particles – eventually the many new particles pass on to infect other host cells. Outside living cells virus particles can be made to form crystals, a characteristic of non-living matter. Viruses are responsible for many diseases; measles, poliomyelitis, chicken pox, influenza and the common cold are among those to which man is prone. Foot and mouth disease of cattle and distemper of dogs are virus infections. Among plants, mosaic diseases of potatoes and tobacco and curly top of sugar beet are caused by viruses. There are also viruses known as phages which destroy bacteria. A plant disease caused by a virus may be transmitted to a healthy plant by handling or by insect vectors which feed on plant juices. Aphids and leaf hoppers are important vectors.

Division Bryophyta

The liverworts and mosses are probably an evolutionary side branch. They are small land plants without vascular tissue or true roots and are mostly confined to damp places as their leaves are not covered by cuticle and hence have no protection from desiccation. Water is also needed for fertilization. Mosses and liverworts show

alternation of generations between a haploid **gametophyte** and a diploid **sporophyte** which obtains its food wholly or partly from the gametophyte. Asexual reproduction by means of gemmae, small multicellular structures which become detached from the plant, is common.

Class Hepaticae

Most liverworts are thalloid but there are some leafy species, they bear unicellular rhizoids pegging them to the ground in wet soil or to the surface of damp walls. In *Pellia,* a common species, **antheridia** producing sperm are found sunken in the mid-rib region, and **archegonia** each producing an egg cell are located under a flap of tissue, the involucre. The sperm reach the eggs by swimming in a film of water; after fertilization the zygote grows into the sporophyte consisting of foot, seta and capsule. Meiosis occurs at spore formation. The capsule opens, the four valves fold back and the spores are discharged by hygroscopic movements of elators, special cells within the capsule. The sporophyte has no green tissue and is parasitic on the gametophyte.

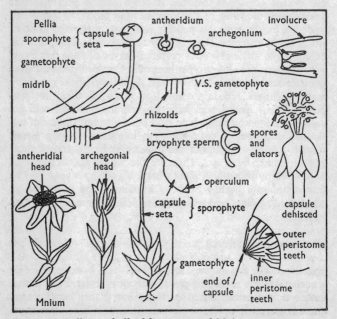

Figure 16. Pellia, a thalloid liverwort and Mnium, a moss

Class Musci

Moss plants usually grow in large groups, often forming 'cushions' which serve for mutual support, water conservation and facilitation of fertilization. The gametophyte has simple leaves spirally arranged on the stem, archegonia and antheridia being produced in the terminal buds, usually on separate plants. The sperm are transferred to the female archegonia by rain splash, after fertilization the zygote grows into the sporophyte, the capsule having some green tissue and therefore showing some independence. At the distal end of the capsule an operculum or lid falls off when the spores are ripe exposing peristome teeth which make hygroscopic movements aiding dispersal of the spores. *Funaria*, *Polytrichum* and *Mnium* are common moss species.

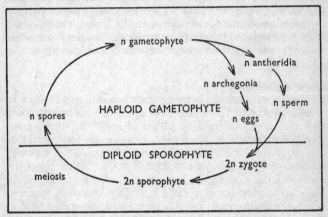

Figure 17. The life cycle of a liverwort or moss

Division Pteridophyta

The *Pteridophyta* were a large and dominant group in Carboniferous times and their fossilized remains form the major part of our present day coal. The ferns have established themselves as the most successful group of the *Pteridophyta* today. The *Pteridophyta* are vascular plants showing alternation of generations, the diploid sporophyte has become the dominant plant, it is independent of the gametophyte and shows improved adaptations for land life, such as cuticle on the leaves and stem. A few species are heterosporous (have two types of spores) a phenomenon which indicates a way in which higher plants may have evolved.

Order Filicales

The ferns are widespread, most are shade-loving plants varying in size from tree ferns to minute water-living species. *Dryopteris* is a common fern producing fronds from a rhizome growing obliquely in the soil, the frond appears above the surface coiled up, a characteristic of the group. The central rachis of the frond bears ramenta, brown scales, and the underside of the frond has groups of sporangia, the sori, each group protected by an umbrella-shaped indusium. The individual sporangia are stalked and roughly biconvex in shape, bearing a single row of special cells, the annulus and flat thin-walled cells, the stomium. Water evaporates from the annulus, creating tension which ruptures the sporangium at the stomium. Further tension in the annulus cells results in water inside suddenly vaporizing, the torn portion of the sporanguim returns to its former position flinging out the spores. A spore grows into a gametophyte or prothallus, a structure resembling a minute liverwort and bearing archegonia and antheridia on the underside. Fertilization occurs when water is present and the zygote grows into a diploid sporophyte.

Order Equisetales

Horsetails have rhizomes bearing upright branched shoots which in some species reach 1·5 m. The ribbed stems have hollow internodes and solid nodes sheathed by whorls of small simple non-green leaves, the stems being green and taking over the photosynthesis. The structures which bear sporangia are specialized sporangiophores, they are grouped into **strobili** or cones at the top of the main stem. In some species they occur on separate fertile shoots. Each sporangiophore is a stalked, roughly hexagonal structure borne at right angles to the main stem, sporangia are attached to the underside. The horsetails are **homosporous**, that is all the spores are alike, they bear strap-like structures which make hygroscopic movements aiding dispersal. The gametophyte is pin-head sized and bears delicate upright photosynthetic plates.

Order Lycopodiales

Species of *Lycopodium* have a branched prostrate main stem and upright branches about 20 cm high. All the stems are clothed by small green leaves and the prostrate stem is pegged to the ground by adventitious roots. Sporangia are borne in the axils of some of the leaves which are then called **sporophylls**. In some species the sporophylls are smaller than the leaves, brownish in colour and grouped together at the top of an upright branch into a cone or strobilus. The gametophytes are sometimes subterranean. The

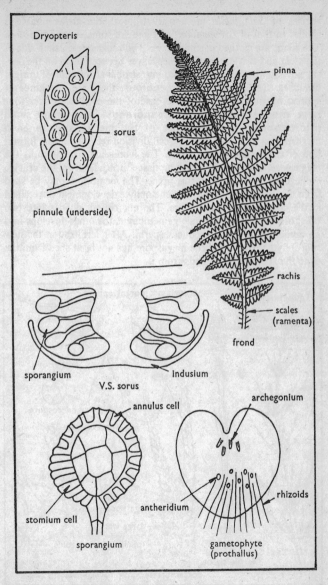

Figure 18. Dryopteris, a common fern

species of *Selaginella* are mostly tropical, the growth habit is similar to that of *Lycopodium* but there are some climbing species. The stems are clothed in small leaves, two ranks one on each side of the stem and two ranks of smaller leaves between them on the dorsal side. Sporophylls are grouped into strobili at the ends of upright branches. *Selaginella* is **heterosporous**, there are two kinds of spores, **megasporangia** at the base of the cone each bear four large **megaspores** and **microsporangia** bear many small **microspores**. One or more of the megaspores in each megasporangium may develop, cell division resulting in the formation of the female gametophyte. The increasing size ruptures the megaspore wall and gametophyte tissue protrudes from the cracks, archegonia developing on this tissue. The megaspore may be shed from the cone at any stage of gametophyte development or retained in the cone and fertilized there. The microspore divides into two cells, one represents the male gametophyte, the other develops into an antheridium which produces sperm. After fertilization the new sporophyte grows up, if the megaspore has not been shed from the cone the sporophyte extends from it.

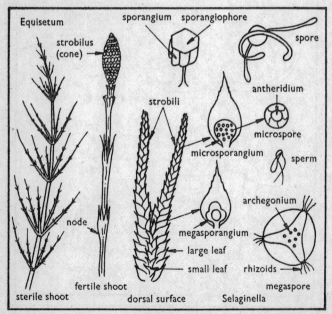

Figure 19. Equisetum, a horsetail and Selaginella, a clubmoss

Division Spermatophyta

Class Gymnospermae

These plants have naked seeds, that is they are not surrounded by a protective case like the ovary wall in the *Angiospermae*. There are many fossil members of the group, the so-called 'seed ferns' were gymnosperms. Today the conifers are the most important, they include pine, fir, spruce, yew and others; most of them bear cones. *Pinus sylvestris*, the Scots pine, is a tall tree bearing needle-shaped evergreen leaves growing in pairs from dwarf shoots on the twigs. The male cones are borne in groups, each replacing a dwarf shoot in position; each individual cone is about 1 cm long and consists of spirally arranged microsporophylls on a central axis, each having two microsporangia on the underside containing haploid microspores. The nucleus of the microspore divides several times forming a pollen grain, bearing two air sacs. Vast quantities of pollen are shed and dispersed by the wind. The female cones appear in spring at the tips of young branches, each consists of megasporophylls or cone scales spirally placed round the cone axis,

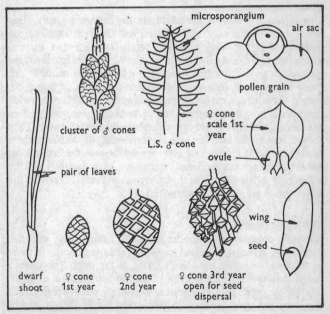

Figure 20. Pinus sylvestris

51

each cone scale bears two ovules on the upper surface (an **ovule** is a megasporangium with a protective layer of cells, the integument). Four megaspores are produced, one develops into the female gametophyte and bears archegonia. Pollen grains are blown between the cone scales and lodge near the female gametophyte. A pollen grain germinates forming a pollen tube, several nuclear divisions take place but no cell walls are formed between them, the pollen tube with two sperm nuclei and several vegetative nuclei is the male gemetophyte. Fertilization of the egg cells in the archegonia by sperm nuclei does not take place until a year after pollination. Although several eggs may become fertilized usually only one develops into an embryo bearing several cotyledons and a radicle. The embryo is embedded in the female gametophyte and the whole is protected by layers formed from the integument, the entire structure is the seed which bears a wing. A year after fertilization and two years after pollination the seed is ready for wind dispersal. In some gymnosperms there is a motile sperm and water is needed for fertilization.

Class Angiospermae

The dominant plants of the world are the flowering plants, their characteristic features being the flower and the fruit. The flower is typically a shoot bearing sepals, petals, stamens and carpels, themselves greatly modified leaves. Ovules which ripen into seeds are enclosed in an ovary which ripens into a fruit. Many plants in this group are of great economic importance providing us with food, timber, fibres, drugs, rubber, dyes, resins and others. There is a wide range in size from the minute floating duckweed (*Lemna*) to large trees like the oak, with shrubs and various herbaceous plants between. They are well adapted for land life, even in exceptionally dry habitats, as the cacti show. All have dispensed with the need for water for fertilization, motile sperm are not produced, archegonia have vanished and the pollen tube grows directly to the embryo sac. (Further details of the reproduction are given in Chapter 12.)

Sub-class Dicotyledones

The class contains trees, shrubs and herbs having seeds with two cotyledons, reticulately veined leaves, floral parts typically in fours or fives and vascular bundles in a ring in the stem. The class is further sub-divided on the basis of certain features, for example, whether the petals are free, joined or absent, the relative positions of the ovary and the other floral parts and whether the carpels are free or joined. Keys in most floras are based on such a scheme.

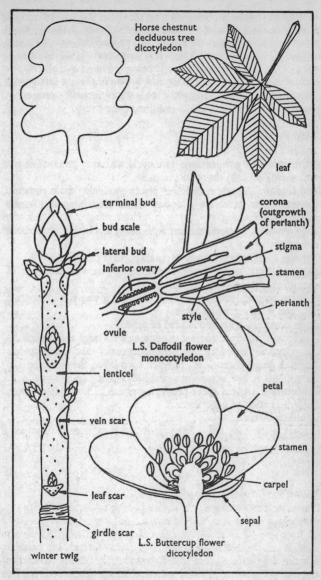

Horse chestnut
deciduous tree
dicotyledon

leaf

terminal bud

bud scale

lateral bud

inferior ovary

ovule

lenticel

vein scar

leaf scar

girdle scar

winter twig

corona
(outgrowth
of perianth)

stigma

stamen

perianth

style

L.S. Daffodil flower
monocotyledon

petal

stamen

carpel

sepal

L.S. Buttercup flower
dicotyledon

Figure 21. Angiosperms

Sub-class Monocotyledones

A smaller class than the *Dicotyledones* containing mainly small plants and a few large ones such as the palms. The seeds have one cotyledon, parallel-veined leaves and floral parts in threes or multiples of three, the vascular bundles being scattered in the stem. The grasses, ancestors of modern cereals, are an important family with reduced floral parts. Diagnostic characters include presence or absence of a perianth and the position of the ovary.

Key terms

Alternation of generations Life cycle with two generations one reproducing sexually the other asexually.

Antheridium Structure in lower plants producing male gametes.

Archegonium Structure in lower plants containing the female gamete (egg).

Coenocyte Protoplasmic mass with many nuclei but no division into cells.

Conidia Externally produced asexual spores of some fungi.

Gametophyte Haploid gamete-producing phase in life cycle of plant. (See Alternation of generations.)

Heterosporous Having two kinds of spores giving rise to separate male and female gametophytes.

Homosporous Having one kind of spore.

Megasporangium Structure containing four large megaspores.

Microsporangium Structure containing many small microspores.

Ovule A megasporangium protected by a layer, the integument.

Sporophyll A leaf, sometimes modified, bearing sporangia.

Sporophyte Diploid spore-producing phase in life cycle of plant. (See Alternation of generations.)

Strobilus A cone.

Thallus Plant body not differentiated into root, stem and leaves.

Chapter 4
Basic Biochemistry

Biochemistry is the study of chemical substances and chemical processes in living organisms.

Carbohydrates

The group of carbohydrates includes sugars, starch, glycogen and cellulose. Starch is a storage product in green plants, while animals and some fungi store glycogen. These carbohydrate storage products can be converted to sugar which is used in respiration to provide energy. Cellulose is a structural material in plants, a few animals are capable of breaking it down to sugar.

Carbohydrates are compounds of carbon, hydrogen and oxygen, in the majority of them the ratio of hydrogen to oxygen is $2 : 1$ as in water.

Monosaccharides
Monosaccharides or single sugars have the general formula $(CH_2O)_n$. In triose sugars, $n = 3$; in pentose sugars, $n = 5$; and in hexose sugars $n = 6$. Structurally, hexose sugars consist of a ring of five carbon atoms and one oxygen atom, with side branches. The carbon atoms are numbered in a clockwise direction starting with the one furthest to the right. Each side branch is attached to a particular carbon atom, the position of the side groups determining the nature of the sugar and its properties. Consider the following formulae of glucose, the commonest sugar in the body of a mammal; simplified formulae are shown on the right hand side.

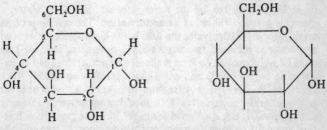

α–glucose (α–glucopyranose)

55

Compare α and β-glucose and note that the H and OH groups have been changed over at position 1, this results in two glucose sugars with slightly different properties. A different arrangement produces fructose, another common hexose sugar occurring in some fruits and in honey.

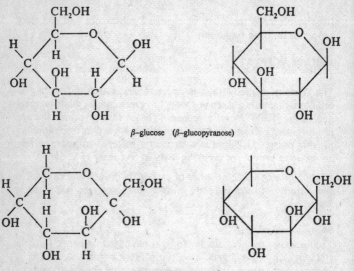

β–glucose   (β–glucopyranose)

fructose (fructopyranose)

The six membered ring structure for the hexoses is called a pyranose ring so names such as glucopyranose and fructopyranose are sometimes used. The hexose sugars form units from which complex carbohydrates may be built.

Disaccharides

A disaccharide or double sugar consists of two units of hexose sugar linked together by the removal of a molecule of water, a chemical reaction known as a **condensation**. The reverse process takes place by **hydrolysis**, the link in the disaccharide is broken and water is replaced, two hexose sugar units being formed. Two units of α-glucose link to form maltose, a disaccharide found in germinating barley (malt) and some other germinating seeds. When fructose is part of a disaccharide, such as sucrose, or polysaccharide, such as inulin (a food storage material in many Compositae), it has a different form, the furanose ring. Thus fructose can exist as fructofuranose or fructopyranose. Sucrose is the

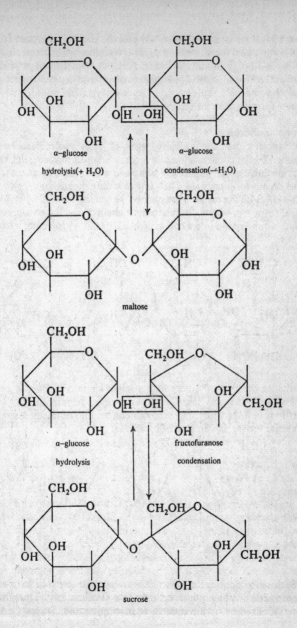

CH₂OH ... O

α–glucose

hydrolysis(+ H₂O)

α–glucose

condensation(– H₂O)

maltose

α–glucose

hydrolysis

fructofuranose

condensation

sucrose

57

result of a condensation between α-glucose and fructose. Sucrose is the commonest form in which sugar is translocated in plants, it also forms a storage product in some. It is our domestic sugar and is extracted from cultivated sugar cane and sugar beet. All monosaccharides and disaccharides are crystalline and dissolve in water forming a sweet tasting solution.

Polysaccharides

Polysaccharides are carbohydrates of high molecular weight formed by the condensation of a large number of hexose units, they are insoluble or only sparingly soluble in water, have no sweet taste and do not form crystals. Their low solubility means that they have little effect on the osmotic pressure of the cell sap and thus they form ideal storage products. Starch forms a chain of 1–4 linked α-glucose units wound round into a coil with the OH groups projecting into the centre.

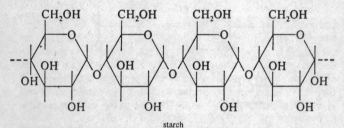

starch

Cellulose consists of a very long straight chain of β-glucose units linked in such a way that OH groups project from both sides and form cross links with other cellulose chains, this results in a strong material for the building of cell walls.

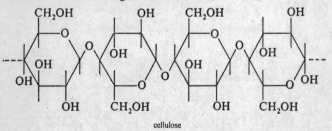

cellulose

Cellulose is important commercially, wood pulp providing the raw material from which paper, cellophane and rayon can be manufactured. Cellulose derivatives are used in lacquers and in films. Cotton

58

is cellulose in an almost pure form used in the manufacture of fibres. Chitin is another structural polysaccharide, a long chain molecule with attached amino (NH_2) groups.

Fats

Fats and oils are important food reserve materials in plants and animals. In plants they are found mainly in fruits, seeds and spores, occurring in the form of globules. About 90% of all seeds store oil, a fact often overlooked in temperate regions where starch-storing grain is cultivated. Many of the oils are of economic importance, for example, oil obtained from palms, olives, almonds, cotton seed and linseed. Fat stored in the dermis of the mammalian skin serves for food storage and acts as a heat insulator. In the middle layer of the plasma membrane of cells, fat is combined with phosphoric acid to form a phospholipid.

Natural fats and oils belong to the group of lipids, compounds composed of carbon, hydrogen and oxygen only, but having a lower proportion of oxygen than carbohydrates. There is no precise distinction between a fat and an oil but compounds of this type are called fats if they are solid at normal room temperature and oils if they are liquid. Fats are compounds of fatty (alkanoic) acids and glycerol (propantriol), the alkanoic acids being mainly palmitic (hexadecanoic), stearic (octadecanoic) and oleic (cis-octadec-9-enoic). The basic formula for an alkanoic acid is $R(CH_2)_nCOOH$

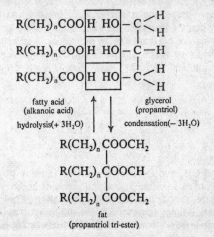

where R is an alkyl group like CH_3 or C_2H_5. In stearic (octadecanoic) acid, for example, $R = CH_3$ and $n = 16$, so that the general formula is $CH_3(CH_2)_{16}COOH$. All the bonds have been used here, so the fat is said to be **saturated**. In some alkanoic acids not all the bonds are used, double bonds occur, in which case the fat is **unsaturated**. To form a fat, three molecules of alkanoic acid react with one molecule of propantriol, three molecules of water being lost in the condensation reaction as the link is brought about. The alkanoic acid molecules involved may be all of the same kind or of different types.

Proteins

Proteins make up a considerable proportion of the dry weight of living things. They are present in the cell sap, protoplasm and as a solid food reserve in seeds and vegetative reproductive structures such as bulbs and tubers; they are components of plasma membranes, walls of cell organelles and are major constituents of muscles, connective tissue, hair and feathers. Cell metabolism is under the control of enzymes which are themselves proteins.

Proteins contain carbon, hydrogen, oxygen and nitrogen, some also contain phosphorus and/or sulphur. They are built up of **amino acid** units of which over twenty naturally occurring ones are known. The number of amino acid units in a protein may range from a few to thousands, but they are mostly large molecules, some contain only a selection of the possible amino acids, others contain all of them. The particular amino acids present and the order in which they occur determines the individuality of the protein. Structural proteins are particular to an individual. Amino acids have a common basic structure, $NH_2.CH.R.COOH$, the simplest amino acid is glycine (aminoethanoic acid), here R is a hydrogen atom. In

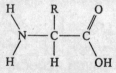

glycine (aminoethanoic acid)

alanine $R = CH_3$ and in valine $R = C_3H_7$. In more complex amino acids R contains an additional amino group or carboxyl group or a ring structure. Just as two hexose sugar molecules link together by a condensation reaction to form a disaccharide, so two amino acid molecules link together in a similar way to form a **dipeptide**. The

peptide bond —CO—NH— is a characteristic feature of all compounds formed from the condensation of amino acids. Dipeptides can link up in a similar way to form **polypeptides** which may be folded or branched; several polypeptide chains cross linked at intervals form a protein. Strong proteins are formed when the links contain sulphur atoms. One end of a polypeptide chain has a basic amino group which enables it to react with an acidic substance, while the opposite end of the chain has an acidic carboxyl group capable of combining with a basic substance. These properties are of value when compounds have to be assembled in the cell.

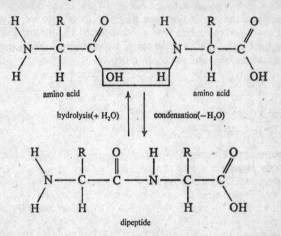

Proteins are large molecules and do not form true solutions but colloidal suspensions, thus a large surface area is available on which water and other substances may be absorbed and retained in position within the cell.

Conjugated proteins
A protein may combine with a non-protein substance forming a conjugated protein, the non-protein part being the prosthetic group. Mucus is a complex compound of protein with carbohydrate; in haemoglobin the protein is joined to an iron-containing pigment and in the vitellin of egg yolk the prosthetic group is phosphoric acid.

Nucleic acids

All living things, including bacteria and viruses, contain nucleic acids, the same nucleic acids being found in both plant and animal cells. Nucleic acids are like proteins in that they form long chains made up of units, the chains are longer than those of protein and the units are more complex than the amino acids which link to form the protein chain. The units making up nucleic acids are **nucleotides**. A nucleotide consists of **phosphoric acid, a 5-carbon (pentose) sugar** and an **organic base**. The sugar is ribose in RNA (ribose nucleic acid) and deoxyribose in DNA (deoxyribose nucleic acid). There are five possible organic bases; cytosine, uracil, adenine and guanine in RNA which is found mainly in the cytoplasm; cytosine, thymine, adenine and guanine in DNA which is confined to the nucleus. These organic bases are of two types, the pyrimidine type which includes cytosine, thymine and uracil and the purine type which includes adenine and guanine. In a nucleotide, condensation reactions have linked the phosphoric acid and the organic base to the sugar.

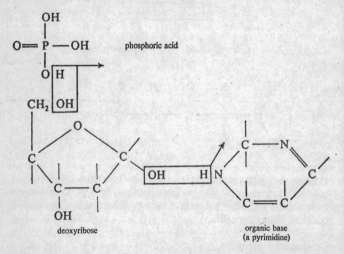

phosphoric acid

deoxyribose

organic base
(a pyrimidine)

There are only four possible bases in either RNA or DNA, so there are only four different nucleotides in each. Hundreds of nucleotides are linked together by further condensation reactions between the sugar unit of one nucleotide and the phosphoric acid unit of another so that a chain is built up with the organic bases projecting sideways. In RNA the phosphate and ribose sugar units are alternate and identical, in DNA the phosphate and deoxyribose sugar units are also alternate and identical; the bases however, vary. The precise sequences are meaningful, it is coded information which determines the organism's development. It was shown that in DNA

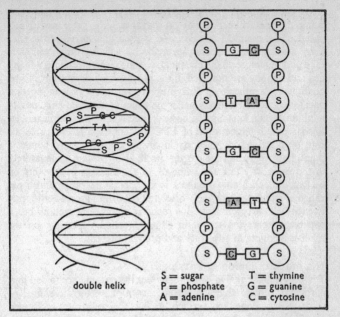

double helix

S = sugar T = thymine
P = phosphate G = guanine
A = adenine C = cytosine

Figure 22. The structure of DNA

there are always equal numbers of molecules of adenine and thymine and equal numbers of guanine and cytosine, this led Watson and Crick (1953) to suggest that DNA exists in the form of two phosphate-sugar strands (like the side supports of a ladder) held together by pairs of bases joined by hydrogen bonds (like the rungs of a ladder). The pairs of bases are adenine and thymine or cytosine and guanine, that is one purine and one pyramidine. The whole structure is coiled like a spiral staircase, the phosphate-sugar strands forming a **double helix.** It is essential that the genetic material should be able to produce an exact copy of itself; the Watson-Crick model shows a way in which this could take place; it will be considered again (see page 266).

Enzymes

The sum total of all the chemical reactions which take place in a living cell is the **metabolism** of that cell, the substances which take part in these reactions are metabolites. When metabolites are transformed into a product the reaction proceeds in a series of steps, each step being catalysed by an enzyme and the route taken being the metabolic pathway. A **catalyst** is a substance which speeds up a chemical reaction and is itself unchanged at the end. Enzymes are organic catalysts made by a living organism, they take part in almost all the chemical reactions which occur in a living cell and as they are not used in the process they do not have to be continually synthesized. Enzymes consist of a protein portion usually bound to a co-enzyme. Some vitamins act as co-enzymes, in addition certain ions may be needed as activators. In chemical reactions a rise in temperature of 10°C will approximately double the rate of reaction; in reactions involving enzymes there comes a point, however, when the enzyme itself, being protein, is denatured, in the same way that the white of an egg changes irrevocably on boiling. For each enzyme there is a temperature range and a pH range at which the enzyme works best. Enzymes are **specific**, that is each will carry out only one reaction or type of reaction, but is capable of carrying it out in either direction depending on the relative amounts of substrate and product present.

The mode of action of enzymes

The polypeptide chains which make up the enzyme are folded in a particular way so that the surface has a characteristic shape; at some point along its surface it fits the substrate molecules exactly, — this is the **active site** of the enzyme. The substrate molecules are thus brought together and form a substrate-enzyme complex, the product is then released and the enzyme is freed to react with further substrate molecules. The process may be summarized as follows:

$$\text{Enzyme} \rightleftharpoons \text{Enzyme-Substrate} \rightleftharpoons \text{Enzyme-Product} \rightleftharpoons \text{Enzyme}$$
$$+ \qquad\qquad \text{complex} \qquad\qquad \text{complex} \qquad\qquad +$$
$$\text{Substrate} \qquad\qquad\qquad\qquad\qquad\qquad\qquad\qquad\qquad \text{Product}$$

This suggested explanation of the way in which enzymes work is the **lock and key hypothesis.** The enzyme fits the substrate like a key in a padlock, it can be used to lock or unlock the padlock leaving the key unchanged; that is it can combine or separate the substrate molecules leaving the enzyme unchanged. Where enzymes carry out more than one reaction they are always of the same type and we can consider the analogy of a master key which will operate a number of locks with a basic similarity in the design. There is experimental evidence to support the lock and key theory. If the reaction, $AB \rightleftharpoons A + B$ is considered and the amount of substrate is increased without increasing the amount of enzyme, the rate of reaction increases at first and then proceeds at a constant rate. Continuing the analogy, at first the number of padlocks unlocked can be increased by increasing the number of padlocks, but a point is reached where the keys are working as fast as they can; what is wanted is more keys, and if more keys (enzymes) are added the reaction speeds up again. A rise in temperature speeds an enzyme reaction. Can the lock and key hypothesis explain this? In order for the padlock to be unlocked it must come in contact with the key, that is the enzyme must come in contact with the substrate molecule; raising the temperature makes molecules move faster and a collision is more likely. At higher temperatures the enzyme is denatured, the key is deformed.

Enzyme activators

Salivary amylase (ptyalin) which converts starch to maltose is activated by the presence of chloride ions, and thrombase (thrombokinase) is activated by calcium ions. Thrombase converts soluble fibrinogen in the blood plasma to insoluble fibrin bringing about blood clotting. The presence of iron or copper is necessary for the action of some oxidase enzymes.

Enzyme inhibitors

Some substances inhibit enzyme reactions so that the reaction slows down or ceases altogether. Mercury and arsenic attach themselves to the active site of the enzyme preventing the substrate fitting there. Cyanides are other powerful inhibitors. Some types of inhibitors work by distorting the shape of the enzyme molecule.

The classification of enzymes

The following are some of the more important groups of enzymes:—

Hydrolytic enzymes (hydrolases) These catalyse the hydrolysis or condensation of substrates by the addition or removal of the elements of water.

$$AB + HOH \rightleftharpoons AH + BOH$$

In this group are the esterases catalysing the hydrolysis of esters, e.g. lipase converts fat to fatty acid and glycerol.

Carbohydrases hydrolyse carbohydrates, e.g. amylase changes starch to maltose. Proteases attack the peptide bond in protein, e.g. pepsin which breaks protein into proteoses and peptones. All these enzymes will, of course, carry out the reaction in reverse, the condensation.

5

Oxidases and dehydrogenases (oxidoreductases) Enzymes in this group catalyse oxidation and reduction reactions, e.g. cytochrome oxidase. In respiration cytochrome is a hydrogen acceptor, cytochrome oxidase catalyses the removal of the hydrogen which combines with oxygen to form water, leaving the cytochrome in the oxidised state again.

Carboxylases Carboxylases are enzymes attacking the —C—C— link, e.g. enzymes involved in the removal of carbon from acids in respiration and liberating it as carbon dioxide.

Transferases These catalyse the removal of a chemical group from one substrate and its attachment to another.

$$AB + C \rightleftharpoons A + BC$$

Isomerases These catalyse internal rearrangement of molecules bringing about the change of one isomer into another.

$$ABC \rightleftharpoons ACB$$

Co-enzymes

Some enzymes work only in the presence of a co-enzyme, a substance which carries a chemical group from one enzyme to another. Vitamins of the B group are important co-enzymes. Nicotinamide in the form of nicotinamide adenine dinucleotide (NAD) or as the phosphate (NADP) acts as a co-enzyme for dehydrogenases. Pantothenic acid (co-enzyme A) is part of a transferase enzyme important in the Kreb's cycle. Riboflavine (B_2), biotin, thiamin (B_1), pyridoxine (B_6), folic acid, and cyanobalmin (B_{12}) also act as co-enzymes.

Analytical techniques

X-ray crystallography

X-ray crystallography is a valuable technique for investigating the shape of a molecule. A beam of X-rays is fired at a crystal of the substance, the atoms in the crystal deflect the rays on to a photographic plate behind the crystal, forming a pattern, the X-ray diffraction pattern. The crystal is turned between each firing to build up a series of patterns. Interpreting the patterns was a slow and difficult process in 1913 when Sir Lawrence Bragg worked out the structure of sodium chloride, but high speed computers have made it possible to study the molecular configuration of complex molecules such as nucleic acids; their structure was elucidated by Watson and Crick in 1953 during their research on the chemistry of the gene.

Spectrophotometry

Spectrophotometry is a technique used for the quantitative determination of minute amounts of chemical substances. One of the properties of chemical substances is that they show maximum absorption of light of different wavelengths. By measuring the percentage absorption at certain wavelengths and comparing it with solutions of known concentration, the amount of substance present can be determined.

Radioactive tracers

A particularly useful technique for studying metabolic pathways is by the use of radioactive **isotopes**. The atoms of an element are not exactly alike, they have the same chemical properties but they differ in atomic mass and other physical properties; these different atoms are called isotopes. Some isotopes are radioactive, such as ^{14}C, that is carbon with an atomic weight of fourteen instead of the usual twelve. The radioactive isotopes can be detected by means of a Geiger counter or by photographic methods and the element is said to be **'labelled'**. For example, if carbon dioxide is prepared using ^{14}C and a green plant placed in an atmosphere containing the gas, the labelled carbon is later found in the leaves. Analysis of the chemical compounds in the leaves, perhaps by chromatography will reveal the identity of the compounds containing the ^{14}C. This technique was used by Calvin (1949) in his studies of the metabolic pathway of photosynthesis. Isotopes which are not radioactive can be detected and measured by a mass spectrometer which separates them owing to their difference in atomic mass.

Manometry

Many processes involve a change in gas volumes, e.g. respiration. These changes can be measured accurately by means of a special manometer. Changes in gas volume can then be recorded under different experimental conditions.

Chromatography

Chromatography is particularly useful for separating and identifying components in a mixture of closely related chemical compounds, e.g. amino acids or chlorophyll. It relies on the fact that the components have different adsorptions. A concentrated spot of the mixture is placed at one end of a strip of absorbant paper which is then suspended in a suitable solvent or solvent mixture. As the solvent front creeps up the paper the individual compounds in the mixture, having different adsorptions, travel at different speeds and become separated. Columns of suitable material may be used instead of paper, or even liquid. A calculation based on the distances travelled by the solvent front and by the substance to be identified gives a figure, the Rf value, which is an aid to identification.

Key terms

Amino acid Chemical compound of the basic formula $NH_2.CH.R.COOH$ from which proteins are built.

Co-enzyme A carrier substance transferring a chemical group from one enzyme to another.

Condensation The linking of chemical compounds by the removal of a molecule of water between them.

Conjugated protein A protein combined with a non-protein part.

Dipeptide Product of the condensation of two amino acid units.

Disaccharide A double sugar formed by the condensation of two hexose sugar units.

Enzyme A catalyst made by a living cell.

Hexose A sugar of the general formula $C_6H_{12}O_6$ e.g. glucose.

Hydrolysis A chemical reaction often involving the splitting of a chemical compound into smaller units by the addition of a molecule of water at the linkage.

Isotopes Atoms of an element with similar chemical properties but different physical properties.

Monosaccharide A single sugar having the general formula $(CH_2O)_n$.

Nucleic acid Long chain compound built up of nucleotide units.

Nucleotide A chemical compound consisting of phosphoric acid, a pentose (5-carbon) sugar and an organic base.

Oxidation The removal of electrons from a substance. In a narrow sense the addition of oxygen or the removal of hydrogen.

Polypeptide Product of the condensation of many amino acid units.

Polysaccharide Carbohydrate of high molecular weight formed by the condensation of many hexose units.

Reduction The addition of electrons to a substance. In a narrow sense the addition of hydrogen or the removal of oxygen.

Saturated (compound) One in which all the chemical bonds are used.

Unsaturated (compound) One in which not all the chemical bonds are used, i.e. there may be double bonds etc.

Chapter 5
Cells and Tissues

Living organisms are composed of cells, in most of them the cells are **eukaryotic**, that is they are complex and have a definite nucleus and organelles but in bacteria and blue-green algae the cells are simpler, they lack a distinct nucleus and organelles and are said to be **prokaryotic**. In unicellular organisms the single cell is responsible for carrying out all the activities associated with living material. In more advanced animals and plants many cells have become specialized to carry out a particular function. In higher organisms groups of cells of similar structure and function form **tissues**, tissues may be collected together to form **organs**, distinct structural and functional units. The study of cells is **cytology**, that of tissues **histology**.

The microscopic structure of the cell

An animal cell is on average about 10 μm in diameter. It consists of a mass of protoplasm bounded by a **plasma membrane**, the protoplasm being differentiated into a **nucleus** and its surrounding granular **cytoplasm**. The nucleus is bounded by the **nuclear membrane** and contains the **nucleolus** and chromatin granules. Outside the nuclear membrane is the **centriole**, a structure concerned with spindle formation in mitosis. Plant cells have the protoplasm enclosed within a **cell wall**, usually composed of cellulose. There is a large **central vacuole** containing **cell sap**; the presence of this means that the cytoplasm forms a layer lining the cell wall and it therefore has two plasma membranes, the outer one next to the cell wall and an inner one, the **tonoplast**, next to the central vacuole. The nucleus may be found in the lining cytoplasm or suspended in the vacuole by strands of cytoplasm. The cell wall consists of a fine layer of calcium pectate produced by the cell, and on this the cellulose is deposited. Neighbouring cells are held together by the fusion of the pectate layers, the boundary between them becoming the **middle lamella**. The cellulose wall has fine pores through which pass threads of cytoplasm called **plasmodesmata**. Within the cytoplasm there may be colourless **leucoplasts** which contain stored food and **chloroplasts** containing chlorophyll.

The light microscope is not able to reveal any greater details of cell structure, but the electron microscope is capable of a magnification of about 250,000 times compared with about 1,000 times using the ordinary light microscope.

The ultrastructure of the cell

The electron microscope reveals that inside the plasma membrane the cytoplasm is differentiated into a number of structures called **organelles;** these include the **endoplasmic reticulum, ribosomes, Golgi body, mitochondria, lysosomes** and **centrioles.** The matrix of the cytoplasm may contain granules, oil drops and vacuoles filled with fluid.

The plasma membrane

The electron microscope shows that the plasma membrane consists of three layers, two similar layers enclosing a dissimilar middle layer, like a sandwich. The triple-layered membrane is supporting evidence for the theory put forward by Danielli and Davson in the 1930s that the plasma membrane consists of a double layer of lipid molecules enclosed between protein layers. Substances which are oil soluble penetrate the cell easily, this suggests that the plasma membrane contains lipid. The lipid molecules are likely to be orientated in a particular way, a molecule of fat has polar groups, a hydrocarbon end which is insoluble in water and a glycerol end which is water soluble. A film of fatty material on water will have the molecules orientated at right angles to the surface with the hydrocarbon groups pointing outwards and the glycerol groups attracted to the water, thus a monomolecular layer, or monolayer is formed. However, the monolayer is formed only when there is a water to air surface, whereas in a cell there will be water on both sides of the plasma membrane, but when two monolayers of this type are in contact the hydrocarbon ends are attracted together to form a bimolecular layer. The bimolecular layer alone would not be strong enough and would not account for the elasticity of the plasma membrane. Danielli and Davson suggested that the lipid layer was sandwiched between two protein layers. From experimental work involving the speeds at which various substances penetrated the membrane, they calculated the lipid layer to be about $6 \cdot 0$ nm thick with protein layers of about $1 \cdot 0$ nm on either side. These figures agree very closely with those obtained by electron microscopy. Furthermore the suggested orientation of the lipid and protein molecules in the membrane is confirmed by X-ray diffraction techniques.

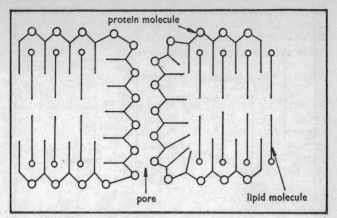

Figure 23. The structure of the plasma membrane

The endoplasmic reticulum

Much of the cytoplasm of the cell is occupied by the endoplasmic reticulum, a system of intercommunicating tubes lined by a membrane which is continuous with the nuclear membrane. One side of the membrane faces the lumen of the tube, the other side is in contact with the cytoplasmic matrix where, attached to the membrane there are numerous ribosomes. These are particles containing ribonucleic acid and are known to be sites of protein synthesis. The endoplasmic reticulum appears to form a kind of transport system within the cell. Substances such as digestive enzymes can be transported out of the cell, and there is free communication between the nucleus and cytoplasm by means of minute pores in the nuclear membrane. Certain areas of the endoplasmic reticulum are devoid of ribosomes, one of these is the Golgi body and it has been suggested that other such regions are concerned with the production and transport of lipids.

The Golgi body

The Golgi body is a dense area in the cytoplasm in a region where the endoplasmic reticulum has no ribosomes. It consists of layers of flattened tubes without ribosomes, the ends of which form small vesicles. Substances produced by the cell are transported to the Golgi body where they are assembled and stored.

Mitochondria

Mitochondria are minute rounded rods measuring about $0.7\,\mu$m in

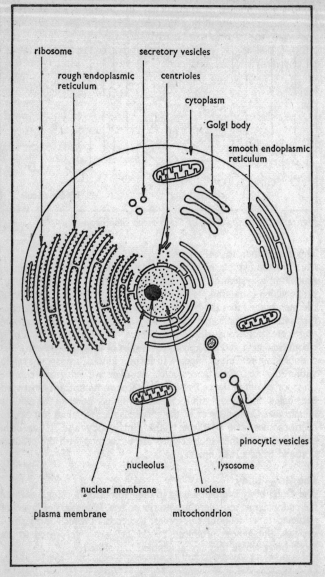

ribosome

rough endoplasmic reticulum

secretory vesicles

centrioles

cytoplasm

Golgi body

smooth endoplasmic reticulum

pinocytic vesicles

nucleolus

lysosome

nuclear membrane

nucleus

plasma membrane

mitochondrion

Figure 24. The ultrastructure of an animal cell

diameter and varying in length. They are present in the matrix of the cytoplasm. The wall of a mitochondrion consists of an outer layer separated by a narrow liquid-filled space from the inner layer which is pleated at intervals forming partitions called **cristae** which project into the interior of the organelle. Mitochondria are the centres of energy production in the cell, the amount of energy used by a cell is directly related to the number of mitochondria present. The chemical reactions of respiration which result in the production of energy are catalysed by enzymes present on the walls of the cristae and inner membrane of the mitochondrion.

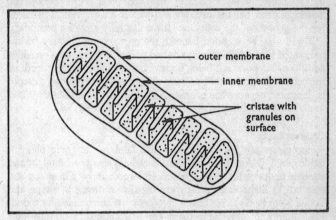

Figure 25. The structure of a mitochondrion

Lysosomes
The lysosomes are spherical bodies containing enzymes. One of their functions is to destroy old and worn out parts of the cell. The part to be destroyed is surrounded by a membrane, lysosomes move towards this sac and discharge enzymes into it bringing about digestion, the products then being absorbed into the cytoplasmic matrix. Lysosomes are important in cells which engulf large particles, such as white blood cells and *Amoeba*.

Centrioles
Every animal cell contains two centrioles near the nucleus, each consists of paired filaments arranged in a hollow cylinder. The centrioles separate at mitosis each giving rise to spindle fibres to which the chromosomes become attached. Centrioles are also concerned with the formation of cilia and flagella.

The ultrastructure of additional features in the plant cell

Cell walls

As the plant cell grows it synthesizes cellulose which is laid down outside the plasma membrane forming the foundation of the primary cell wall. The cellulose is deposited in parallel strands called microfibrils each composed of about 2,000 cellulose chains. Subsequent layers of microfibrils are laid down at an angle to those in the previous layer. Spaces may be filled with pectates or hemicelluloses, but the primary cell wall is always elastic to allow for the growth of the cell. Once the cell is fully grown a secondary cell wall may be secreted beneath the primary one. It may be impregnated with lignin as in xylem and sclerenchyma, and it provides additional support, but being impermeable it results in the death of the cell. In the corky cells of bark, a layer of fatty material, suberin, is deposited between the primary and secondary walls, again this is impermeable and brings about the death of the cell.

Chloroplasts

Chloroplasts are the organelles which contain the green pigment chlorophyll. Chlorophyll absorbs the radiant energy of sunlight and enables photosynthesis to proceed. Chloroplasts vary in shape and size but in higher plants they are usually biconvex in shape and about 5 μm in diameter. Each chloroplast is surrounded by a double membrane and inside there are large numbers of **lamellae**

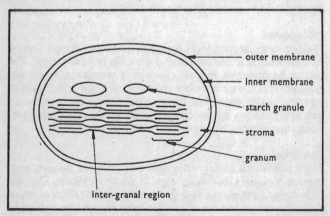

Figure 26. The structure of a chloroplast

74

arranged parallel to one another. Each lamella consists of two membranes close together but with a space between. In the lamella are two regions, the granal and the intergranal. In the granal region the constituent membranes are slightly further apart and a third membrane is found between them. The granal regions of adjacent lamellae coincide, each group forming a **granum**. The chlorophyll molecules are arranged on the lamellae in such a way as to receive the maximum amount of light. Surrounding the lamellae is the fluid **stroma**, it contains enzymes and starch granules. When illuminated, isolated lamellae liberate oxygen and it seems likely that the light reaction of photosynthesis takes place here. Examination of broken grana under the electron microscope shows numerous granules called quantosomes which contain a high proportion of chlorophyll.

Animal tissues

Although cells are basically similar and possess the organelles revealed by the electron microscope, they vary in size, shape and contents. The structure of the cell is admirably suited to the function it has to perform. Even in a lowly animal such as *Hydra* there are several different types of cells, while in the complex structure of the mammalian body there is a considerable degree of cell specialization.

Epithelium

Epithelium is lining tissue, it covers the external and internal surfaces of the body. Except in the skin it is one cell thick and consists of cells held firmly together and attached to a basement membrane. In **squamous** epithelium the cells are flattened and ideally suited to forming the walls of blood capillaries and alveoli where the thin layer allows gases to diffuse through easily. In the trachea the epithelial cells are **ciliated**, the cilia wafting a layer of mucus upwards and away from the lungs carrying with it trapped dust particles. **Columnar** epithelium has elongated cells, it lines the intestines and is concerned with the absorption of digested food. Among the columnar cells there may be special secretory cells called goblet cells which produce mucus to aid the passage of solid material along the gut. The mixture of columnar and glandular cells may be called **glandular** epithelium. In the skin there are a number of layers of epithelium, the innermost layer remains capable of dividing and pushing the others towards the surface where they become progressively flatter and drier and are eventually shed. This multilayer is **stratified** epithelium.

Connective tissue

Connective tissue is strong and holds organs and tissues in place. The commonest type is **areolar** tissue which consists of a matrix in which are embedded several types of cells and fibres. There are the fibroblasts, bundles of parallel collagen fibres and a network of elastic fibres. Mast cells secrete the matrix; there may also be fat storage cells and large amoeboid cells which engulf foreign particles.

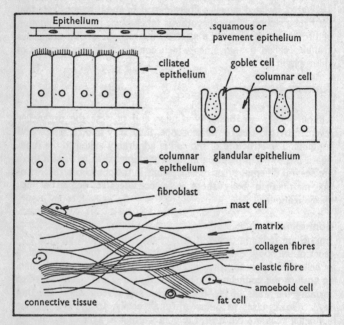

Figure 27. Epithelium and connective tissue

Skeletal tissue

The skeleton is composed of **bone** and **cartilage**. The cartilage which forms the temporary skeleton of the foetus is gradually replaced by bone but remains on the articular surfaces of the bones. Cartilage is less rigid than bone, simple or hyaline cartilage consists of chrondroblasts which secrete the slightly elastic matrix. Bone contains much calcium phosphate, the surface layer of bone is hard bone and the inside consists of spongy bone, the spaces being filled with red bone marrow. The central cavity in the long bones is filled with yellow bone marrow. The calcium phosphate is secreted by cells called osteoblasts, they are arranged in a series of rings round nerves and blood vessels.

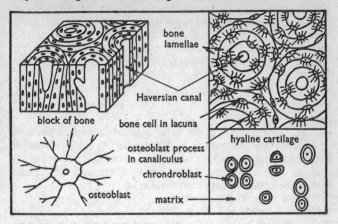

Figure 28. Cartilage and bone tissues

Muscular tissue

There are three types of muscular tissue; **striated** muscle makes up the muscles attached to the skeleton, **cardiac** muscle is found in the heart and smooth **unstriated** muscle occurs in the gut wall and blood vessels. Smooth muscle is associated with involuntary

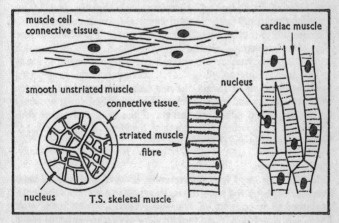

Figure 29. Muscular tissue

movements, it is composed of sheets of closely packed parallel fibres held together by connective tissue. Cardiac muscle consists of anastomosing cells with little connective tissue, it is faintly striated. The structure of striated muscle is dealt with in Chapter 11.

Nervous tissue
The structure of nervous tissue is considered in Chapter 10.

Plant tissues

Meristematic tissue
In higher plants meristematic tissue is found in the root tip, stem apex and in the cambium. It is characterized by small thin-walled cells containing a prominent nucleus, dense contents and no central vacuole. New cells formed by the activity of the meristematic cells become differentiated into specialized cells.

Epidermal tissue
Epidermal cells are rather flat and sometimes irregular in shape so that they may interlock like pieces in a jigsaw puzzle. They are protective in function and may have the outer cellulose wall impregnated with waxy substances forming the cuticle which is waterproof and prevents evaporation from the cells.

Mechanical tissue
Parenchyma is a tissue consisting of living thin-walled cells which are rounded in shape and therefore pack together leaving intercellular spaces. Their role as mechanical tissue is due entirely to their turgidity; they are particularly important in seedlings before any other mechanical tissues have developed. Most cells which carry out photosynthesis are parenchymatous, modified in shape as in the palisade mesophyll of leaves, and containing chloroplasts. **Collenchyma** also consists of living cells, their support being due to both turgidity and extra cellulose thickening laid down unevenly on the walls and filling the corners of the cells. **Sclerenchyma** fibres are long tapering cells with thick lignified walls, the deposit of lignin resulting in the death of the cell.

Vascular tissue
Xylem is concerned with the transport of water and mineral salts from the roots up the stem to the leaves. It is a complex tissue; in angiosperms it consists of tracheids, vessels, parenchyma and fibres. No vessels are found in the xylem of gymnosperms or lower plants. A tracheid is a cell with somewhat chisel-shaped ends, the

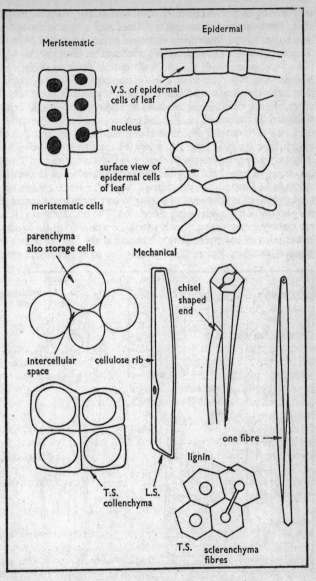

Meristematic

Epidermal

V.S. of epidermal cells of leaf

nucleus

surface view of epidermal cells of leaf

meristematic cells

parenchyma also storage cells

Mechanical

chisel shaped end

Intercellular space

cellulose rib

T.S. collenchyma

L.S.

one fibre

lignin

T.S.   sclerenchyma fibres

Figure 30. Meristematic, epidermal and mechanical tissues

walls are lignified and therefore when mature the cell is no longer alive. The thickening is not uniform, there may be many circular or oval bordered pits, these occur between adjacent tracheids. A vessel element is a single lignified cell; a vessel consists of vessel elements placed end to end with the end walls broken down or perforated. Vessels vary in length from a few centimetres to several metres, they have simple pits and bordered pits, the former occur where adjacent cells have unlignified areas coinciding, the two cells being separated by the middle lamella and primary walls only. The secondary wall in a vessel is deposited in different forms, the first formed vessels have lignin in rings, these are the annular vessels; they are followed by vessels with the thickening in the form of spirals. These two types of vessel are found in the protoxylem which is the first xylem to be formed. The structure of the protoxylem permits a certain amount of longitudinal stretching to take place in the region of the plant which is undergoing elongation. The next formed xylem, the metaxylem, contains vessels which have sclariform thickening, in the form of bars; reticulate thickening in the form of a net; or pitted thickening. Xylem fibres are similar to sclerenchyma, and

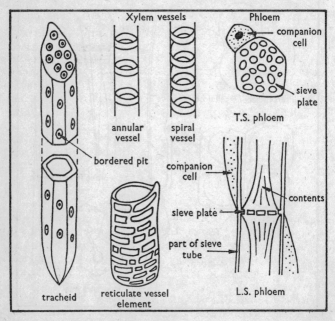

Figure 31. Xylem and phloem tissues

80

xylem parenchyma stores water and sometimes food materials.

Phloem is concerned with the translocation of food materials from the leaves to other parts of the plant. In angiosperms it consists of sieve tubes and companion cells, fibres and parenchyma; in gymnosperms there are no companion cells. A sieve tube element and its companion cell are formed by the division of a single cell, but the cell destined to become the sieve tube element loses its nucleus and the contents become greatly changed, the centre of the cell being occupied by a proteinaceous mass while the companion cell develops normally. A sieve tube consists of sieve tube elements placed end to end, the end walls being perforated and forming a sieve plate. Cytoplasmic strands pass through the sieve plate so that adjacent cells are in communication. Sieve areas may also be found on the side walls of the sieve tube elements.

The passage of substances in and out of cells

Diffusion

Diffusion is the movement of molecules or ions from a region of high concentration to one of low concentration. Diffusion can occur in gases or in liquids. The rate of diffusion is inversely proportional to the distance over which the diffusion takes place. In other words, as molecules move from a region of high concentration to one of low concentration they move at a progressively slower speed. Some organisms obtain oxygen for respiration by diffusion over their surface and get rid of carbon dioxide the same way. The size of the organism for which this method can be satisfactory is limited for two reasons; firstly, the larger the organism the lower is its surface area to volume ratio, so that larger organisms simply would not have sufficient surface to allow them to obtain enough oxygen. Secondly, the larger the organism the slower will be the rate at which the oxygen will diffuse to deeper regions.

Active transport

Molecules and ions diffuse from a region of high concentration to one of low concentration, therefore the process of diffusion cannot be used to explain the fact that cells often accumulate certain ions so that they are present in a higher concentration inside the cell than outside. In other words they have entered the cell against the diffusion gradient. This involves an expenditure of energy on the part of the cell in a process called active transport the energy being supplied by respiration. Temperature, oxygen concentration and various enzyme inhibitors such as cyanide affect both the rate of respiration and the rate of active transport. One mechanism that has been suggested to explain active transport has postulated the presence of carrier molecules, a carrier collecting an ion or molecule at the outer surface of the plasma membrane and conveying it across to the cytoplasm. The movement of the carrier molecules backwards and forwards across the plasma membrane would require energy.

Osmosis

The plasma membrane of a cell is **semi-permeable**, that is it will allow some substances to pass through in preference to others. Small molecules will be able to cross the membrane but larger ones will be impeded. Natural membranes such as pig's bladder and artificial ones such as cellophane and Visking tubing are examples of semi-permeable membranes. The process of osmosis can be demonstrated with the simple apparatus shown in Fig. 32. The level of the liquid in the glass tubing rises, this may be explained by the fact that on one side of the membrane there are water molecules, on the other side there are both sugar molecules and water molecules. All the molecules are in a state of motion, colliding with each other and with the membrane. The membrane may be regarded as having small holes through which water molecules can pass but the larger sugar molecules cannot. Water molecules will thus pass in both directions but there are fewer water molecules in the sugar solution than in the water outside, so more water molecules will pass into the sugar solution than will move in the opposite direction. Osmosis may be defined as the passage of water from a weak solution to a strong solution through a semi-permeable membrane. As the water level in the glass tubing rises, a hydrostatic pressure develops, pressing on the semi-permeable membrane, so that in time no further water enters. The head of pressure developed by the solution is its **osmotic pressure**. The more concentrated the solution the greater the osmotic pressure. The same phenomenon will take place with other solutions such as those of mineral salts. If a cell such as a red blood cell is placed in water or a solute concentration lower than that inside the cell, water enters by osmosis and the cell swells up; the osmotic pressure of the liquid outside is said to be **hypotonic** to the cell. If the cell does not change in size when placed in a solution, the osmotic pressure and the solute concentration of the solution outside are the same as that in the cell or **isotonic**. If the red blood cell is placed in a solution of higher solute concentration and therefore higher osmotic pressure than that inside the cell, the cell will shrink, the external solution is **hypertonic** to the cell. If cells are to function normally they need to be either in an isotonic solution or to be equipped with a means of **osmoregulation** to enable them to exist in hypertonic or hypotonic media. The contractile vacuole of freshwater protozoa is one such osmoregulatory mechanism. The solutes in the organism cause water to enter by osmosis and this has to be collected and expelled or the organism would swell up and burst. Small marine organisms have body fluids isotonic with sea water, no contractile vacuoles are necessary.

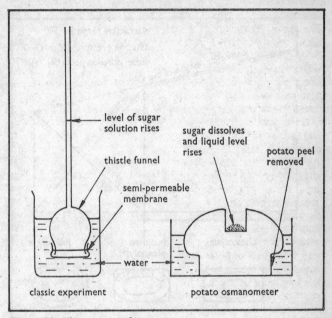

Figure 32. The process of osmosis

In a plant cell the cell wall is permeable, the plasma membrane and the tonoplast behave as semi-permeable membranes. As a plant cell takes up water the volume of the cell sap increases and presses the cytoplasm against the cell wall, this is the turgor pressure. When the cell wall can stretch no more the cell is fully turgid. If the turgid plant cell is now placed in a hypertonic solution, water passes out of the cell by osmosis, the volume of the cell sap is reduced, the cytoplasm draws away from the cell wall and the cell is said to be plasmolysed – the process is **plasmolysis**. If the plasmolysed cell is placed in a hypotonic solution, water enters the cell with a force which is the **suction pressure** (diffusion pressure deficit). This equals the osmotic pressure of the cell sap. When the cytoplasm touches the cell wall again, the wall exerts a pressure on the contents, this is the **wall pressure**, so now the suction pressure is equal to the osmotic pressure minus the wall pressure. The cell continues to increase in volume, as it does so the wall pressure increases and the suction pressure decreases until at full turgor the suction pressure is zero, and the osmotic pressure and wall pressure are now equal.

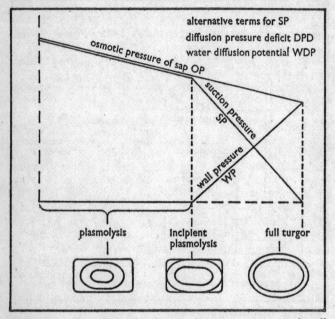

Figure 33. The relationship between osmotic, suction and wall pressures

Phagocytosis

Some cells are able to take in relatively large particles; *Amoeba* may feed on smaller protozoa, and white blood cells will engulf certain bacteria. A cup-shaped depression forms at the surface of the cell, the particle is enclosed and cytoplasm gradually closes over it leaving the particle in a food vacuole where it is digested by means of enzymes. The cells are capable of selecting suitable particles and rejecting others.

Pinocytosis

On the surface of cells fine channels have been observed, they are formed by little tucks in the plasma membrane. Minute vacuoles are pinched off at the base of the channels and they migrate towards the centre of the cell. This is an additional method of transporting liquids into the cell, although the liquid is still separated from the cytoplasm by the plasma membrane at the boundary of the vacuole and the cytoplasm.

Key terms

Centriole Cell structure present outside nuclear membrane, concerned in spindle formation during cell division.

Collenchyma Plant tissue of living cells with additional cellulose thickening particularly in the corners of the cells.

Diffusion The movement of molecules or ions from a region of high concentration to one of low concentration.

Diffusion pressure deficit Suction pressure.

Endoplasmic reticulum System of long narrow channels in cell cytoplasm bordered by thin membranes.

Epithelium A covering tissue in animals.

Eukaryotic (cell) Genetic material on chromosomes in a nucleus separated from the cytoplasm by a nuclear membrane. Structural unit in most organisms. See prokaryotic.

Golgi body Structure present in cell cytoplasm consisting of a series of parallel flattened sacs.

Hypertonic (solution) One with a higher osmotic pressure.

Hypotonic (solution) One with a lower osmotic pressure.

Isotonic (solution) One with the same osmotic pressure.

Lysosomes Cell bodies containing enzymes destroying worn out parts of cell.

Mitochondria Bodies in cell cytoplasm containing enzymes important in production of energy.

Organelle A permanent structure with a particular function in a cell.

Osmoregulation Control of the osmotic pressure within an organism.

Osmosis The movement of water across a semi-permeable membrane from a weak solution to a stronger solution.

Osmotic pressure The pressure required to stop the movement of water across a semi-permeable membrane.

Parenchyma Plant tissue consisting of living thin walled cells.

Plasma membrane Thin membrane of fat and protein covering surface of cytoplasm in cells, and bordering cell vacuole in plant cells.

Plasmodesmata Fine cytoplasmic strands connecting adjacent plant cells through minute pores in the cellulose wall.

Plasmolysis The withdrawal of the cytoplasm from the cell wall in a plant cell.

Prokaryotic (cell) One having no nuclear membrane separating the genetic material (filaments of DNA) from the cytoplasm. Typical of bacteria and blue-green algae.

Ribosomes Sites of protein synthesis in cells. Formed of protein and RNA.

Sclerenchyma (fibres) Long tapering dead cells with thick walls of lignin giving mechanical support.

Suction pressure In osmosis the force with which water enters a cell.

Tracheid Lignified element of xylem formed from a single cell.

Vessel Water conducting structure in xylem of angiosperms, consisting of a series of dead lignified elements placed end to end.

Wall pressure In osmosis the inward pressure exerted by the cell wall.

Water diffusion potential Suction pressure.

Chapter 6
Nutrition

All living organisms need a source of energy for cellular and body activities, and substrates for the synthesis of all material necessary for proper functioning, growth and reproduction. The nutrition of an organism is the obtaining and utilization of materials from the external environment that satisfies these requirements. Living organisms fall into two groups nutritionally; **autotrophs** which utilize the simple inorganic compounds carbon dioxide and water as starting materials, and **heterotrophs** which obtain complex organic compounds. There are two types of autotrophic nutrition depending on the source of energy used; most autotrophs use light energy in the familiar process of **photosynthesis**, but some bacteria are **chemosynthetic,** they obtain energy by a respiratory process involving the oxidation of certain simple inorganic materials in the environment. The term holophytic is also in use meaning the nutrition of green plants. The heterotrophs show greater variety in their mode of life; most animals are **holozoic**, obtaining organic food by consuming the body material of plants and animals and digesting it internally by means of enzymes. Many bacteria and fungi are **saprophytes** feeding on decaying plant and animal matter by secreting enzymes on to it and absorbing the soluble products of digestion. Some animals and plants are **parasites**, taking food from living plants and animals. Other ways of life are **symbiosis** in which two living organisms, usually an autotroph and a heterotroph, live in close association for mutual benefit; and **commensalism** in which the commensal gains and the host is neither benefitted nor exploited.

Food chains, food webs and energy levels

In an **ecosystem**, a natural community of plants and animals, the organisms are linked nutritionally. There are producers, autotrophic organisms, mainly green plants which synthesize organic food, and there are consumers, the heterotrophs, consisting of primary consumers, the herbivores which feed on the green plants, and secondary consumers, carnivores which feed on the herbivores. Lastly there are decomposers, saprophytes, they are responsible for recycling the materials for the autotrophs. In any ecosystem the energy trapped by an autotroph is transferred to a primary consumer as it feeds upon it. In turn it is passed to a predatory secondary consumer and so on along a food chain. Food chains may be short, for example; grass – rabbit – fox, or longer, but they rarely exceed five organisms. In most ecosystems the herbivore will have a choice of food plants and a carnivore will have a choice of prey so that a more complex relationship, a food web, will be built up. When a herbivore consumes plants only about 20% of the energy locked up in them becomes incorporated into the animal's body, 80% is lost as heat in respiration, in urine and in faeces. When the herbivore is eaten by a carnivore a similar loss of energy occurs. The number of organisms in a food chain is therefore limited, as is the total amount of living material which can exist at each **trophic level**, – the **biomass**. The biomass is progressively lower at each trophic level and the number of organisms contained in it is fewer at each level, the effect being accentuated by the fact that the larger animals are at the top of the food chains. The loss of energy at each level accounts for the fact that there are only a few organisms in a food chain. The progressive drop in numbers and biomass at each trophic level can be shown diagrammatically as a pyramid of numbers and pyramid of biomass.

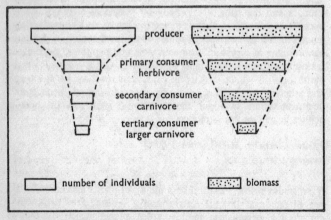

Figure 34. Pyramid of numbers and pyramid of biomass

If these facts are considered in relation to the diet of man, it means that a high percentage of meat in the diet is expensive in energy terms. To obtain the maximum amount of energy from the land man needs to be near the base of the food chain. In poorer countries this is exactly the position he occupies, the staple diet is a vegetable crop such as rice or maize. However, where the land is poor and unsuitable for agriculture, sheep and goats may be raised to build useful protein from poor vegetation. Unfortunately some areas of poor vegetation are the result of the goats' indiscriminate feeding habits which prevent regeneration and bring about soil erosion.

Chemosynthetic autotrophs

Certain bacteria oxidize substances in the environment, for example, some may convert nitrites to nitrates, others iron[11] salts to iron[111] salts, a third group hydrogen sulphide to water and sulphur. These oxidation reactions are a special kind of respiration and the energy obtained from them is used to fix the carbon from carbon dioxide into an organic form. Chemosynthesis is a less efficient process than photosynthesis, the starting materials are less readily available than sunlight and only small amounts of energy are obtained from the oxidation reactions.

Photosynthetic autotrophs

Photosynthesis is the method of nutrition used by all green plants. Water and carbon dioxide are converted to sugar using light energy from the sun which is trapped by chlorophyll. There are also certain bacteria which are able to make their food in this way. All animals are ultimately dependent on plants for their food, contributing carbon dioxide, a waste product of their respiration, for use as a raw material by the green plants; these in turn produce oxygen as a waste product of photosynthesis, the excess over their respiratory requirements being available for animal respiration. The two groups of living organisms are thus completely interdependent.

The products of photosynthesis

To show that oxygen is produced in photosynthesis some pieces of a water plant such as *Elodea* are placed under an inverted filter funnel in a tall beaker. The apparatus is filled with water and a test tube filled with water is inverted over the stem of the funnel. A small quantity of sodium bicarbonate may be stirred in the water to guard against any possible shortage of carbon dioxide. The apparatus is then exposed to bright light, and bubbles of gas arise from the water weed and collect in the test tube. When sufficient gas has been collected it may be tested by the insertion of a glowing splint. The splint will burst into flames showing that oxygen is present.

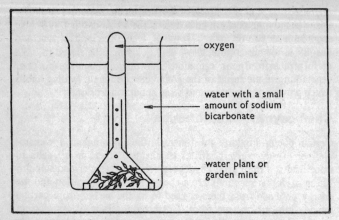

Figure 35. To show that oxygen is evolved in photosynthesis

To show that starch is produced in photosynthesis a green leaf is dipped into boiling water to break open the cells; soaked in alcohol, warmed if necessary, to dissolve out the chlorophyll; washed free of alcohol and tested with iodine solution. A blue colour indicates the presence of starch. The hexose sugar formed during photosynthesis is used for energy and growth or converted to starch for storage purposes in the plant.

The conditions necessary for photosynthesis

For photosynthesis to take place the plant needs water, carbon dioxide, light, chlorophyll and a suitable temperature. The process of photosynthesis alone, however, will not ensure a healthy plant, for it needs a source of nitrogen to build proteins; this and other vital elements are obtained in the form of ions by the roots. Water enters the plant mainly through the root hairs, these contain osmotically active substances in the cell sap which are separated from the soil water by the cell wall and cytoplasm. Water enters the root hairs by osmosis passing freely through the fully permeable cell wall and across two semi-permeable membranes, the plasma membrane and the tonoplast, bordering the cytoplasm on each side, and reaches the cell sap. The sap is diluted and water will now pass by osmosis from it to the adjacent cell in the cortex. The gradient of suction pressures maintained across the cortex from the stele to the epidermis ensures the passage of water across the cortex to the vascular tissue in the centre of the root. The processes of transpiration, capillarity and root pressure account for the upward transport of water in the xylem to the leaves. The optimum temperature for photosynthesis in most plants is about 28 to 30°C, above this the enzymes gradually become denatured.

Starch being a substance which is easy to identify chemically, its presence forms a convenient means of determining whether or not photosynthesis has taken place. When demonstrating that light, carbon dioxide or chlorophyll is essential for photosynthesis the first step is to destarch the plant, this is done by placing the plant in the dark for 24 hours, when it will use up its store of starch in the leaves. A leaf is then tested to confirm that the plant is starch free.

To show that carbon dioxide is necessary for photosynthesis, a destarched plant is taken and a leaf inserted into a flask containing a little sodium hydroxide solution, a second leaf is inserted into a similar flask containing water, to act as a control. The plant is then exposed to bright light for 6 to 8 hours, after that the leaves are picked and tested for starch. The leaf from the flask in which the sodium hydroxide has absorbed the carbon dioxide will be free of starch.

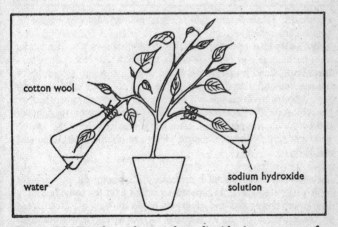

Figure 36. To show that carbon dioxide is necessary for photosynthesis

To show that light is necessary for photosynthesis, some stencils are cut from black paper and fixed to the leaves of a destarched potted plant. The plant is then exposed to bright light for 6 to 8 hours, the stencils being removed at the end of that time and the leaves picked and tested for starch. The leaves will show a pattern of blue staining with iodine solution which corresponds to the cut out portions of the stencil, proving that starch is formed only where the leaf has been exposed to light.

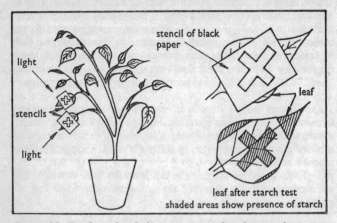

Figure 37. To show that light is necessary for photosynthesis

The **absorption spectrum** of chlorophyll shows that it absorbs light in the blue and red ends of the spectrum. An absorption spectrum is obtained by passing a beam of light through a solution of chlorophyll and then through a prism. Any colours found in a complete spectrum which are not represented have been absorbed by the chlorophyll. Experiments exposing green leaves to light of different colours and then estimating quantitatively the starch produced, show that the highest yields are obtained with blue and red light.

To show that chlorophyll is necessary for photosynthesis a plant with variegated leaves is exposed to bright light for some hours. A few leaves are picked and diagrams made showing the green areas of the leaves. They are then tested for starch and it will be found that the regions which have been stained blue with iodine solution correspond to the areas in which chlorophyll was present, showing that starch is produced only in the presence of chlorophyll. Alternatively, a few circles cut with a cork borer may be taken from a green area and a non-green area of a variegated leaf, tested for starch and compared.

The concept of limiting factors

When a process requires a number of different conditions for its success, the rate at which it will proceed depends on the factor which is closest to its minimum value. For photosynthesis to take place in a green plant, light, carbon dioxide and a suitable temperature are required. In the natural environment light is a **limiting factor** for many plants all the time and there is constant competition to reach the light. Early in the day temperature may be a limiting factor and for plants growing in open situations with plenty of light and a suitable temperature in the middle of the day, carbon dioxide may be the limiting factor. In the hours of darkness a plant is using its food reserves for respiration, when daylight returns and photosynthesis commences there comes a time when the rate at which carbohydrate is being synthesized is exactly equal to the rate at which it is being used in respiration, this is the **compensation point**. The time taken for a plant which has been in the dark to reach its compensation point in the light, is the **compensation period**.

Leaf structure

The leaf is thin and flat to present a large surface area to the light, the thinness also ensures that gases have a minimum distance over which to diffuse. The structure is supported by the midrib and veins containing vascular and mechanical tissues, and by the turgidity of the cells. Figure 38 shows a small portion of a vertical section through the lamina of a dicotyledonous leaf. It is bounded on each surface by a single layer of epidermal cells which have a covering of waterproof **cuticle**. Beneath the **upper epidermis** is a layer of **palisade cells**, elongated cells with the long axis at right angles to the surface of the leaf, they contain chloroplasts and have intercellular spaces. Below the palisade layer there are loosely packed **spongy mesophyll** cells with large intercellular spaces, they contain chloroplasts but fewer than the cells of the palisade layer. In the **lower epidermis** are **stomata**, pores bounded by a pair of **guard cells** which lead internally to a sub-stomatal air space.

Leaf function

Carbon dioxide enters the leaf through the stomata and diffuses through the intercellular spaces to the chloroplasts. Water is drawn up from the soil through the roots and stem and into the veins of the leaf, it passes out of the xylem vessels into the surrounding cells. It evaporates from the walls of the mesophyll cells of the leaf and diffuses into the sub-stomatal air space and out through the stomata.

The moist walls of the cells are essential for the diffusion of gases in and out of the cells. Oxygen produced in photosynthesis diffuses out of the stomata and sugar is translocated away from the leaf in the phloem. The opening and closing of the stomata can control the movement of gases in and out of the leaf. When the stomata are closed some photosynthesis can still take place using the carbon dioxide from respiration, and respiration can proceed using the oxygen produced in photosynthesis, but obviously for photosynthesis to proceed at more than a minimal rate carbon dioxide must be taken in from outside.

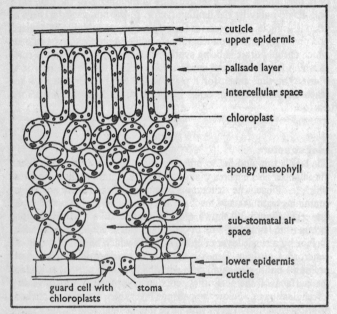

Figure 38. V.S. of part of the lamina of a dicotyledonous leaf

Structure and function of stomata

The guard cells are sausage shaped and their walls are unevenly thickened, the portion of the wall facing the stoma being thicker than elsewhere. The guard cells are the only cells of the epidermis to contain chloroplasts and carry out photosynthesis. The sugar produced increases the concentration of the cell sap and raises the osmotic pressure causing water to be drawn into the guard cells by osmosis from the surrounding epidermal cells, thus increasing their turgidity. The thinner part of the cell wall stretches but the thickened portion cannot so each guard cell becomes more curved and the thickened walls pull apart opening the pore.

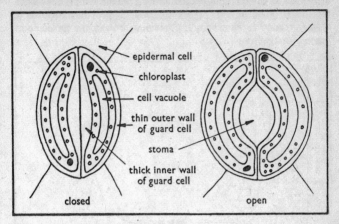

Figure 39. Closed and open stomata

This theory of stomatal opening cannot be the whole story because the stomata open too rapidly when photosynthesis is resumed in daylight. One theory depends on the fact that the conversion of starch to sugar proceeds more rapidly under conditions of high pH the reverse process being favoured when the pH is low. During the hours of darkness carbon dioxide from respiration accumulates in the leaf and the carbonic acid results in the lowering of the pH which favours the conversion of sugar to starch. When daylight returns and photosynthesis commences, the carbon dioxide is used, the pH rises and the conversion of starch to sugar proceeds, raising the osmotic pressure in the guard cells and opening the stomata. The opening and closing of the stomata brings about some control over the movement of gases and water vapour to and from the leaf.

Chloroplasts and chlorophyll
The structure of chloroplasts has been mentioned in Chapter 5. The green colouring matter of a leaf; 'chlorophyll' is really a mixture of pigments. This can be shown readily by the technique of paper chromatography. From the extracted colouring matter five pigments can be separated; **chlorophyll a** (blue-green), **chlorophyll b** (yellow-green), **xanthophyll** (yellow) and **carotene** (orange); the fifth, phaeophytin is believed to be a breakdown product, it is grey-brown in colour. Chlorophylls a and b absorb

light in the blue and red regions of the spectrum, while xanthophyll and carotene absorb it in the blue-violet. Chemically chlorophyll is a complex organic compound containing magnesium, it belongs to the group of porphyrins. The red blood pigment haemoglobin is closely related to chlorophyll, containing iron in the molecule in place of magnesium.

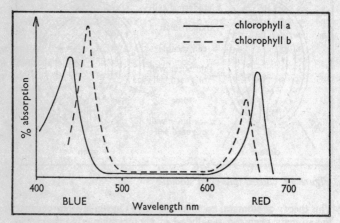

Figure 40. Absorption spectra of chlorophyll pigments

The chemistry of photosynthesis
The equation

$$6CO_2 + 6H_2O \xrightarrow[\text{chlorophyll}]{\text{light}} C_6H_{12}O_6 + 6O_2 \uparrow$$

summarizes the process of photosynthesis but tells us nothing about the stages in the process. Warburg showed that the total amount of carbon fixed by a plant given alternate periods of light and dark was greater than that fixed by a plant given continuous light, although the total amount of light was the same in each case. This suggests that part of the process of photosynthesis is not dependent upon light. Other evidence came from a comparison of the rates of photosynthesis of two groups of plants, one given light of high intensity, the other light of low intensity; both groups being supplied with adequate carbon dioxide. For the group with intense illumination a rise of 10°C doubled the rate of photosynthesis, the other group showed no increase. This shows that part of the process of photosynthesis is an ordinary thermochemical reaction and not a photochemical one which would be unaffected by a temperature

96

change. Another contribution to the understanding of the process of photosynthesis came from the use of water containing the oxygen isotope ^{18}O. When water containing this isotope was supplied to the plant the oxygen evolved during photosynthesis was $^{18}O_2$ proving that it must have come from the water and not the carbon dioxide. The elucidation of the chemical pathways of photosynthesis is due in the main to Calvin in the U.S.A. He used carbon dioxide containing the carbon isotope ^{14}C and supplied this to cultures of unicellular algae, exposing them to light for varying lengths of time, then killing the cells by plunging them into boiling alcohol and examining the products. After 5 seconds exposure he found phosphoglyceric acid; after 30 seconds exposure, triose phosphate and after 90 seconds, sugars.

Photosynthesis proceeds in two major stages, the light stage and a stage which is independent of light, – the dark stage.

Light stage This involves the formation of adenosine triphosphate (ATP) which provides energy for carbohydrate synthesis and the splitting of water photochemically to produce hydrogen atoms to reduce carbon dioxide. When light reaches a chlorophyll molecule an electron becomes 'excited', leaves the molecule and is taken up by an electron carrier; it is then passed through a series of electron carriers which are at different energy levels. In this process it loses energy which is used to synthesize ATP (from ADP and phosphate), and it finally returns to the chlorophyll molecule which has been positively charged and unstable during the travels of the electron. For each circuit of an electron two molecules of ATP are formed. This process is **photophosphorylation**. In the water there will be some hydrogen ions (H^+) and hydroxyl ions (OH^-), formed by the dissociation of water. From time to time a hydrogen ion will capture an electron emitted from a chlorophyll molecule and form a hydrogen atom. The hydrogen atom is collected by a hydrogen carrier, nicotinamide adenosine dinucleotide phosphate (NADP) which then becomes reduced. This reduced NADP is important in the dark stage. The hydroxyl ion gives up its electron to the chlorophyll and forms water and oxygen

$$4(OH) \rightarrow 2H_2O + O_2 \uparrow$$

Dark stage In this stage carbon dioxide is reduced and carbohydrate synthesized in a series of reactions. The 5-carbon compound ribulose diphosphate takes up carbon dioxide forming an unstable compound which breaks up into two molecules of 3-carbon phosphoglyceric acid.

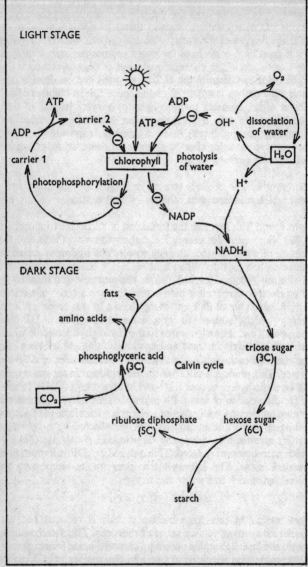

Figure 41. The chemistry of photosynthesis

98

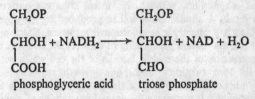

$$\begin{array}{ccc}
\begin{array}{l}
CH_2OP \\
| \\
C = O \\
| \\
CHOH \\
| \\
CHOH \\
| \\
CH_2OP
\end{array}
+ H_2O + CO_2 \longrightarrow &
\begin{array}{l}
CH_2OP \\
| \\
CHOH \\
| \\
COOH
\end{array}
+
\begin{array}{l}
COOH \\
| \\
CHOH \\
| \\
CH_2OP
\end{array}
\end{array}$$

ribulose diphosphate   2 mols. phosphoglyceric acid

The products of the light stage are now utilized. The phosphoglyceric acid is reduced to triose phosphate by the hydrogen carried by the NADP, the energy being supplied by the ATP.

$$\begin{array}{l}
CH_2OP \\
| \\
CHOH \\
| \\
COOH
\end{array}
+ NADH_2 \longrightarrow
\begin{array}{l}
CH_2OP \\
| \\
CHOH \\
| \\
CHO
\end{array}
+ NAD + H_2O$$

    phosphoglyceric acid   triose phosphate

The triose phosphate is now converted to hexose (6-carbon) sugar in a series of stages drawing upon ATP for the necessary energy. Some sugar is converted to starch for storage but a portion undergoes another series of reactions to regenerate ribulose diphosphate. This circuit of reactions; ribulose diphosphate – phosphoglyceric acid – triose sugar – hexose sugar – ribulose diphosphate is the **Calvin cycle**. Calvin also showed by the use of radioactive carbon that phosphoglyceric acid is a versatile compound from which lipids and amino acids can be synthesized by the plant. Separation of chloroplast components by means of a high speed centrifuge has shown that the light reactions are associated with the lamellae and the dark reactions with the stroma.

Synthesis of fats and amino acids

In the synthesis of fats and amino acids, phosphoglyceric acid is a key substance. Fats are formed from fatty acids and glycerol. Glycerol is closely related to triose sugars and fatty acids may be synthesized from acetyl co-enzyme A which has been produced from phosphoglyceric acid via pyruvic acid. Amino acids are produced by phosphoglyceric acid entering the Krebs cycle and being transformed into α-ketoglutaric acid which reacts with ammonia to form an amino acid, glutamic acid, this can be converted to other amino acids. The nitrogen necessary to form the ammonia comes from the nitrates absorbed by the roots.

Elements needed by the plant

In addition to carbon, hydrogen and oxygen obtained from water and carbon dioxide, the plant requires seven major elements and a number of minor ones which are obtained in the form of ions from the soil water. When the plant is unable to obtain a particular element it develops symptoms which are characteristic of the deficiency. Nitrogen is a constituent of all protein and therefore its absence results ultimately in cessation of growth. Sulphur and/or phosphorus are present in some proteins, and in addition phosphorus is a constituent of DNA, RNA and ATP; absence of these elements will cause poor growth. The chlorophyll molecule contains magnesium, without this metal chlorosis and reduced growth result. A similar effect will be produced by the absence of iron which is a precursor in chlorophyll synthesis. Calcium is important for the normal functioning of membranes and it is used in the construction of the middle lamella of the cell walls, without it the cells lose turgidity and poor growth results. Reduced photosynthesis and yellowing of the leaves result from a lack of potassium which is necessary for normal functioning of membranes and is required for the activity of certain enzymes. Elements required in trace amounts include boron, molybdenum, copper and zinc.

Measuring the rate of photosynthesis

The rate of photosynthesis can be determined by measuring the amount of oxygen evolved in a given time. A shoot of the water plant, *Elodea*, is convenient for the purpose. The effect of light of different intensities on the rate of photosynthesis can also be measured in the same way; a special piece of apparatus, a photosynthometer is available for the purpose. A simpler way of comparing the rate of photosynthesis under different conditions is to take a shoot of *Elodea* and place it upside down in a test tube or small measuring cylinder of the water in which the plant has been growing. In the light, bubbles should issue from the cut end of the stem, if necessary the stem can be trimmed until this is achieved. If the bubbles are not then issued at an even rate the stem may be fitted into a short length, 3 to 4 cm, of glass tubing of suitable bore which has been drawn out to form a narrow jet at the opposite end. The number of bubbles issuing from the jet in a given time may then be counted.

Holozoic heterotrophs

Animals other than parasites, together with a few specialized plants, belong to this group. They need a source of organic food obtained from the body materials of other animals or plants which they digest, mostly internally, by means of enzymes. The majority need protein, carbohydrate and fat, but the relative amounts needed and the form in which they are taken in differs considerably. Every conceivable type of food which conforms to these requirements is utilized by some living organism and the range of feeding mechanisms developed to make use of them is very wide. Animals may be placed into categories on the basis of the type of food eaten, thus there are **carnivores**, the meat eaters; **herbivores**, plant eaters and **omnivores** which consume both types of food. This system is most useful when considering the chordates. When dealing with lower animals it is convenient to consider firstly the large particle feeders, secondly the small particle feeders including the **filter feeders** which obtain their nourishment from fragments suspended in the water; thirdly **deposit feeders** which take in fragments which have collected on the substratum or extract particles of nutritious matter from a mass of inert material; and lastly the **liquid feeders** which consume juices of plant and animal origin. This group however merges into the group of parasites and illustrates the problems involved in dividing living organisms into groups. It serves as a reminder that classification is man made and clear cut divisions are not to be expected.

Food is **ingested**, broken down by the process of **digestion** into simple soluble products which can be **absorbed** into the body, then **assimilated** into complex materials needed by the body or used as a source of energy in respiration, the indigestible remains being **egested**.

Dietary requirements of man
Man requires a source of protein, carbohydrate and fat together with vitamins, a variety of mineral salts and water. When these are obtained in the proper proportions, man is said to have a balanced diet. The overall quantity of food must be sufficient to provide the energy required for metabolism. Protein is obtained mainly from meat, fish, eggs and milk; carbohydrate from cereals and their

products, sugar and root vegetables; fat from 'fat' meat, animal and vegetable oils. An adult man will require enough food to provide about 11 to 15 MJ daily, of which 6 g/MJ should be protein. A varied diet ensures a supply of the necessary mineral salts. The only elements likely to be in short supply are calcium essential for bones and teeth, found in milk and cheese; iron needed for haemoglobin, present in red meat and green vegetables; iodine a constituent of thyroxine produced by the thyroid gland, present in sea food and most drinking water; and fluorine, also present in drinking water in most areas, which assists in preventing dental caries. Man needs to have a source of the fat soluble vitamins, A, D, E and K, although vitamin D is synthesized in the skin when exposed to sunlight. Water soluble vitamins of the B group and vitamin C are also essential. Vitamin K is found in spinach and is synthesized by microorganisms in the gut, it is needed for the production of prothrombin concerned in the blood clotting mechanism.

The principles of digestion

Food is subjected to mechanical and chemical breakdown processes. Firstly it may be chopped up by teeth to aid transport and to expose a greatly increased surface area for chemical digestion. The food is then moved along some kind of gut by the activity of muscles which also assist in mixing the food with digestive juices containing enzymes secreted by cells in the gut wall or in glands associated with it. The enzymes belong to three major categories, each of which attacks one of the food groups, thus there are proteases acting on proteins, carbohydrases acting on carbohydrates and lipases which attack fat. Within each category there are a number of enzymes, each carrying out one particular step in the breakdown, and often requiring particular conditions which are met by additional secretions. Eventually the proteins are transformed into amino acids, the carbohydrates into simple sugars and the fat into fatty acids and glycerol. The end products of digestion are soluble substances of small molecular size which can pass through the gut wall. The gut wall itself may be folded or bear villi to increase the surface area for absorption. Once absorbed these vital materials are transported to the tissues, often by some kind of blood system, where they are assimilated or used in respiration.

Digestion in man

The incisors bite off the food and the pre-molars and molars crush it in the buccal cavity, mixing it with saliva from the salivary glands of which there are three pairs. Saliva has a neutral or slightly alkaline reaction and consists of mucus and an enzyme, salivary amylase (ptyalin), which begins the digestion of starch to maltose. Saliva also serves to assist the passage of food down the oesophagus. The tongue forms the chewed food into a bolus and manoeuvres it to the back of the buccal cavity. The action of swallowing forces the food through the pharynx into the oesophagus, the epiglottis closing over the glottis to prevent food entering the trachea. Peristaltic action squeezes the bolus down the oesophagus, the cardiac sphincter relaxes and it enters the stomach. Stimulation of the stomach lining causes a hormone, gastrin, to be secreted by the stomach wall, it stimulates the gastric glands to produce gastric juice. Churning movements of the stomach mix the food with gastric juice containing rennin which coagulates caseinogen, the soluble milk protein, turning it into insoluble casein. Casein and other proteins are acted upon by another enzyme, pepsin, and broken down into polypeptides. These two enzymes work best in an acid medium which is provided by hydrochloric acid secreted by the oxyntic cells in the gastric glands. The resulting chyme is moved towards the pyloric sphincter which relaxes at intervals allowing small amounts to pass through into the duodenum, where it encounters bile which has flowed down the bile duct from the gall bladder in the liver. Bile contains sodium bicarbonate which neutralizes the acid from the stomach and bile salts, sodium glycocholate and sodium taurocholate, which emulsify fat (now present as oil at body temperature), breaking it into minute droplets, thus increasing the surface area for enzyme action. The yellow-green colour of the bile is due to waste pigments, bilirubin and biliverdin, formed when old red blood cells are broken down in the liver. Bile itself contains no enzymes. The chyme also meets pancreatic juice which flows along the pancreatic duct from the pancreas, its release being stimulated by the hormone, secretin. This juice contains amylase changing starch to maltose; lipase converting fat to fatty acids and glycerol; together with trypsinogen and chymotrypsinogen, inactive precursors of protein digesting enzymes. Enterokinase, in the intestinal juice secreted by cells in the wall of the small intestine, activates trypsinogen converting it to trypsin. Trypsin then converts chymotrypsinogen into active chymotrypsin. These enzymes attack protein bonds producing mainly polypeptides. Other constituents of intestinal juice are enzymes hydrolysing disaccharides to monosaccharides; maltase converting maltose to glucose; sucrase hydrolysing sucrose to glucose and fructose; lactase changing lactose to glucose and galactose; together with peptidases, enzymes capable of breaking down polypeptides to amino acids. At the same time food is mixed with various secretions by contractions of the muscular wall, the

103

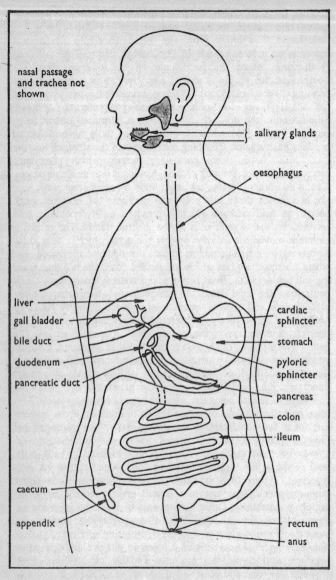

nasal passage and trachea not shown

salivary glands

oesophagus

liver

gall bladder

bile duct

duodenum

pancreatic duct

cardiac sphincter

stomach

pyloric sphincter

pancreas

colon

ileum

caecum

appendix

rectum

anus

Figure 42. The alimentary canal of man

resulting liquid containing the final products of digestion is chyle, it is from this that absorption takes place.

The surface of the ileum is covered by numerous villi and the cells bordering these bear minute microvilli. The surface area of the intestine is therefore very greatly increased. The villi are supplied with a network of capillaries; sugars and amino acids diffuse from the chyle through the epithelium lining the villi and into the blood system. The capillaries convey these materials to the hepatic portal vein which transports them to the liver. Fatty acids and glycerol are absorbed by the epithelial cells of the villi and passed to the lymph vessels (lacteals) as minute droplets of oil; they are eventually distributed by the blood as the lymphatic system itself opens into the veins. Mineral salts and vitamins are also absorbed in the ileum but the main absorptive region for water is the colon. Indigestible remains are passed out of the gut as faeces.

When glucose reaches the liver in the hepatic portal vein, it may be utilized for respiration there, passed on into the blood circulation, or converted to glycogen for storage in the liver. Its fate is largely determined by the level of glucose in the blood which is maintained at about 80 to 100 mg/dm^3, by hormone control (see page 200). Only a limited amount of glycogen can be stored in the liver, a small amount is held in muscles, but any excess is converted to fat and stored. Amino acids reaching the liver are sorted, those required are passed on into the circulation. Proteins and amino acids cannot be stored so excess amino acids are deaminated, the amino group removed combines with carbon dioxide to form waste urea and the residue is utilized.

Digestion in herbivorous mammals

Herbivores have to digest large quantities of food in order to obtain sufficient protein. In the cells of the plant material the cytoplasm occupies a thin layer lining the cellulose cell wall, the centre of the cell being occupied by a large cell vacuole. The presence of the cell wall means that the protein of the cytoplasm is protected and not readily available for digestion. Only some lower animals, bacteria and fungi synthesize cellulose digesting enzymes, so large herbivores rely on grinding the plant material between the ridged molars in order to break the cell walls and expose the contents. Cellulose digesting bacteria inhabit the caecum of the animal and when the food arrives there most of the protein has been digested and the herbivore is able to benefit from the soluble carbohydrate which the bacteria produce by the digestion of the cellulose cell walls.

Among the **ruminants** such as sheep, oxen and deer, the food is swallowed without much mastication by the aid of copious saliva. It is stored temporarily in the rumen, a portion of the complex stomach. Here there are micro-organisms which begin to break down the cellulose using some of the products for their own growth and reproduction; with the warmth and abundant food material they multiply rapidly. The ruminant chews the cud, that is, it regurgitates the stored food a small portion at a time, masticates it thoroughly and swallows it again. The second time it by-passes the rumen and goes into further chambers of the stomach where both ingested food and micro-organisms are digested, the animal benefitting from the additional food material provided by the micro-organisms and their activities.

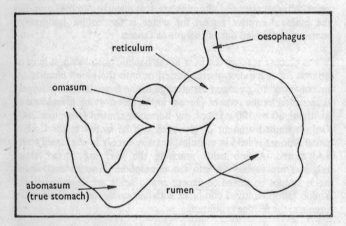

Figure 43. The stomach of a cow

Digestion in carnivorous mammals
The diet of a carnivore consists of a very large proportion of protein, the only indigestible protein being feathers, hair and exoskeletons of insects. The animal confines mastication of the food to chopping the flesh and crushing the bones into suitable sized pieces for swallowing. The chemical breakdown of protein is faster than that of carbohydrate and fat, and absorption of amino acids is rapid. For these reasons the alimentary canal can be much shorter than in the herbivore.

Teeth in mammals
Only in mammals is there mastication of food by specialized teeth,

unlike the simple pegs of the lower vertebrates. There are four types of teeth, **incisors** at the front of the mouth for cutting; **canines** on each side of them for seizing prey and ripping flesh; **pre-molars** and **molars** for crushing, grinding and shearing. In different mammals there are variations in the total number, and number of each type, their relative size, shape and structure and kind of chewing surface—differences related to the animal's diet. In many herbivores, incisors in the top jaw have been replaced by a horny pad, the lower chisel shaped incisors closing on to it to crop the vegetation. The sharp edge of these incisors is maintained by the posterior surface of the teeth wearing away faster than the anterior surface owing to the fact that the hard enamel is much thinner on the posterior side. Canines are often absent, a considerable gap, the **diastema**, taking their place, allowing the tongue to move freely during manipulation of the bulky food. In rodents upper and lower incisors are well developed, in the region of the diastema the cheeks can be sucked in to divide the buccal cavity into anterior and posterior regions so that material gnawed off by the incisors can either be dropped or passed to the posterior region to be ground and swallowed. The pre-molars and molars in herbivores are used for grinding; in some species the lower jaw moves from side to side, in others backwards and forwards. Not only is the food ground but the cement, enamel and dentine of the teeth is worn down. The enamel is the hardest material so it is the least worn and stands up in sharp edged ridges. The teeth of the lower and upper jaws having been ground down together have ridges which fit each other perfect-

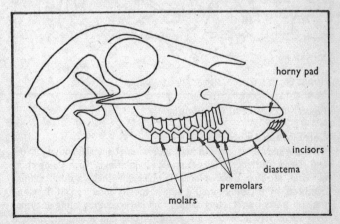

horny pad

incisors

diastema

premolars

molars

Figure 44. The dentition of a sheep

ly. The permanent teeth in herbivores grow throughout life to compensate for continual wear.

In the carnivore the incisors grip and pull off fragments of meat from bones, they are also used in grooming. When seizing its prey the animal makes use of the large pointed canines to get a firm grasp and tear the flesh from the bones. The pre-molars and molars are cusped, bones are crushed to fragments between them and the pieces swallowed. On either side of the jaw there is an opposing pair of massive sharp edged **carnassial** teeth, they are the greatly enlarged last upper pre-molar and first lower molar, and they occur at a place where the greatest force can be exerted. When the jaws are closed the carnassials sweep past each other like the blades of a pair of shears and snip off chunks of flesh. A relatively short time is spent in feeding compared with the herbivores, there is no grinding of the food and therefore the wear on the teeth is considerably less and they do not continue to grow throughout life.

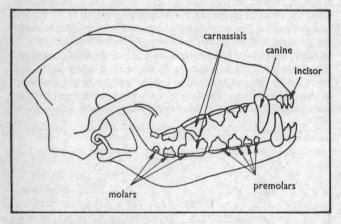

Figure 45. The dentition of a dog

Carnivorous plants

Carnivorous plants grow in acid soils where bacterial activity is low and release of mineral salts from dead material is slow. Being short of vital nitrates these plants supplement their normal photosynthesis by trapping small animals, mostly insects, and digesting the soft parts by secreting a fluid rich in protein digesting enzymes over them. The amino acids are absorbed and assimilated. Most plants of this type are tropical or sub-tropical like the pitcher plants, but sundews which trap insects by means of sticky glandular hairs on the leaf, and bladderwort an aquatic plant with tiny traps, are both British.

Lower organisms. Large particle feeders

In the coelenterates *Hydra* feeds on whole organisms such as water fleas (see Chapter 2). In the annelids the carnivorous polychaete *Nereis* everts a muscular pharynx through the mouth to seize crustaceans and other annelids, the pharynx is then drawn back and the organism swallowed. In many arthropods there are specialized organs for reducing the size of the food particles prior to digestion. In some of the crustaceans mouthparts seize the food, while lobsters, crabs and crayfish grasp the food with toothed edged pincers which pass it with the help of the maxillipeds, to the mouthparts. The mouthparts and maxillipeds shred the food into suitable sized pieces. Carnivorous insects feed mainly on other insects, seizing them by the anterior pair of legs as in the mantids and dragonflies, or by the mouthparts as in some beetles. The food is held to the mouth and broken up by the mouthparts.

Small particle feeders

One means of capturing small particles is by means of pseudopodia. *Amoeba* is capable of distinguishing between particles which are suitable for food and those which are not. Pseudopodia surround a suitable particle so that it is completely enclosed in a drop of water in the cytoplasm, forming a food vacuole into which enzymes are secreted. At first the vacuole shows an acid reaction, later an alkaline one. The products of digestion are absorbed into the cytoplasm and assimilated, the indigestible remains being left behind as *Amoeba* moves on.

Many invertebrate phyla contain animals which make use of rapidly beating cilia to create a current of water drawing food particles towards a collecting point. In *Paramecium* spirally arranged cilia waft particles down the oral groove (see Chapter 2). The bivalve molluscs such as clams and mussels show highly developed methods of ciliary feeding. The gills which in other molluscs are respiratory organs only, are enlarged and modified to form feeding organs. There are two folded gills, each forming a double gill, one on each side of the body separated by the foot which extends into the mantle cavity on the ventral side. The gills are covered by cilia and mucus and have minute holes in the surface. Each half of the folded gill has partitions between the inner and outer walls which divide the interior into a series of vertical water tubes opening into a dorsal gill passage which runs horizontally at the fold. Beating of the cilia draws water and particles through the inhalent siphon, into the mantle cavity and then through the pores in the gill surfaces where particles are trapped by mucus. The water then passes up the water tubes, back along the dorsal gill passage and out of the exhalent siphon. Cilia on the gills move the mucus forward to the labial palps, a pair of folds on each side of the mouth. Food particles and mucus are carried to a groove between the palps which leads to the mouth, they pass through the oesophagus to the stomach. Particles unsuitable for food, such as sand, drop off the gill surface and are wafted away by the cilia on the mantle and expelled.

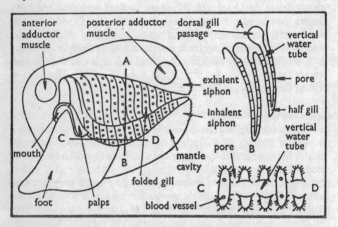

Figure 46. Feeding mechanism of a bivalve mollusc

Many crustaceans have a fringe of bristles on some of the appendages which collect particles as movement of the limbs causes a current of water to pass between the bristles. The fragments are then passed to the mouth. Barnacles, incapable of locomotion when adult, retain their limbs for feeding. When covered by the tide the shell valves open, the legs are thrust out making sweeping movements to collect particles. Filter feeding in the chordates is uncommon, but the basking shark filters off particles using special fringes on the gills. The filter feeding whales collect krill, the larger components of plankton, sieving it from the water by means of plates attached to the roof of the mouth.

Many of the deposit feeders are animals swallowing large quantities

110

of mud, silt or earth which makes up their environment; most of them are aquatic but the earthworm is a terrestrial example. There is no selection of the food, the animal passes the mass of the material slowly through the gut digesting and absorbing the organic matter which consists of plant and animal remains and smaller organisms inhabiting the environment.

Liquid feeders
Butterflies and moths suck nectar from flowers, uncoiling a long proboscis for drawing up the liquid. In the housefly the proboscis ends in two channelled pads which are pressed to the food, saliva is pumped along the channels on to the food which is softened or dissolved, the soluble part is then sucked back. This method of feeding makes the housefly a danger to health. There are many organisms which visit a host animal or plant for feeding but otherwise live independently; aphids, mosquitoes, leeches and blood-sucking flies live in this way. They are not permanently associated with a host and are not therefore complete parasites.

Parasitic nutrition
In the course of their visits from one host to another, many of the liquid feeders mentioned in the last section are themselves carriers of disease-causing parasites; such animals are **vectors**. This is one way in which parasites overcome the problem of reaching new hosts and they may undergo reproductive stages within the vector, greatly increasing their numbers. A parasite is an organism which exists in close association with a living host, deriving nourishment from it and causing it some harm. The host may sustain tissue damage, or in extreme cases be killed; or it may suffer from the effects of the parasite utilizing some of its food supply or from the effects of toxic wastes produced by the parasite. Parasitism is known in many groups of animals, in bacteria and fungi and in angiosperms. There are many bacterial diseases of plants and animals. Tetanus, typhoid and diptheria are examples of those affecting man. Viruses too, are parasitic causing the common cold, influenza and poliomyelitis in man; distemper in dogs; foot and mouth disease in cattle and mosaic diseases in plants. There are large **endoparasites** such as tapeworms and small parasitic protozoa which spend their lives in a nutrient medium absorbing it over the surface of the body, or others like the nematodes and liver flukes which suck up the nutrient solution. There are **ectoparasites** such as fleas and lice which live on the surface of the host, in crevices or in cavities such as the nostrils and anal opening; these pierce the skin to suck from the host.

Fungi can attack animals; ringworm and athlete's foot are two diseases of man, thrush is a disease man shares with other animals, and the aquatic fungus *Saprolegnia* is a parasite of fish. There are many fungal diseases of plants, the parasite gains entry through a wound or through the stomata. Germinating spores of some fungi are able to penetrate through the cuticle of higher plants and gain entry in this way. Many fungi such as the rusts can survive only so long as the host is living, they are the **obligate parasites**; others may kill the host but continue to live on the dead remains as saprophytes, these are the **facultative parasites**. *Pythium* is a fungus attacking young seedlings causing them to 'damp off', the fungus then continues to live on them and other organic material in the soil. Dodder is a non-green flowering plant which parasitizes heather and nettles producing haustoria which enter the host and penetrate between the xylem and phloem, the xylem of the parasite being continuous with that of the host; with the haustoria strategically placed it obtains both food and water. The semi-parasite mistletoe relies on the host for water and some food, but it has some green tissue and is able to make some food of its own.

Saprophytic nutrition

Saprophytes need a source of organic food, they feed on dead animal and plant material by secreting enzymes on to it and absorbing the soluble products. Many bacteria and fungi are saprophytes, they are of vital importance in breaking down all dead animals and plants, allowing the elements of which they are composed to be recycled for use again by green plants. The natural process of decay can cause hardship and economic disaster if conditions are such that saprophytes are able to destroy stored food, fabrics, leather and other organic materials; destructive processes which are particularly liable to take place in the warm moist atmosphere of tropical regions. In the environment there is competition among saprophytes for available food material and some species gain an advantage by secreting substances which are toxic to other organisms. Great use has been made of these antibiotic substances to control bacterial infections in man and animals. Penicillin produced by the fungus *Penicillium* was the first of a number of antibiotics now in use.

Symbiosis

When dissimilar organisms live together in close association to their mutual benefit, a state of symbiosis exists. Sometimes the association is so close that the **symbionts** appear as a single organism as in the lichens. A lichen consists of an association between a fungus and an alga, the alga producing sugars and oxygen which can be utilized by the fungus which in turn provides water and mineral salts. The mycelium provides shelter for the algal cells and hyphae anchor the whole structure to the substratum. The lichens are very hardy plants, they can exist in exposed and inhospitable regions where neither algae nor fungi alone would be likely to survive. Another close association is that between the green hydra *Chlorohydra viridissima* and the green alga *Chlorella* which lives in the endodermal cells of the hydra. It has been shown that this is a true symbiotic relationship, for if the hydra is kept in the dark the alga still survives, showing that it must be obtaining essential nutrients from the hydra. Also if the hydra is kept in the light but not fed, it survives longer than similar species of hydra lacking *Chlorella*, indicating that some of the food made by the alga must be available to it. The *Chlorella* is protected and receives carbon dioxide from the hydra's respiration and nitrogen compounds from its metabolic waste, while *Chlorohydra* has the benefit of carbohydrates and oxygen synthesized by the alga.

Many vertebrates and invertebrates have protozoa, bacteria and simple fungi inhabiting the gut. They exist in a state of symbiosis with the host and in return for protection and food they supply the host with water soluble vitamins, particularly those of the B group, vitamin K and amino acids. The host obtains these products either from excess manufactured by the micro-organisms or by digesting them after their death. In animals having a mixed diet they play little part in the actual process of digestion. Where the diet of the host is highly specialized the host may also rely on the symbionts in the gut for some part of the process of digestion as in the ruminant (see page 106). A major part of the digestive process is carried out by the symbionts in the gut of termites where they are largely responsible for the breakdown of the wood.

Some seed plants are involved in a symbiotic relationship with fungi. A mycorrhizal association is the association of soil fungi with plant roots, the best known being that between tree roots and various larger fungi such as species of *Amanita*, *Russula*, *Lactarius* and *Boletus*. The affected roots are shorter, stouter and more branched forming a coral-like mass. The fungal hyphae form a sheath round the root tips and penetrate between the cortical cells. When the mycelium associates itself with the root in this way it forms an ectotrophic mycorrhiza. The sheath of hyphae forms a water absorbing layer which takes the place of the root hairs. All green orchids and saprophytic orchids have a **mycorrhizal** association in the wild. The most common fungus involved is *Rhizoctonia* which forms an endotrophic mycorrhiza, the hyphae penetrating into the cortical cells of the orchid root. Orchids have minute seeds and their successful germination and growth is due to the supply of essential carbohydrate and vitamins to them by the fungus, which associates itself with the orchid from the earliest stage of development.

Commensalism

A state of commensalism is one of association between two organisms in which the commensal gains and the host neither gains nor loses. Well authenticated examples are not easy to find but one is between a coelenterate *Hydractinia echinata* and a hermit crab *Pagurus bernhardus*. The hydroid is attached to a whelk shell inhabited by the crab and is in an excellent position for receiving fragments of food which drift in its direction when the crab feeds.

Key terms

Absorption spectrum The pattern obtained after passing a beam of light through the substance then through a prism. The colours absorbed show as dark bands in the spectrum.

Assimilation The synthesis of complex materials needed by an organism from simpler materials, often the products of digestion.

Autotrophic (nutrition) Form of nutrition characteristic of green plants and certain bacteria in which simple inorganic compounds are used as starting materials.

Biomass The total mass of living material.

Calvin cycle The cycle of reactions in the dark stage of photosynthesis involving the production of sugars from ribulose diphosphate and carbon dioxide.

Chemosynthesis Synthesis brought about by using the energy gained from the oxidation of inorganic compounds.

Commensalism Association between two organisms in which one (the commensal) gains and the host neither gains nor loses.

Compensation point The point at which the rate carbohydrate is being made in photosynthesis equals the rate of its use in respiration.

Ecosystem A natural community of plants and animals.

Ectotrophic (mycorrhiza) One in which the fungal hyphae penetrate between but not into the cells of the root cortex.

Endotrophic (mycorrhiza) One in which the fungal hyphae penetrate into the cells of the root cortex.

Facultative (parasite) An organism which can live as a parasite or a saprophyte.

Heterotrophic (nutrition) One involving a source of complex organic compounds.

Holophytic (nutrition) The nutrition of green plants.

Holozoic (nutrition) The nutrition of animals digesting organic food internally by means of enzymes.

Limiting factor When a process requires a number of different conditions the rate at which it will proceed depends on the factor closest to the minimum value – this is the limiting factor.

Mycorrhiza An association of a fungus with the roots of higher plants.

Obligate (parasite) An organism obliged to live as a parasite.

Parasite An organism which lives in close association with a host organism, derives nourishment from it and causes some harm.

Photolysis The splitting of water by energy from light.

Photophosphorylation A reaction in which light energy is transformed into chemical energy by the formation of ATP from ADP and phosphate.

Ruminant Animal which chews the cud.

Saprophyte An organism deriving nourishment from dead plant or animal material by extracellular digestion.

Symbiont One of the organisms in a symbiotic relationship.

Trophic level Feeding level consisting of organisms with similar feeding habits.

Chapter 7
Respiration

Respiration occurs in all living cells. It is the process from which an organism derives energy for all metabolic processes. In the majority of organisms energy is released by the breakdown of organic compounds, particularly carbohydrates. In **aerobic** respiration the process requires the consumption of free oxygen with carbon dioxide produced, but energy can be released by **anaerobic** respiration, the breakdown of substances without the consumption of oxygen, although much less energy is liberated by this means. Few organisms fall strictly into the group of aerobes or anaerobes; a few bacteria are strict anaerobes in that they do not make use of free oxygen at all, on the other hand many organisms which respire aerobically when free oxygen is available are able to respire anaerobically for short periods. Yeast cells will break down sugar in the presence of oxygen forming carbon dioxide and water, but when deprived of oxygen they will continue to respire anaerobically producing carbon dioxide and ethanol until the concentration of the latter rises to a level which kills the yeast cells. Where a local shortage of oxygen occurs in an organism which respires aerobically, the particular tissue concerned may respire anaerobically for a short time incurring an **oxygen debt** which is repaid later. This may occur in vertebrate muscle during vigorous activity when the supply of oxygen cannot keep pace with the demand, and the muscle cells respire anaerobically with the accumulation of lactic acid which is disposed of later when free oxygen becomes available. True respiration, as defined above, is sometimes called internal, tissue or cell respiration to distinguish it from external respiration or breathing. Breathing is the mechanical process associated with gas exchange in respiration.

The material broken down in respiration, the respiratory substrate, is commonly the carbohydrate, glucose. Although the equation

$$C_6H_{12}O_6 + 6O_2 \rightarrow 6H_2O + 6CO_2 + 2880 \text{ kJ}$$

represents the overall process of aerobic respiration, the breakdown of glucose takes place in a number of stages, some of the chemical energy contained in the glucose being transferred to compounds in the cell capable of storing energy, and some being lost as heat. The final breakdown products of the glucose are metabolic waste products and are eliminated by the cell.

Energy storing compounds

An important energy storing compound **adenosine triphosphate (ATP)** is present in all living cells. It is most likely the supplier of energy for every activity in both animals and plants. Energy is needed for muscular movement, nerve conduction, for the movement of ions and solutes against a concentration gradient and other functions; so it is essential that there should be a supply of energy readily available. ATP is a nucleotide made up of adenosine, a complex organic molecule attached to a chain of three phosphate groups A—P—P ~ P. Adenosine is derived from adenine, a purine base, and a sugar, ribose. When the terminal phosphate group is detached, a hydrolysis brought about by the enzyme adenosine triphosphatase, energy is released to the extent of about 33 kJ per mole, and adenosine diphosphate remains.

$$ATP + H_2O \rightarrow ADP + H_3PO_4 + 33 \text{ kJ}$$

As a relatively large amount of energy is released when the terminal phosphate bond is broken, this bond is described as an energy-rich or high-energy bond and it is distinguished from the others by being written with a wavy line. The energy-rich phosphate bond can be transferred to other compounds such as creatine for storage, leaving the ADP free to pick up another energy-rich phosphate bond. The phosphocreatine thus formed in skeletal muscle will give up the ~ P when required. Not all the energy available in the energy-rich phosphate bond can be used for biological purposes however, some of it is lost as heat. When the ATP has given up the terminal phosphate bond releasing the free energy and become ADP, it needs to be recharged. The energy released during the chemical processes which together constitute respiration, is used to build up the ATP. ATP is the readily available source of energy, it can be broken down and built up again speedily wherever it is required in the cell. It is produced in the cell where it is needed, it cannot be transported.

The hydrogen carrier system

In the breakdown of sugar during respiration some of the steps in the process are exergonic (energy is released). This energy is available for the synthesis of ATP from ADP and phosphate. Comparatively little energy can be obtained in this way and the majority comes from the use of the hydrogen carrier system. For certain steps to take place in the breakdown of sugar, hydrogen atoms have to be removed, this process is dehydrogenation and it is carried out by the action of a dehydrogenase enzyme. Two hydrogen atoms are taken up by a **hydrogen carrier** which is thereby reduced; the hydrogen atoms are then passed on to a second carrier which becomes reduced, the first then becoming re-oxidized. In this transfer some energy is released and is utilized for the synthesis of ATP. There are further carriers, the one reached by the hydrogen atoms becomes reduced, the one they have left being re-oxidized. Finally the hydrogen combines with oxygen forming water. At each stage there is a release of energy for ATP synthesis. The first carrier is nicotinamide adenine dinucleotide (**NAD**) formed from a vitamin of the B group, nicotinic acid. The second carrier is flavine adenine dinucleotide (**FAD**), a derivative of vitamin B_2. The third is **cytochrome**, a protein pigment with a prosthetic group containing iron, and the fourth is an enzyme, **cytochrome oxidase**. The first three carriers are co-enzymes, they are involved in handing on the hydrogen removed by the dehydrogenase enzyme, to the enzyme cytochrome oxidase which passes it on to oxygen, forming water. Each time two hydrogen atoms pass through the carrier system sufficient energy is released to synthesize three molecules of ATP.

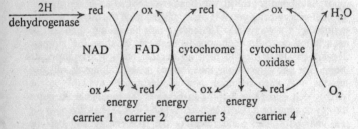

The chemistry of respiration

Glycolysis

Carbohydrates are the main respiratory substrates. The first stages of the breakdown do not require oxygen, so regardless of whether an organism respires aerobically or anaerobically the initial processes of carbohydrate breakdown proceed along a common pathway, step by step, leading to the formation of pyruvic acid. These reactions are collectively known as **glycolysis**. The first step in glycolysis is the **phosphorylation** of sugar, that is adding phosphate groups to the sugar. Carbohydrates such as starch and glycogen may also be phosphorylated to form 6-carbon phosphorylated sugars. Phosphorylation is an energy-consuming (endergonic) process and both energy and phosphate groups are supplied by the ATP molecules donating the terminal high-energy phosphate group. Two phosphate groups are added to each sugar molecule using two molecules of ATP. The phosphorylated sugar then splits into two molecules of a 3-carbon, triose sugar, which are converted to pyruvic acid, enough energy being released at this stage to synthesize two molecules of ATP. Although in the first stage of the conversion of triose sugar to pyruvic acid two hydrogen atoms are taken from the triose sugar and picked up by NAD, they are not passed through the carrier system during anaerobic respiration. In plant respiration the $NADH_2$ is utilized to reduce the acetaldehyde (ethanal) formed from pyruvic acid to ethanol, and in animal muscles to reduce the pyruvic acid to lactic acid, the freed NAD is then returned to the system once more. Pyruvic acid is an important intermediate compound, as the respiratory pathway branches at this point. The route taken depends on whether the respiration is aerobic or anaerobic. If oxygen is present the next stage takes place in the mitochondria where pyruvic acid is converted into 2-carbon acetyl co-enzyme A which enters the **Krebs cycle**. When pyruvic acid is converted to acetyl co-enzyme A, carbon dioxide is released and two hydrogen atoms are transported into the carrier system which releases sufficient energy to synthesize three molecules of ATP. Acetyl co-enzyme A is a key substance in respiration; when fat is used as the respiratory substrate it is converted to acetyl co-enzyme A. Protein is first hydrolysed to amino acids which are deaminated and these enter the Krebs cycle or join the breakdown system at pyruvic acid.

The Krebs cycle (citric acid cycle)

Acetyl co-enzyme A reacts with the 4-carbon oxaloacetic acid to form 6-carbon citric acid. A series of reactions now takes place in which the citric acid is changed back to oxaloacetic acid. This series of reactions makes up the Krebs cycle. At various points in the cycle carbon dioxide is released and hydrogen atoms removed from the substrate by a dehydrogenase enzyme are passed to the carrier system with the subsequent formation of ATP. Four of the stages involve the removal of hydrogen in this way, but not every pair of hydrogen atoms passing through the carrier system provides sufficient energy for the synthesis of three molecules of ATP, in one case there are only two molecules produced. One stage in the Krebs cycle provides energy for the direct synthesis of one molecule of ATP. Most of the energy for the synthesis of ATP is provided by the Krebs cycle. The total amount of energy produced by the breakdown of one molecule of hexose sugar aerobically, is sufficient to synthesize 38 molecules of ATP. In glycolysis 2ATP are produced; the conversion of two molecules of pyruvic acid to acetyl co-enzyme A yields 2×3ATP, and 2×12ATP are formed when this acetyl co-enzyme A goes round the Krebs cycle. 2×3ATP formed during the conversion of two molecules of triose sugar to pyruvic acid, are added to the total. The total amount of energy obtained is 60% of the theoretical energy content, showing that living organisms are very efficient when compared with machines. The Krebs cycle is a continuous one, during each circuit about 16% of the original material is lost in the form of carbon dioxide and hydrogen atoms, the energy being used to convert ADP to ATP. The role of the oxygen is to pick up the unwanted carbon and hydrogen atoms.

It is believed that the reactions of the Krebs cycle take place in the matrix of the mitochondria while the reactions involving hydrogen transfer occur on the cristae and inner membrane. Strictly speaking it is not hydrogen itself but electrons which are transferred from one carrier to another.

Anaerobic respiration

Most of the energy produced in aerobic respiration is made available in the Krebs cycle by the hydrogen carrier system which relies on oxygen being present to collect the hydrogen at the end. In anaerobic respiration it is not possible to break down the respiratory substrate completely, instead of carbon dioxide and water being formed, lactic acid is produced in animals, and ethanol and carbon dioxide in plants. Anaerobic respiration in plants is also known as **fermentation**.

$$C_6H_{12}O_6 \rightarrow 2CH_3CH_2OH + 2CO_2 + 210 \text{ kJ} \quad \text{In plants}$$
$$\text{ethanol}$$

$$C_6H_{12}O_6 \rightarrow CH_3CH(OH)COOH + 150 \text{ kJ} \quad \text{In animals}$$
$$\text{lactic acid}$$

Comparing these equations it is clear that anaerobic respiration in animals produces less energy than anaerobic respiration in plants. The yield of energy is poor in any case when compared with that obtained by aerobic respiration.

$$C_6H_{12}O_6 \rightarrow 6H_2O + 6CO_2 + 2880 \text{ kJ}$$

Considering the three equations together, it is clear that in aerobic respiration about nineteen times as much energy is produced than is made available by anaerobic respiration in animals, and about four-

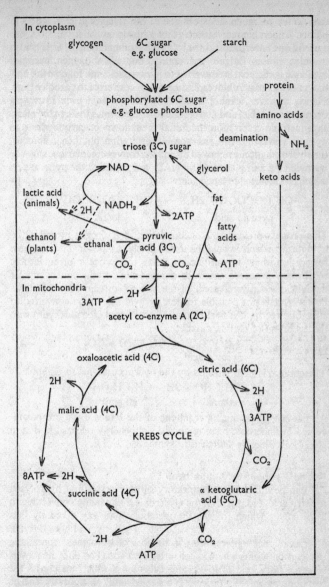

Figure 47. Respiratory pathways

121

teen times as much as is obtained from anaerobic respiration in plants. Anaerobic respiration is thus a highly inefficient process, but a useful one nevertheless. In animals the accumulation of lactic acid in muscles causes fatigue and cramp, but when oxygen becomes available lactic acid is converted to pyruvic acid and follows the normal pathway of aerobic respiration or is reconverted to carbohydrate. Plants, however, cannot break down the ethanol even if oxygen becomes available, and at a certain level it becomes toxic to the plant. In anaerobic respiration the initial breakdown of carbohydrate to pyruvic acid is the same as in aerobic respiration, but then in animals, the hydrogen atoms removed during the conversion of triose sugar to pyruvic acid and picked up by NAD, are passed to the pyruvic acid which is converted to lactic acid.

$$CH_3COCOOH + 2H\text{-----} \rightarrow CH_3CH(OH)COOH$$
$$\text{pyruvic acid} \qquad\qquad\qquad \text{lactic acid}$$

This process prevents the accumulation of hydrogen atoms in the cytoplasm which would be more likely to occur in anaerobic respiration than in aerobic, because the process of anaerobic respiration proceeds faster to compensate for the much smaller amount of energy released. In the anaerobic respiration of plants however, it is not possible for the pyruvic acid to be converted to ethanol directly, it is first changed into ethanal (acetaldehyde) with the evolution of carbon dioxide.

$$CH_3COCOOH \rightarrow CH_3CHO + CO_2$$
$$\text{pyruvic acid} \qquad \text{ethanal}$$

The ethanal is then reduced by the hydrogen atoms to ethanol.

$$CH_3CHO + 2H \rightarrow CH_3CH_2OH$$
$$\text{ethanal} \qquad\qquad \text{ethanol}$$

As the energy-producing reactions of the Krebs cycle are not involved in anaerobic respiration, the only energy released is that in glycolysis which is sufficient to synthesize 2ATP.

Fat as a respiratory substrate

Fat can be utilized as a respiratory substrate, it is first hydrolysed to fatty acid and glycerol, the glycerol is then readily convertible to triose sugar which follows the metabolic pathway taken by that formed from a carbohydrate substrate. The fatty acid goes through a series of reactions resulting in the loss of a fragment containing two carbon atoms which is converted into acetyl co-enzyme A, this leaves a fatty acid of lower molecular mass which undergoes the reactions again. The process is repeated until all the fatty acid is metabolized. The breakdown of fatty acids takes place in the mitochondria where carriers present pick up the hydrogen atoms removed and pass them through the carrier system, the energy released being used to form ATP. The acetyl co-enzyme A produced enters the Krebs cycle resulting in the formation of more ATP. Altogether the oxidation of one molecule of a fatty acid with six carbon atoms produces sufficient energy to form 44ATP compared with 38ATP from a 6-carbon sugar.

Protein as a respiratory substrate

Protein is not normally used as a respiratory substrate, the body will use first of all the carbohydrate and fat reserves and when these are exhausted protein will be metabolized; at this stage starvation has set in. Protein from skeletal muscle will be the first to be used. Initially the protein is broken down to amino acids which are deaminated, that is, split into a carbohydrate portion which can be utilized and an amino group which is waste. The carbohydrate portion enters the respiratory pathway of carbohydrate at an appropriate point according to its nature.

Factors affecting respiration

Temperature

The optimum temperature for respiration in homoiothermic animals is about 37°C, in poikilothermic animals and in plants it may be different. Arctic algae and the algae of hot springs, for example, have different optimum temperatures for respiration.

The concentration of oxygen

If more than 2% of oxygen is available, respiration will normally proceed by the aerobic pathway following glycolysis.

The respiratory substrate

The nature of the respiratory substrate will obviously determine the relative amount of energy released, and will affect the relative amounts of oxygen consumed and carbon dioxide produced.

Respiratory quotient

The **respiratory quotient** (RQ) is the amount of carbon dioxide produced, divided by the amount of oxygen consumed, in a given time

$$RQ = \frac{CO_2 \text{ produced}}{O_2 \text{ consumed}}$$

The RQ provides useful information about the nature of the substrate being respired. Where the substrate is carbohydrate $RQ = 1$. From the equation,

$$C_6H_{12}O_6 + 6O_2 \rightarrow 6CO_2 + 6H_2O + energy$$

$$RQ = \frac{6CO_2}{6O_2} = 1$$

The theoretical RQs for the oxidation of fat and protein can be calculated from the equations and are $0 \cdot 7$ and $0 \cdot 9$ respectively. In practice a mixture of substrates is often utilized, so that the RQ falls between $0 \cdot 7$ and $1 \cdot 0$. If this is so it is likely that a mixture of carbohydrate and fat is being used, as protein is utilized only under extreme conditions. An RQ greater than $1 \cdot 0$ indicates a shortage of oxygen and the production of some carbon dioxide from anaerobic respiration.

Oxygen uptake in respiration

The fact that oxygen is absorbed during aerobic respiration can be demonstrated by attaching to a manometer a vessel maintained at constant temperature, and containing suitable living material supplied with a means of absorbing the carbon dioxide produced. It is possible to measure the amount of oxygen consumed directly, by passing dry air free of carbon dioxide through a vessel containing a small mammal then drawing it through containers of chemicals to

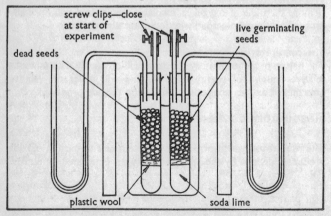

Figure 48. The uptake of oxygen in respiration

absorb water and carbon dioxide. The mammal and containers are weighed at the beginning and end of the experiment and the loss in weight of the mammal compared with the total gain in weight of the water-absorbing and carbon dioxide-absorbing containers. The difference in mass will be the mass of the oxygen consumed.

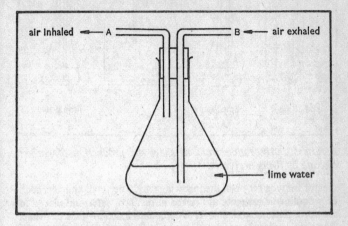

Figure 49. The carbon dioxide content of inspired and expired air

The production of carbon dioxide

The production of carbon dioxide in respiration can be shown by bubbling expired gas through lime water, which quickly turns milky. In man the difference between inspired and expired air is easily demonstrated using a gas washing bottle. Twenty inspirations are taken through A (see figure 49), the air being exhaled into the atmosphere. After noting any change in the lime water, twenty expirations are made at B, air being inhaled from the atmosphere. A more general method for animals and plants is to set up an absorption train on the lines of that shown in figure 50. First of all, air is drawn through soda lime to remove carbon dioxide, then through lime water to make sure that all the carbon dioxide has been removed. Next the treated air is passed through a container with the animal or plant (a blacked-out container for a green plant to prevent photosynthesis), then bubbled through lime water, noting any change. For very small organisms a more sensitive test for carbon dioxide is necessary. A simple experiment using bicarbonate in-

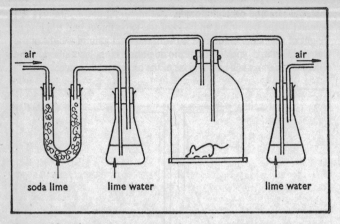

Figure 50. Absorption train to show the production of carbon dioxide by living organisms

dicator may be set up in the following way. The small animals, such as woodlice or maggots are rinsed in distilled water and placed in the wire gauze container over bicarbonate indicator in a test tube. The carbon dioxide produced results in a colour change from pink to yellow, which can be compared with a control. Small pieces of plant material and yeast also give good results. Green plant

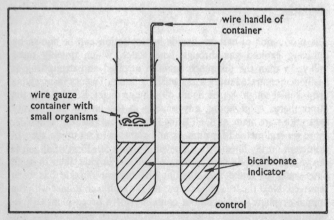

Figure 51. Apparatus to show the production of carbon dioxide by small organisms

material must be protected from light.

To show that carbon dioxide is produced during anaerobic respiration in plants, a yeast suspension is prepared using a 5% glucose solution made up with water which has been boiled to expel oxygen. Some of the suspension is poured into a test tube and covered with a thin layer of medicinal paraffin. The gas evolved is allowed to bubble through lime water. A control may be set up using a boiled yeast suspension.

The production of heat

Heat production in plants can be shown by enclosing soaked seeds in a vacuum flask fitted with a thermometer inserted through a rubber bung. The experimental flask should contain live seeds, the control flask boiled seeds. Both should be treated by soaking in dilute sodium hypochlorite solution (a 20% solution of domestic bleach) for ten minutes, to kill bacteria and fungal spores.

Metabolic rate

Respiration is the process producing energy in living organisms, the rate of energy expenditure being metabolism. Information about the metabolic rate can be obtained by investigating the rate of consumption of oxygen. Alternatively, the amount of energy produced in a given time can be measured, this involves measuring the heat produced.

The rate of oxygen consumption

The rate of oxygen consumption and carbon dioxide production can be determined by using a Douglas bag. This is a light gas proof bag which can be worn by the subject and attached to his mouth by a flexible tube fitted with valves which allow air to be breathed in from the atmosphere, but direct expired air into the bag. An additional tube allows air to be tapped off for gas analysis. At the end of a given time the total volume of air produced can be measured, and the oxygen consumed and the carbon dioxide produced can be calculated. The bag can be worn during various activities, and the effect of these on the metabolic rate determined.

The rate of oxygen consumption can also be calculated by using a recording **spirometer**. This works on the same principle as a gasometer. There is an air tight container floating on water, the lid having an attached pen which is made to record the movements of the lid on a kymograph, a rotating cylindrical drum. The container is filled with oxygen, the subject breathes in and out of this closed space through a flexible tube which leads into it after passing through a canister of soda lime, to absorb the carbon dioxide. As the subject breathes in and out the lid moves up and down, tracing peaks and troughs on the kymograph. The oxygen in the container is gradually used up and as the carbon dioxide is absorbed, the volume of the gas decreases. The recording paper on the kymograph is calibrated for volume on the vertical scale and for time on the horizontal scale, so from the tracing the volume of oxygen used in a given time can be calculated. The spirometer can also be used to measure the oxygen consumption during and after exercise.

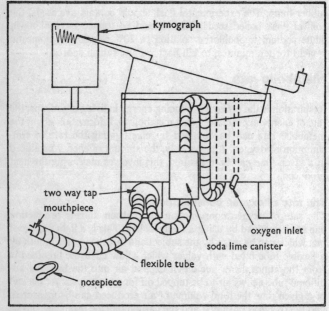

Figure 52. A recording spirometer

By using a bicycle joulometer, the amount of energy used can be shown to be directly proportional to the amount of oxygen consumed. The subject pedals the joulometer, the work done is measured, and at the same time he can be breathing into a Douglas bag.

The amount of heat produced

The amount of heat produced in a given time is measured by confining the subject to a special thermally insulated cabinet, a **calorimeter**. Water is circulated through the cabinet and the change in temperature recorded. A high degree of muscular activity increases energy production tenfold, but even when the subject is resting there is still some energy produced, for it is required for the action of the heart, breathing and the maintenance of body temperature. This minimal amount of energy expended is the **basal metabolic rate (BMR)**. It is expressed as the number of kilojoules per square metre of surface per hour. An average figure for man is 4·2 kJ but it varies with age and at different times in the same individual. It also varies between the sexes, a woman has a lower BMR. The variation in BMR within the individual is partly due to differences between the body temperature and the surroundings, obviously the greater the temperature difference the higher will be the expenditure of energy in the body. **Homoiothermic** animals such as mice and small birds have a large surface area in relation to their volume and consequently they lose a lot of heat, to compensate for this they have a high rate of respiration, which in turn means they spend a good deal of time in feeding. On the other hand, some large mammals, especially those living in hot climates, have a small surface area in relation to their volume and have difficulty in losing heat, they have a relatively slow rate of respiration. In **poikilothermic** animals the rate of respiration is in the main determined by the temperature of the environment, but on average it is much lower than that of a homoiothermic animal of the same size.

The energy value of food

The material oxidized in respiration to produce energy comes from the food. The amount of energy provided by any particular food can be determined directly by oxidizing a known amount of it and measuring the heat produced. The piece of apparatus used for this purpose is a **bomb calorimeter**. It has a strong steel container which can be sealed tightly. A small amount of the material to be oxidized is weighed into a small crucible and placed inside, oxygen is passed into the bomb and the material is ignited by means of an electric coil. A water jacket containing a known amount of water surrounds the calorimeter, the temperature being recorded before and after firing. From the rise in temperature the amount of heat produced can be calculated. Fat produces the most heat, one gramme yields about 38 kJ, one gramme of protein about 22 kJ and one gramme of carbohydrate about 17 kJ. These figures are the

energy values (calorific values). Just as a machine has an energy balance, the amount of energy put in (fuel) equalling the amount of energy given out (work and heat), the same is true of ourselves. The total amount of energy provided by the food is equal to the heat produced together with the energy expended during activities. This only applies if the body mass is unchanged. If a person is losing mass he is burning up his fat reserves, so that the total energy produced will be greater than the total energy value of the food consumed. If he is gaining mass, the total energy value of the food exceeds energy expenditure and the surplus will be stored in the body. There is considerable variation in energy requirements, it depends on age, sex and the degree of activity. An adult man requires somewhere in the region of 11,000 to 15,000 kJ (11 to 15 MJ) daily. These are recommended figures published by the United Nations Food and Agriculture Organization (FAO). It is clear from these that a large proportion of the population of the world has a diet which fails to provide the recommended energy value.

The exchange of gases in animals

For respiration to take place oxygen must be absorbed into the body. In small animals such as protozoa, there is a sufficiently large surface area in relation to the volume of the body for oxygen to be absorbed without the need for a special respiratory surface. In somewhat larger animals such as flatworms, the surface area is still adequate and the body is thin enough to allow for diffusion of gases through the surface to all parts. In annelids, however, the diameter of the body is too great for simple diffusion to provide adequate supplies of oxygen throughout the body, and to allow for carbon dioxide to be removed efficiently; remembering that the rate of diffusion is inversely proportional to the distance travelled. Although the surface area is not increased, the annelids absorb oxygen through the thin cuticle into the blood capillaries near the surface, which join the dorsal vessel; a simple blood system therefore, aids the distribution of the oxygen. Respiratory surfaces in all animals have certain features in common. They have to be large enough for adequate gas exchange, which may involve various kinds of structural devices to increase the surface area, they must be thin enough to allow gases to pass through easily, and they must be moist so that oxygen and carbon dioxide can pass through in solution. The more active the animal the greater will be the oxygen requirement.

Exchange of gases in insects

Insects are of small size, but they are very active creatures with a high metabolic rate associated with an efficient system of gas exchange. The respiratory system consists of fine tubes, **tracheae** which lead from the surface to the interior. The lining of the tracheae is no different from that covering the surface of the body, and the tubes are kept open by supporting rings or spirals. The external openings, **spiracles**, are able in some cases to open and close by muscular action. Internally the tracheae branch into many fine thin-walled **tracheoles** which penetrate into the tissues and are permeable to liquids and gases.

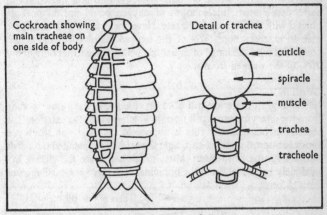

Figure 53. Part of the tracheal system of an insect

The system works efficiently because the spiracles giving access to the atmosphere are never far from the finest tracheoles; it could not supply a larger body structure, and that is one of the factors limiting the size of insects. As oxygen diffuses through the walls of the tracheoles into the tissues, more diffuses in from outside. In most insects improvement to the system is made by an active ventilating mechanism, usually pulsating movements of the abdomen. Water loss is a problem for insects, and the spiracles may be closed temporarily to control it. Some control is exercised over the rate at which oxygen reaches the tissues, by the fact that great muscular activity results in the accumulation of lactic acid. This brings about an increase in the osmotic pressure of the tissue fluid, water is withdrawn from the tracheoles creating more space for air.

Exchange of gases in fish

Gills for the exchange of respiratory gases are found in many different aquatic animals. The water gives the gills support and prevents them drying out. Gills are outgrowths of the body rather than invaginations like lungs, and they are associated with some mechanical means of renewing the supply of water over them, bearing fresh oxygen and flushing away waste carbon dioxide. They are delicate structures of large surface area having a rich supply of blood. This flows in capillaries near the surface, and contains a respiratory pigment which combines readily with oxygen. The amount of oxygen which can dissolve in water is not more than 1% compared with air which contains 20%; even with the most efficient extraction system this amount of oxygen could not support an animal with a high metabolic rate. Nevertheless, the gills of fish are able to extract about 50% of the oxygen dissolved in the water, compared with the lungs of mammals which can extract only about 20% of the oxygen from the air.

Dogfish
In the dogfish there are **gill slits** on either side, each one opening from the pharynx into a **gill pouch** which leads to the exterior. The septum in between the slits is supported on the inner side by a **branchial arch** made of cartilage; the septum is extended outwards into a flap, the **branchial valve**, which can close the gill slit immediately behind it. From the branchial arch there is a cartilaginous

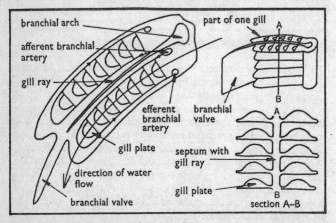

Figure 54. Gill filaments of the dogfish

132

gill ray which passes outwards to support the septum. On either side of the septum are attached thin delicate **gill filaments**. At the base of each gill near the arch is an **afferent branchial artery** which carries deoxygenated blood to the gill from the heart; on either side of this vessel there is an **efferent branchial artery** which takes oxygenated blood away from the gill to the dorsal aorta. The two are joined by capillaries in the **gill plates**.

Ventilation of the gills is effected by the fish contracting muscles which lower the floor of the pharynx, creating a suction which causes the branchial valves to close over the gill slits, and water to enter the mouth and spiracles. When the cavity is full of water the

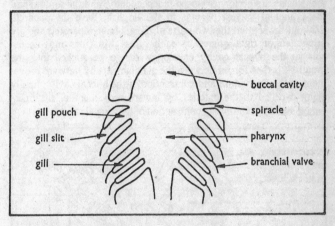

Figure 55. L.S. of the pharynx of the dogfish

mouth and spiracles close, the floor of the pharynx rises forcing water over the gills, opening the branchial valves and passing out to the exterior. The main direction of the flow of the water is parallel to the long axis of the gill filaments, and little passes between the gill plates owing to the presence of the septum; this means that as deoxygenated blood reaches the gill filaments it is flowing in the same general direction as the water. At first it will pick up oxygen readily, but as it flows along, the oxygen level in the blood rises while that in the water decreases; in other words, the concentration gradient is decreasing all the time until finally the oxygen content of the blood will be in equilibrium with that in the water. This equilibrium point is only 50% of the maximum possible saturation with oxygen. Parallel flow is therefore not very efficient.

Teleost fish

In bony fish, such as cod and haddock, the gill filaments are arranged in such a way that the blood and the water flow in opposite directions; this is the **counterflow** system, which makes it possible for blood to approach closer to the maximum saturation with oxygen. As the blood flows along the filament it first meets water which has given up much of its oxygen, but as it flows along the filament with its oxygen content rising, it meets water with a progressively higher oxygen content. Thus the same concentration gradient is maintained all along the filament enabling the blood to take up oxygen to 80% of the maximum possible saturation. In a bony fish the gills are covered by a muscular flap, the **operculum**, the gill slits are no longer closed independently, and the septum and the branchial valves, present in the dogfish, have disappeared. Without the septum the two parts of the gill have separated and are orientated at right angles to each other. Muscular movements enlarge the buccal cavity causing water to be sucked into the mouth, it is then forced between the gill filaments by outward movement of the operculum and contraction of the buccal cavity; finally being expelled to the exterior by inward movement of the operculum aided by continuing contraction of the buccal cavity.

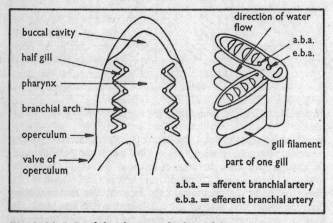

Figure 56. L.S. of the pharynx of a bony fish

The exchange of gases in animals with lungs

Lung fish of Devonian times appear to be the first vertebrates to

134

possess lungs, they are extensions of the pharynx, like the swim bladder of the teleost fish. In the frog the absorption of oxygen from lungs is additional to that obtained by absorption through the damp permeable skin, and through the highly vascular membrane lining the buccal cavity. The ventilation of the lungs relies on the alternate lowering and raising of the floor of the buccal cavity. Reptiles rely on rib movements for the ventilation mechanism. In birds which are very active animals, the exchange of gases is highly efficient, all the air in the lungs is changed and the breathing rate can be very rapid. In the pigeon it can rise to over 400 per minute during flight. When the ribs and sternum make outward movements, air is drawn in and passes down the trachea to the bronchi which pass into the lungs giving off branches to the lung tissue. The bronchi then continue through the lungs, branch and lead into air sacs, of which there are nine occupying a large proportion of the body cavity. Some of the air sacs lead into cavities in the bones. The air sacs themselves do not play any part in gas exchange. Inward movement of the ribs and sternum forces air from the sacs through the bronchioles in the lungs and then out of the body. Gas exchange takes place in the bronchioles.

The exchange of gases in man
The **lungs** are situated in the **thoracic cavity** which is bounded by the **ribs** at the sides and the **diaphragm** at the base. Round each lung is the **pleural cavity** lined by **pleural membranes**, the cavity is kept moist. Inspiration takes place by an upward and outward movement of the ribs brought about by the contraction of the intercostal muscles, and simultaneous lowering of the diaphragm by muscular contraction. These movements cause the pressure to be lowered in the pleural cavities and then in the lungs, resulting in air being sucked in from the outside. It is warmed and moistened as it passes through the nose, and then on down the trachea, through the **bronchi** to the lungs. The reverse process takes place in expiration, the ribs being lowered and the diaphragm raised.

The lung tissue consists of a system of **bronchioles**, tubes resulting from the progressive branching of the bronchi, each terminating in a group of **alveoli**. The alveoli are surrounded by an extensive capillary network, and it is through the extremely thin walls of the alveoli and blood capillaries, that exchange of gases takes place. Although the alveoli are minute the total surface area they provide in the two lungs is about 70 m^2. During breathing while at rest, some 500 cm^3 of air is inspired and expired during each breath or respiratory cycle. This is the **tidal volume**. The volume of air breathed per minute is the **ventilation rate**. With deep breathing it is possible to take in about seven times as much air as the tidal volume, the extra air is the **inspiratory reserve volume**. Similarly, at the end of a normal breathing cycle it is possible to force out additional air equal to about twice the tidal volume, this is the **expiratory reserve volume**. The total volume which can be expired after breathing in the maximum possible, is the **vital capacity**. The vital capacity of an average man is about $4 \cdot 5 \text{ dm}^3$. Even then there is a **residual volume** in the lungs of about $1 \cdot 5 \text{ dm}^3$.

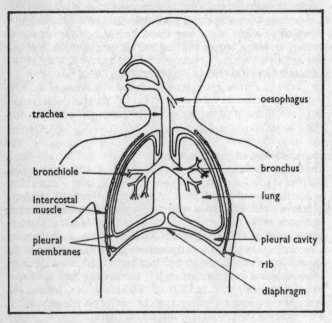

Figure 57. The respiratory system of man

Inspired air has a high oxygen content and a low carbon dioxide content, the blood in the capillaries reaching the alveoli has a high carbon dioxide content and a low oxygen content; the concentration gradient thus favours the diffusion of oxygen from the alveoli to the blood, and the diffusion of carbon dioxide in the opposite direction. Increasing the carbon dioxide concentration of inspired air results in a rapid increase in the ventilation rate. This has been shown by using a spirometer without the carbon dioxide absorber, the subject is then breathing air with a rising carbon dioxide content and a decreasing oxygen content. (Warning. It is dangerous to breathe air with a high carbon dioxide content.) It can be shown that the increase in ventilation rate is not due to a decreasing oxygen content, by using the spirometer with the carbon dioxide absorber in place between the subject and the reservoir of air, there is then no increase in the carbon dioxide content. Although the oxygen content is decreasing a much longer time elapses before there is any increase at all in the ventilation rate.

There are some circumstances under which breathing ceases but if the right treatment is available it may be started again. Electric shock, drowning, inhalation of smoke during a fire or of poisonous gases such as carbon monoxide may be a cause of respiratory failure. Giving artificial respiration may well save a life and anyone may learn readily how to perform mouth to mouth resuscitation ('kiss of life').

Respiratory carriers

Oxygen has a low solubility in water and in blood plasma, therefore the amount which can be transported in this way is limited. The oxygen requirements of many animals can be met only by having a respiratory carrier in the blood capable of combining with oxygen rapidly and being swept away from the respiratory surface. One respiratory carrier is haemocyanin, a blue or colourless compound containing copper which is present as copper[1] in the deoxygenated condition as as copper[11] when oxygenated. It is a less efficient respiratory carrier than haemoglobin. It is present in the blood of many crustaceans and cephalopods. Haemoglobin is present in the chordates and in several invertebrate groups such as annelids, molluscs and arthropods. It is an iron-containing pigment attached to a protein; its oxygen carrying mechanism is a complex one, not relying on the state of oxidation of the iron which is always in the iron[11] state (see page 141).

Key terms

Aerobe An organism using oxygen in respiration.
Anaerobe An organism respiring without the use of oxygen.
ATP Adenosine triphosphate, a nucleotide present in all living cells which releases energy in a controlled form for cell activities.
Breathing Ventilation. External respiration.
Citric acid cycle See Krebs cycle.

Dehydrogenation The removal of hydrogen atoms from a chemical compound.

Endergonic (reaction) One requiring energy.

Exergonic (reaction) One releasing energy.

Expiratory reserve volume Air which can be expelled from the lungs in addition to the tidal volume.

FAD Flavine adenine dinucleotide, a co-enzyme hydrogen carrier.

Fermentation Anaerobic respiration in plants producing ethanol and carbon dioxide.

Glycolysis First stage of respiration involving the conversion of glucose to pyruvic acid, a common pathway shared by aerobic and anaerobic processes.

Homoiothermic Having a constant body temperature.

Inspiratory reserve volume Air which can be taken into the lungs in excess of the tidal volume.

Krebs cycle Cycle of reactions in aerobic respiration in which energy is released to synthesize ATP. From pyruvic acid, formed in glycolysis, acetyl co-enzyme A is produced and enters the Krebs cycle.

Metabolic rate The rate at which an organism expends energy. Basal M.R., the rate at rest.

NAD Nicotinamide adenine dinucleotide; a co-enzyme, one of a series of carriers passing hydrogen atoms, removed during respiration reactions, to oxygen.

Oxygen debt The additional oxygen consumed by an animal after vigorous activity.

Phosphorylation The combination of an organic molecule with phosphate, e.g. formation of glucose phosphate in respiration.

Poikilothermic Varying body temperature associated with changes in the temperature of the surroundings.

Residual volume Air remaining in the lungs after a maximum expiration.

Respiration 1) The chemical reactions from which all living cells derive energy (= internal, cell or tissue respiration). 2) Breathing (= ventilation, external respiration).

Respiratory pathway Series of steps in the chemical breakdown of a respiratory substrate.

Respiratory quotient (RQ) The amount of carbon dioxide produced divided by the amount of oxygen used, in the same period of time.

Respiratory substrate Material metabolized by an organism to provide energy.

Tidal volume Air taken in and expelled during one respiratory cycle.

Ventilation rate Volume of air breathed per minute, i.e. number of inspirations per minute × the tidal volume.

Vital capacity Total volume of air which can be expelled following the maximum inspiration.

Chapter 8
Transport Systems

The blood system in a mammal

Substances needed by the cells of the body have to be distributed to them. In small organisms the process of diffusion may suffice, but in larger animals this is inadequate. In mammals food, oxygen and essential materials are distributed to the cells and their waste products collected by the blood system; blood forms the transport system of the body.

The structure of blood

Blood is a tissue consisting of **red blood cells** (erythrocytes), **white blood cells** (leucocytes) and blood **platelets**, in a liquid, the blood **plasma**.

Red cells

The red cells are minute discs, a drop of blood would contain up to a quarter of a million of them, they have no nucleus, instead there is a circular depression in the centre, the general shape being that of a biconcave disc. The interior of the cell contains the red pigment substance, **haemoglobin**, a conjugated protein consisting basically of four iron-containing prosthetic groups attached to polypeptide chains. The protein part is globin, the prosthetic groups consist of haem, a porphyrin. A red cell has a life span of about four months, new cells continually being produced in the red bone marrow of the ribs, sternum and vertebrae, while old cells are broken down in the liver.

White cells

Most white cells are larger than the red and there is only one white to about 550 red cells. There are various kinds of white cells; the polymorphs are produced in the bone marrow and have granular cytoplasm and an irregular shaped nucleus consisting of rounded masses with narrow constrictions between them; and lymphocytes and monocytes are produced in the lymph glands and have non-granular cytoplasm and a spherical or kidney-shaped nucleus. The polymorphs themselves are of several types, identifiable by their staining reactions.

Platelets

Platelets are minute rounded cell fragments, much smaller than red cells. They are budded off from special cells in the red bone marrow. There are about 40 to every one white cell.

Plasma

Plasma is a pale straw coloured liquid consisting of a solution of many compounds in water, the major ones being various proteins and amino acids, glucose, mineral salts, urea and hormones.

The functions of blood

The transport of oxygen

The red cells carry oxygen to the tissues of the body, their shape ensures a large surface area for the absorption of oxygen from the lungs. It diffuses through the cell membrane and combines with the haemoglobin to form oxy-haemoglobin. A molecule of haemoglobin is capable of combining with four molecules of oxygen, one molecule of oxygen combining with each of the four haem groups. (There is no oxidation of the iron in the haem group.) **Oxy-haemoglobin** which is formed is an unstable compound readily breaking down to haemoglobin and releasing oxygen which diffuses out through the membrane and becomes available to the tissues. The amount of oxygen which will combine with haemoglobin is related to the partial pressure of oxygen in the gas mixture when the solution and the gas are in equilibrium (this takes about 45 minutes). Increasing the partial pressure of oxygen results in an increase in the amount of oxygen combined with haemoglobin, but there is a limit above which no more oxygen can be combined. The solution is then saturated, and the amount of oxygen combined in a unit volume is its **oxygen capacity**. The amount of oxygen combined with haemoglobin is usually expressed as a percentage of the amount combined when it is fully saturated.

The partial pressure of a particular gas in a mixture of gases is the fraction of the total pressure contributed by the gas. For example, air contains 21% of oxygen at normal atmospheric pressure, the partial pressure of oxygen is therefore 21% of one atmosphere or $0.21 \times 760 = 160$ mm Hg, or as 1 mm Hg $= 133$ N/m^2, $160 \times 133 = 21280$ N/m$^2 = 21.28$ kN/m^2. If samples of blood are subjected to oxygen and nitrogen mixtures with different partial pressures of oxygen, allowed to come to equilibrium, and the percentage saturation of the blood with oxygen determined, the results can be plotted on a graph to obtain an **oxygen dissocia-**

tion curve. The curve shows that blood can become as much as 90% saturated with oxygen when the partial pressure is only 6 kN/m² equivalent to less than 6% of oxygen in the air, thus haemoglobin has a high affinity for oxygen. The curve also shows that oxy-haemoglobin gives up oxygen readily when the partial pressure of oxygen is low (below about 4 kN/m²), this will tend to be the state of affairs in tissues using oxygen rapidly, and will result in the oxy-haemoglobin releasing more of its oxygen.

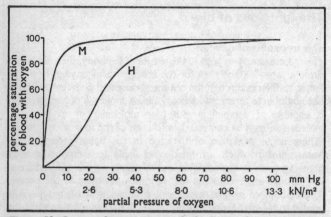

Figure 58. Oxygen dissociation curves for human haemoglobin (H) and myoglobin (M)

If carbon dioxide is introduced into the gas mixture, and the percentage saturation of the blood with oxygen determined at the same partial pressures of oxygen as before, it is found that the dissociation curve is shifted to the right. Increasing the carbon dioxide results in the curve shifting further to the right, in other words a rise in the concentration of carbon dioxide results in the blood taking up less oxygen. It does mean, however, that the oxy-haemoglobin will release oxygen to tissues before the partial pressure of oxygen reaches such a low level. This shifting of the dissociation curve for haemoglobin to the right in the presence of carbon dioxide, is called the **Bohr shift** or Bohr effect, after its discoverer. The Bohr shift favours the uptake of oxygen into the blood surrounding the alveoli in the lungs where the carbon dioxide content is low as it is constantly escaping, and it favours the release of oxygen to the tissues where the carbon dioxide content is high as it is continually released in cell respiration.

142

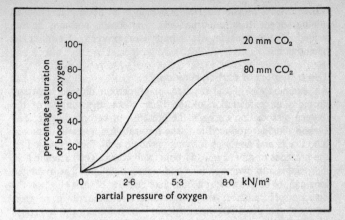

Figure 59. The effect of carbon dioxide on the oxygen dissociation curve for human haemoglobin

Myoglobin is found in muscles, it is closely related to haemoglobin, but has a dissociation curve to the left of that for haemoglobin (see figure 58). This means that it can take up oxygen even more readily than haemoglobin, but it releases it only at very low partial pressures of oxygen; thus it acts as an extra oxygen store and it is found in increasing quantities in more active animals.

Haemoglobins in different species of animals have different oxygen dissociation curves. When the haemoglobin of different species is fully saturated with oxygen this does not mean it is carrying the same amount of oxygen in each case; for example, human blood carries 26 volumes of oxygen for every 100 volumes of blood, whereas in the earthworm the blood carries only 4 volumes. The oxygen dissociation curve of haemoglobin in the human foetus shows a shift to the left of the curve shown by haemoglobin in the adult. This seems a strange fact, but it ensures that the blood of the foetus is able to take up oxygen across the placenta from the blood of the mother.

Haemoglobin has an affinity for carbon monoxide 250 times greater than it has for oxygen, and it combines with it to form a compound known as carboxy-haemoglobin which prevents it from taking up oxygen. Carboxy-haemoglobin dissociates 1000 times more slowly than oxy-haemoglobin, carbon monoxide therefore acts as a poison by interfering with oxygen transport and depriving cells of oxygen.

143

Other blood pigments Haemocyanin is a blood pigment containing copper. It is found in some invertebrates and may be dissolved in the plasma. Its affinity for oxygen is similar to haemoglobin.

The transport of carbon dioxide

An examination of the mechanism of carbon dioxide transport provides an explanation of the Bohr effect, the shifting of the oxygen dissociation curve in the presence of carbon dioxide. The carbon dioxide produced in tissue respiration diffuses into the red blood cells and dissolves forming carbonic acid, this is assisted by the presence of an enzyme, carbonic anhydrase. The carbonic acid dissociates into hydrogen ions and bicarbonate ions. The hydrogen ions cannot be allowed to accumulate because of their effect on the delicate pH balance; they bring about a breakdown of oxy-haemoglobin providing haemoglobin which buffers the hydrogen ions, collecting them to form haemoglobinic acid, a very weak acid, while the released oxygen diffuses to the cells. The result of these reactions is that bicarbonate ions tend to accumulate in the red blood cells and these diffuse out into the plasma. To adjust the charge, negatively charged chloride ions diffuse in from the plasma, this is the **chloride shift**. The situation in the red blood cell may be summarized as follows:

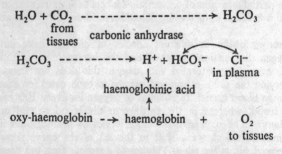

Some carbon dioxide is carried in combination with the amino groups in the haemoglobin molecule and some is dissolved in the plasma, here the plasma proteins act as a buffer by picking up the hydrogen ions.

In the lungs there is a different situation, the partial pressure of oxygen is high and that of carbon dioxide low, which brings about a reversal of the above reactions with the result that oxygen is absorbed by the red cells and carbon dioxide given out.

Defence mechanisms

The white blood cells are mainly responsible for protecting the body against infection. The polymorphs and monocytes are **phagocytic**, that is they ingest and destroy bacteria; they are capable of independent movement, creeping along the walls of blood vessels unhindered by the flow of blood, and even squeezing between the cells of the capillary walls to enter the tissues. A second defence system is brought about by the **lymphocytes**, they react to foreign proteins **(antigens)** in the bacteria entering the body, by initiating the production of other protein substances, **antibodies**. The antibodies react with the antigens causing the bacteria to clump together, and in this **agglutinated** state they are readily disposed of by the phagocytes. Some bacteria produce waste products of metabolism which are highly poisonous to the body, these toxins are neutralized by **antitoxins**, a type of antibody. It used to be thought that antibodies once produced remained in the blood stream for a long time, even for life, conferring **immunity** to the disease. Modern research suggests that immunity is not due to the persistence of the antibodies themselves, but to the fact that once the particular antigen has been encountered and the antibody response set going, the response is much more rapid if the same antigen is met on a subsequent occasion. Every individual is unique and this immune response will be triggered off by foreign protein even that from another individual of the same species, which explains the extreme care taken to match tissues for grafts or transplants and the need to control the immune response or the new tissue will be rejected by the body. Blood for transfusions must also be correctly matched (see page 147). Individuals vary in their degree of sensitivity to particular foreign proteins, a high degree of sensitivity may result in an allergic reaction which may be manifested in hay fever, skin rashes, some types of asthma or violent reactions to some foodstuffs.

Many tissues in the body have their own phagocytes, the macrophages, they are particularly abundant in the liver, spleen, lymph glands and connective tissue; together they make up the reticulo-endothelial system which disposes of foreign invaders.

Immunity to a particular disease acquired by being exposed to infection in the normal course of daily life, is natural immunity. Immunity to a number of diseases can also be brought about by artificial means. This **immunization** may be either active or passive. **Active immunity** results when antigens in the form of dead or weakened disease organisms, constituting the vaccine, are introduced into the body. Antibodies are produced just as if live organisms were present. **Passive immunity** may be achieved by injecting into the body antibodies which have been produced in another animal. The animal, usually a horse, is injected with progressively larger amounts of antigen material over a period of time, the antibody material can be extracted and injected into man. In general active immunity takes longer to build up but is long lasting, passive immunity confers a high degree of protection for a short period.

Blood clotting mechanism

When blood is exposed to air it coagulates, this natural mechanism stops bleeding from a wound and prevents the entry of bacteria into the body. The clot gradually dries and hardens into a scab which remains until healing is completed beneath it, then it falls away. Clotting results from the formation of **fibrin**, a protein produced in the form of fine interlacing fibres which form a meshwork over the wound trapping blood cells. The fibrin is the result of a chemical reaction between **fibrinogen**, a blood protein and **thrombin**, an enzyme. Thrombin is not present in the blood in the vessels, but is formed from prothrombin when the blood is exposed to air. The reactions which bring about its formation are complex, but involve the interaction of prothrombin with vitamin K, calcium ions and thromboplastin, the latter being produced when liquid from damaged cells reacts with disintegrating platelets. The reactions may be summarized as follows:

platelets
+
liquid from damaged cells $\longrightarrow$ thromboplastin
+
blood factors

thromboplastin + prothrombin + vit. K + Ca^{2+} $\longrightarrow$ thrombin

thrombin + fibrinogen $\longrightarrow$ fibrin

Substances transported in the plasma

The transport of waste carbon dioxide from respiration in the form of the ion HCO_3^-, antibodies for defence and materials concerned in blood clotting have already been mentioned in this chapter. A second waste product, urea, is carried from the liver where it is produced, to the kidneys to be filtered from the blood and removed from the body. The endocrine glands are well supplied with blood capillaries and secrete hormones directly into the blood which transports them. Food materials are carried in the plasma; glucose and other monosaccharides, amino acids, fatty acids and glycerol, vitamins and various mineral salts in the form of ions, Na^+, K^+, Mg^{2+}, Ca^{2+}, Cl^-, SO_4^{2-}, PO_4^{3-}. The plasma also distributes water and heat.

Blood groups

Two types of antigen are found in human red blood cells, indicated by the letters A and B; the blood of some individuals contains A, some B, others both A and B, and the remainder neither. In addition two types of antibody, a and b are found in the plasma. A and a cannot be present in the same blood or the red cells would be agglutinated, similarly B and b cannot exist in the same blood. Blood with A in the red cells can have b in the plasma, and blood with B in the red cells can have a in the plasma; where both A and B are found neither a nor b can be present, but both a and b can exist in blood where A and B are absent from the red cells. The international designation for the four major blood groups; A, B, AB, and O, indicates the antigens present in the red cells. Mixing a sample of blood of unknown group with two sera separately, the first containing a and the second b, and checking for agglutination, will indicate to which of the groups the blood sample belongs. In the table below, plus indicates agglutination, minus indicates no agglutination.

Reaction with serum a	+	−	+	−
Reaction with serum b	−	+	+	−
Blood group	A	B	AB	O

In a blood transfusion it is desirable to use blood of the same group, but in an emergency, group O blood may be used, this lacks antigens and those with group O are universal donors. As the amount of blood transfused is normally small it is diluted by the recipient's blood, and the antibodies present in the donor's blood do not cause agglutination. Also, owing to the fact that blood cells have a limited life the donor's cells do not persist in the patient's blood to manufacture antibodies over a period of time. Persons with blood of group AB are universal recipients, there are no antibodies in the blood to react with any antigens introduced from the donor. The important points to consider are the donor's antigens and the recipient's antibodies. In practice after the patient and donor have been grouped, the cells of one are mixed with the serum of the other; the additional tests serving as a check and as a precaution against rare and anomalous reactions. **Serum** is blood plasma without the clotting constituents.

In addition to the antigens A and B, another may be present in the red cells, this is the **Rhesus factor**. Rhesus positive blood has the antigen while Rhesus negative blood lacks it. The corresponding antibody is not normally present in the plasma but it is produced under particular conditions. If Rhesus positive blood is introduced into a person with Rhesus negative blood the recipient manufactures the antibody, but it takes time for the antibody level to build up and the red cells introduced have a limited period of survival, so no further problem arises. If however, a second introduction of Rhesus positive blood occurs at a later stage the antibodies are produced more rapidly and agglutination results. Under normal conditions this could happen in pregnancy when a Rhesus negative mother bears a Rhesus positive child; red cell fragments from the foetus can cross the placenta into the maternal circulation initiating the production of the antibodies which in turn can cross into the blood system of the foetus causing destruction of the red cells. The child may then be stillborn or be seriously anaemic—a 'blue' baby. There is little damage in a first pregnancy of this kind because the antibodies take time to build up in the maternal blood, but in a subsequent pregnancy with a Rhesus positive child, antibodies will be produced rapidly. Modern medical science has now found a way to overcome this problem by giving the mother an anti-Rhesus globulin which protects the red cells of the foetus.

Blood circulatory systems

In some invertebrates particularly the arthropods, blood is not contained in vessels but is within the body cavity, this is an open circulation and the body cavity is known as a **haemocoel**. In insects the haemocoel is divided by a perforated membrane into dorsal and ventral cavities; a muscular tube consisting of a series of heart chambers, each pierced by two pores, is suspended in the dorsal cavity. Blood is pushed forward by waves of muscular contraction, flows through the haemocoel and as the muscles relax it is sucked back through the pores which are equipped with a one-way valve system, into the heart chambers.

In annelids blood circulates in blood vessels forming a **closed system**. There is a main dorsal vessel in which blood flows towards the head and a main ventral vessel in which blood flows posteriorly, the two being connected by five 'hearts' (contractile vessels or pseudohearts) with simple valves.

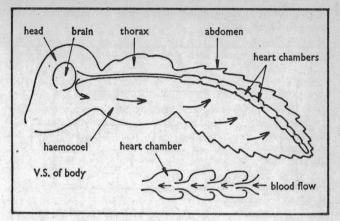

Figure 60. Blood circulation of an insect

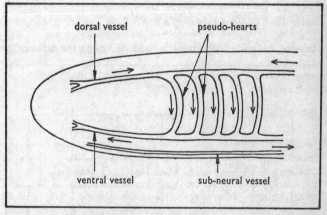

Figure 61. Blood circulation of an annelid

Fish have a closed blood system and there is a **single circulation** of blood. The heart has one auricle and one ventricle, blood is pumped to the gills to be oxygenated and then flows round the body. A system of this type results in blood being supplied to the tissues at a low pressure after it has passed through the capillaries of the gills. Following its passage through capillaries of the body there is a further drop in pressure which creates a problem in returning blood to the heart, this has been solved by the blood flowing slowly in large sinuses which offer less resistance to the blood flow than veins.

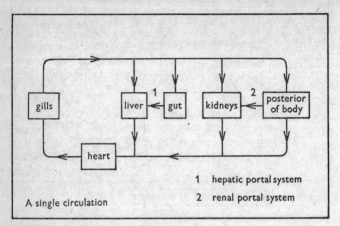

Figure 62. The blood system of a fish

Mammals have evolved a better system of solving the problem of

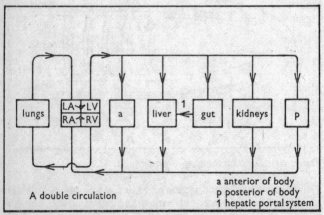

Figure 63. The blood system of a mammal

the drop in pressure of the blood. After it has passed through the capillaries of the lungs to be oxygenated, it returns to the heart and is pumped out again round the body, this is a **double circulation**. Mixing of oxygenated and deoxygenated blood in the heart is prevented by the presence of a longitudinal wall, so that deoxygenated blood flows through the right side and oxygenated blood through the left side.

Amphibians have a double circulation with a partially divided heart of two auricles and one ventricle. In most reptiles there is some division between the ventricles, this being complete in crocodiles.

The mammalian heart

The heart is divided into four chambers, two smaller thin walled **auricles (atria)** and two larger thick walled **ventricles**. It is formed mainly of muscle but has a lining of epithelium, the **endocardium**, and an outer covering of connective tissue and epithelium, the **pericardium**. The pericardium is of two layers with fluid between them. The heart muscle itself is supplied with blood by coronary vessels.

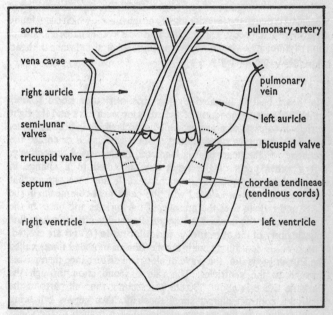

Figure 64. The structure of the mammalian heart

Deoxygenated blood returning from the body in the venae cavae enters the right auricle, the pressure opening the tricuspid valve and

151

allowing it to flow into the right ventricle. When it is full of blood the ventricle contracts forcing the blood into the pulmonary artery; it is prevented from returning to the auricle by the flaps of the tricuspid valve which close the opening, non-elastic **tendinous cords** stop the flaps from turning inside out. When the ventricle relaxes blood cannot be sucked back from the pulmonary artery as the **semi-lunar valves** at its base are closed. The pulmonary artery branches and carries blood to the lungs to be oxygenated, it returns to the left auricle in the pulmonary vein and flows into the left ventricle. The left ventricle is the larger of the two with thicker walls, when it contracts it drives the blood into the aortic arch and thence into the dorsal aorta, branches being given off to the head, forelimbs, internal organs and hind limbs. Blood is collected from the capillary networks into veins which join to form the venae cavae returning blood to the heart. Both sides of the heart contract together **(systole)** and relax together **(diastole)**, completing one **cardiac cycle**; the alternate contracting and relaxing occur about 72 times a minute, in man, throughout life. The smooth working of the heart is due to the functioning of special muscle which is not found elsewhere in the body. This cardiac muscle is even capable of contracting rhythmically when the nerve supply is severed and when the heart is isolated from the body.

The heart beat is initiated by the **sino-auricular node (SAN)** which lies near the junction of the superior vena cava and the right auricle, it consists of a plexus of fine muscle fibres in fibrous tissue. The SAN acts as a **pacemaker,** when it is warmed or cooled the frequency of the heart beat is increased or decreased respectively, but if other parts of the heart are subjected to a change in temperature the frequency is unchanged. It has been shown that electrical changes associated with the heart beat commence in the SAN and radiate over the muscles of the auricles and bases of the veins to reach the junction of the auricles and ventricles where fine muscle fibres of the **auriculo-ventricular node (AVN)** are excited. The AVN is continuous with a collection of modified fibres called the **Purkinje tissue,** the wave of electrical disturbance then passes through to the ventricles. The rate of conduction through the Purkinje tissue is about 500 cm per second, thus all parts of the ventricles contract almost simultaneously. Two nerves can bring about changes in the activity of the SAN, a branch of the vagus nerve has an inhibitory effect, slowing down the rate at which the heart is beating, while a branch of the sympathetic nervous system has an accelerating effect.

Arteries, veins and capillaries

Arteries carry blood from the heart, they have thick muscular walls to withstand the pressure of the blood pumped into them when the heart beats. Veins return the blood to the heart, the pressure of the blood in them is lower and the flow is steadier. Valves at intervals along their length prevent the back flow of blood, while the contraction and relaxation of skeletal muscles assists in driving it towards the heart. In general the venous blood has less food materials and oxygen than arterial blood and it is darker in colour. The exceptions are the hepatic portal vein carrying digested food materials from the small intestine to the liver, the pulmonary vein returning freshly oxygenated blood from the lungs to the heart, and the pulmonary artery taking deoxygenated blood from the heart to the lungs. The major arteries divide repeatedly into smaller and smaller vessels finally becoming a network of capillaries, some so narrow that red blood cells travel through in single file. The capillaries finally join up to form minor veins which unite forming larger veins to conduct blood to the heart.

Plasma, tissue fluid and lymph

Blood enters the capillaries under pressure, the walls are thin so water and small sized molecules are forced through the permeable walls. The escaped liquid is similar to plasma in that it contains, for example, amino acids, glucose, mineral salts and some plasma proteins, but it lacks the larger plasma proteins which cannot escape. This liquid bathes the cells, it is **tissue fluid** and from it the cells take the substances they need. Oxygen diffuses from the blood to the cells and the carbon dioxide produced there diffuses back. White blood cells can squeeze between the cells of the capillary wall and migrate among the tissue cells if required. At the venous end of the capillary network the pressure is considerably lower and water from the tissue fluid is able to go back into the capillaries as the osmotic pressure of the plasma is greater than that of the tissue fluid owing to its higher protein content. The remaining fluid is drained into lymphatics which occur between the cells, these join to form larger ducts which eventually discharge their contents into the veins near the right auricle. The fluid in the lymphatics is **lymph**, it lacks the larger proteins of plasma and much of the materials absorbed by the cells from the tissue fluid, and it contains lymphocytes. **Lymph glands** occur at intervals along the lymph vessels, they manufacture the lymphocytes and antibodies, and destroy bacteria. The lymph system has no pump as the blood system has, the move-

ment of lymph being brought about largely by pressure from contracting skeletal muscles, back flow being prevented by valves.

The uptake of water by plants

The surface area of the region of the root which bears **root hairs** is
increased at least tenfold by their presence, thus forming an effective anchorage and an extensive surface for the absorption of water
by osmosis. Water is also absorbed in the region between the root
hair zone and the root apex where the epidermal cells, like the root
hairs, are not cuticularized. The cell sap in these regions contains
sugars and other osmotically active substances in sufficient quantity
to produce an osmotic pressure greater than that in the soil water,
so that water passes into the root from outside. Once inside the root
hair water travels across the cortex and enters the vascular tissue.
The last cell to give up water to the vascular tissue is left with a
higher concentration of solutes in the cell sap, and thus an **osmotic
gradient** is set up across the cortex tending to draw water from cell
to cell across from the root hair to the vascular tissue. Water may
also be carried in the cytoplasm from cell to cell via the
plasmodesmata or in some cases through the permeable cell wall
and then between the wall and the cytoplasm.

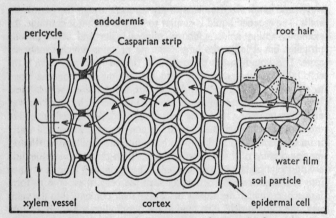

Figure 65. The passage of water across the cortex of a root

It can be shown that xylem is the tissue responsible for carrying
water up the stem, by placing a cut stem in water containing some
red ink or eosin. Some hours later sections of the stem are examined

under the microscope which reveals that the dye is contained only in the xylem. If a cut stem is placed in a solution of picric acid bright yellow staining can be seen later in the xylem, in spite of the fact that picric acid is a powerful poison. This shows that water can still be transported in dead cells. In angiosperms vessels carry the most water up the stem; the vessel elements being open ended form long tubes when placed end to end whereas tracheids offer some resistance to water flow by the perforated end walls.

How water is made to pass from the parenchymatous cortical cells into the xylem is still not fully understood. The evaporation of water from the leaves causes water to be drawn up and into the xylem, but it is not all the story because if the stem of a plant is severed from the rootstock, water continues to flow from the stump, so there must be some force pushing the water up from the roots, this is **root pressure**. Considerable pressures are developed by some plants in this way. The cells of the endodermis may prove to be responsible for this phenomenon, their structure is unique in that each cell possesses a **Casparian strip**, an impermeable strip apparently adhering to the cell wall on one side and the cytoplasm on the other, so that even when the cell is plasmolysed the cytoplasm does not draw away from the wall in the region of the Casparian strip, though it does so elsewhere in the cell. This means water cannot creep between the cell wall and the cytoplasm but is obliged to pass through it. The cells of the endodermis contain starch grains, a food reserve which can be utilized for energy. These two characteristics of the endodermal cells suggest that some active process is involved when water passes through.

In a mature tree such as an ash which may be over 40 m tall, the xylem in the trunk must contain innumerable columns of water, each of microscopic diameter but of considerable length; yet if water is drawn up a piece of tubing by means of a vaccum pump, the column will not rise above 11 m, the normal barometric height of water. However, if a porous pot is attached to a piece of tubing, both filled with water and the end placed in a container of mercury, water will evaporate from the pot drawing up the water which in turn pulls up the mercury. The height reached by the mercury under these conditions can be as much as 1 m, the normal barometric height being 0·76 m. The explanation for this phenomenon appears to lie in the fact that the porous pot is full of narrow channels through which the water passes before evaporating into the air. The water tends to cling to the walls of the channels, there are **forces of adhesion** between the molecules of water and the molecules of the

155

substance of the pot. The narrower the channels the higher will be the proportion of water molecules in contact with the walls and the greater will be the forces of adhesion. These forces will support a column of water above its normal barometric height. The **forces of cohesion**, that is the attraction of the water molecules to each other also prevent the columns of water breaking as they are sucked upwards. The phenomenon of capillarity, the rise of liquid in narrow spaces due to forces of adhesion and cohesion, can be shown by placing pieces of capillary glass tubing in a beaker of water. The height to which the water rises is inversely proportional to the diameter of the tube; for example, water rises 3 cm in a tube of 1 mm bore, 30 cm when the bore is 0·1 mm.

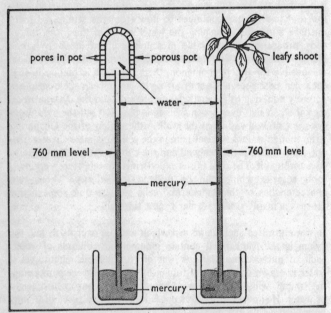

Figure 66. Force of transpiration compared with a physical model

Transpiration

The loss of water vapour from a plant, mainly through the leaves, is transpiration, while the passage of water from the roots through the stem and leaves and into the atmosphere is the transpiration stream. Water evaporates from the walls of the mesophyll cells in the leaf

156

into the intercellular spaces and diffuses into the sub-stomatal space and out through the stomata. The cellulose walls of the mesophyll cells have fine channels which can be compared with those in a porous pot, and thus there are strong forces of adhesion supporting the water columns. As water molecules evaporate, the cohesive forces between them result in more molecules being pulled up to replace them. The cells from which the water has evaporated will be left with a higher osmotic pressure, so they tend to draw water from the next cells bringing about an osmotic gradient, the cells in the centre of the leaf having the lowest osmotic pressure; this gradient helps to draw water from the xylem into the mesophyll cells. Transpiration assists in drawing water into the plant, its passage aids the transport of mineral salts and its evaporation cools the leaves.

Conditions affecting the rate of transpiration

External conditions affecting transpiration are temperature, humidity, air movements, atmospheric pressure, light and the availability of water to the plant roots. An increase in temperature of the air increases its capacity to absorb water vapour therefore bringing about a higher rate of transpiration. Increased humidity, on the other hand, means that the air can take up less water vapour from the plant and transpiration will be reduced. If the humidity is very high, water may accumulate in the leaves eventually oozing on to the surface through the stomata and dripping from the leaves. Some plants have special **hydathodes** in the epidermis near the ends of the xylem tissue, the liquid exuding from them contains mineral salts which may remain as a white deposit as in some saxifrages. The removal of excess water in these ways is **guttation**. Air movements will increase transpiration by carrying away water vapour from the immediate vicinity of the plant and allow more to evaporate from the leaves. The lower the atmospheric pressure the higher will be the rate of transpiration; mountain plants are susceptible to high water losses and have modifications to reduce transpiration. Light causes stomata to open (see page 94), and if water is not available for the roots of the plant it will wilt and obviously this will affect transpiration. Other factors affecting the rate of transpiration are the number of stomata, their structure and location in the leaf.

The control of transpiration

Provided that the roots have plenty of water an increased rate of transpiration will result in more water being absorbed by the roots.

If adequate water is not available transpiration will exceed water uptake and in time the cells will lose their turgidity and the plant will wilt. In colder climates many trees lose their leaves in winter, if they did not do so the water lost in transpiration could not be replaced by the roots from a cold or frozen soil, a condition known as **physiological drought**. Evergreen trees have leaves either with a much reduced surface area such as pine needles or with a thick waxy cuticle and other features such as sunken stomata.

Measuring the rate of transpiration
A small plant can be taken and placed in water in a suitable container. The apparatus is weighed at intervals and the loss in mass recorded. A control is set up at the same time omitting the plant. Alternatively a potted plant may be used with the pot and soil enclosed in a plastic bag and tied firmly round the stem, to prevent loss of mass by the evaporation of water from the pot and soil.

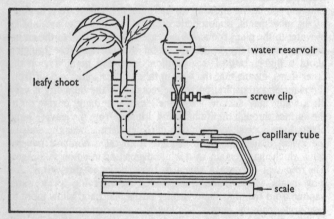

Figure 67. The potometer

From the results the rate of transpiration can be calculated and expressed as mass of water lost per unit area of leaf surface per unit time. The mass of water lost in a given time is known and the leaf area can be found afterwards by placing the leaves on squared paper, tracing round the margins and counting the squares within the outlines (not forgetting that leaves have two sides). Water loss may range from 20 to 200 $g/h/m^2$ during daylight. To compare the rates of transpiration under different conditions it is more convenient to use a **potometer**, this piece of apparatus, however,

158

measures water uptake not water loss, but as rates are being compared any difference between the two may be disregarded. It is essential to ensure that the apparatus is free of air bubbles and to leave it for about 15 minutes to allow it to come to equilibrium with the environment before any readings are taken.

As water evaporates from the leaves, air is drawn into the end of the capillary tube and the meniscus can be seen moving along the scale. This movement can be timed over a fixed distance. The meniscus can be returned to the end of the capillary tube by loosening the screw clip, when water will flow into the capillary tube from the reservoir. Experiments can be carried out to find which surface of the leaf loses most water by smearing the surfaces of (say) the undersides of the leaves with petroleum jelly. A qualitative assessment can be made by attaching small pieces of dry cobalt chloride paper (kept in a desiccator) to both surfaces of a leaf by means of sellotape, and comparing the length of time taken for it to change from blue, the dry state, to pink when damp. The results obtained can be related to the number of stomata on each surface by painting nail varnish on to a small area of each side, peeling it off when dry and examining under the microscope the impressions left by the epidermal cells and stomata.

The uptake of mineral salts

Examination of the ions present in a plant shows that some are present in greater concentration than in the soil water, indicating that the plant is able to take in ions against the concentration gradient. The relative proportions of the ions present in the plant may be quite different from those in the soil water, showing that the plant is able to select certain ions and reject others. The movement of ions from the soil water into the roots of the plant is not a process of simple diffusion but is, at least in part, an active one requiring energy. If roots are deprived of oxygen, ion uptake is hindered, while raising the temperature increases the rate of uptake of some ions. It is possible that the ion needed is collected at the surface of the plasma membrane by a carrier molecule and transported across, the energy required being made available by ATP. When a cation such as K^+ or Mg^{2+} is taken in, an anion which may be OH^- is also picked up to keep the balance of the charge; and when an anion, for example NO_3^- or SO_4^{2-} is needed, a cation, H^+ for instance is taken up. The balance of the charge may also be maintained by the cell exchanging a cation or anion that is needed for one not required.

The uptake of carbon dioxide

In a dorsiventral type of leaf the stomata are more numerous on the lower surface, in a vertical leaf they are distributed equally on either side. Through the stomata carbon dioxide and oxygen are exchanged, and water vapour passes out during transpiration. The opening and closing of the stomata is under the control of the guard cells (see page 94). Whether the stomata are open or closed can be investigated by means of a **porometer**, a piece of apparatus measuring the resistance to the passage of air through a leaf. At the

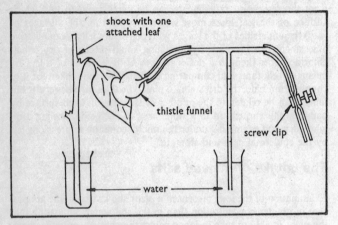

Figure 68. The porometer

beginning of the experiment the air in the funnel attached to the leaf is under reduced pressure. The rate of fall of the water level between the two marks is recorded, this gives a measure of the rate of air flow through the stomata and hence an indication of their condition. In general, stomata close at night and open during the day. In the day, the fact that the stomata open to take in carbon dioxide may lead to a high rate of water loss by transpiration, causing the plant to wilt, however, it usually recovers rapidly during the cooler part of the day. When carbon dioxide diffuses into the stomata it enters the substomatal space and intercellular spaces between the mesophyll cells where it dissolves in the film of water on their surface and diffuses into the cell, here it is used in photosynthesis. This results in a concentration gradient from the atmosphere outside to the mesophyll cells and causes more carbon dioxide to diffuse into the leaf.

Translocation

Translocation is the transport of organic materials made by the plant. Food materials are made in the leaves but need to be taken to the principal growing regions of the stem and roots, and in some plants to storage organs such as bulbs and corms. Translocation takes place in the phloem (see page 81). If a ring of bark is peeled from a tree it separates in the cambial region, so that the phloem is removed in the bark. It is then found that sugar accumulates above the ring. If the plant is supplied with carbon dioxide containing radioactive ^{14}C, this becomes incorporated into the sugar and can be detected in the phloem. Mittler in the U.S.A. has devised an ingenious method of removing some of the phloem contents; he found that aphids feeding from a plant insert the proboscis into the phloem, so by killing them off with carbon dioxide and severing the proboscis, he was left with a fine tube giving access to the phloem. Micro-analysis of the contents showed a high concentration of sugars and amino acids. The rate of movement of sugar in the phloem is between 50 to 100 cm/h, far in excess of that possible by diffusion. Also, it has been found that materials can move in opposite directions in the phloem and that different materials are translocated at different rates, indicating that translocation is probably an active process, which is supported by the fact that oxygen deficiency slows up translocation, while raising the temperature increases the rate of flow. The means by which materials are translocated in the phloem is the subject of considerable controversy, there are two major schools of thought, one favouring the mass flow hypothesis and the other supporting a hypothesis based on protoplasmic streaming. The **mass flow hypothesis** suggests that movement of materials in the phloem is due to the fact that there is a turgor pressure gradient between the cells of the leaves and those of the root, the high turgor pressure in the leaves being due to the manufacture of sugar which raises the osmotic pressure of the cell contents, however, this hypothesis in its basic form is unsatisfactory in that it does not explain all the observed facts. Movement of materials by protoplasmic streaming would mean that translocation is confined to younger phloem, even so some substances, such as injected dyes, appear to move independently of it.

Key terms

Agglutination The sticking together of bacteria brought about by antibodies or of red blood cells when mixed with incompatible blood.

II

161

Antibody Substance produced in the body by lymphocytes to combine with invading antigen.

Antigen Substance foreign to the body, usually protein sometimes carbohydrate, capable of initiating antibody formation.

Antitoxin A type of antibody produced to neutralize the poisonous waste (toxin) produced by some organisms.

Bohr shift (Bohr effect) The effect of carbon dioxide on the dissociation of oxygen in the blood. The oxygen dissociation curve is shifted to the right.

Cardiac cycle One heart beat consisting of a contraction (systole) and a relaxation (diastole).

Casparian strip An impermeable strip round the transverse and radial walls of the cells of the endodermis in plant roots.

Closed circulation The circulation of blood in vessels.

Diastole Phase of the heart beat when the heart muscle is relaxed and the heart is filling with blood.

Erythrocytes Red blood cells.

Guttation Excess water in liquid form exuding from the leaves of plants under conditions of high humidity.

Haemoglobin A red pigment in the red blood cells having a high affinity for oxygen. A conjugated protein consisting of iron-containing groups (haem) attached to protein (globin).

Immunity Protection from a disease conferred by the presence in the body of specific antibodies ready to combine with invading antigens associated with the disease.

Leucocytes White blood cells comprizing polymorphs, lymphocytes and monocytes. Polymorphs and monocytes are phagocytes, ingesting bacteria.

Lymph Liquid returned from tissues in the lymph system, similar to tissue fluid but with less food materials and containing lymphocytes.

Myoglobin A compound found in muscle fibres, closely related to haemoglobin and having an even higher affinity for oxygen.

Open circulation Blood contained in the body cavity and not in vessels e.g. as in arthropods.

Oxygen dissociation curve The curve obtained when the percentage saturation of a sample of blood with oxygen is plotted against the partial pressure of oxygen.

Plasma Liquid part of the blood containing plasma proteins, soluble products of digestion, waste products, hormones etc.

Platelets Minute bodies in mammalian blood concerned in blood clotting.

Rhesus factor An antigen present in the red blood cells of 85% of the population (Rh positive), absent in the remainder (Rh negative).

Root pressure Pressure under which water passes from the cells of the root cortex into the xylem.

Serum Blood plasma without the clotting factors.

Sino-auricular node (SAN) The heart pacemaker.

Systole Phase of the heart beat when the heart muscle is contracted and blood is being pumped into the arteries.

Tissue fluid Liquid forced through capillary walls to bathe the tissues. Similar to plasma but lacking larger plasma proteins.

Translocation The transport in the phloem of the soluble products of photosynthesis.

Chapter 9
Excretion and Osmoregulation

Excretory products

Excretion is the removal from the body of the **waste products of metabolism**. The main waste products of animals are **nitrogenous materials, carbon dioxide** and **water**. Faeces are not an excretory product but are egested food residues which are not the result of metabolism. In green plants the excretory products, water and carbon dioxide, released in respiration are used in photosynthesis, and some of the oxygen produced in photosynthesis is used in respiration, only the excess oxygen actually being eliminated. Thus waste products which have been expelled from the cells are not necessarily eliminated and conversely materials eliminated are not necessarily waste in the sense of being made by the cells for example, excess mineral salts.

Sources of animal excretory products

Nitrogenous waste
Nitrogenous waste is derived from the **deamination** of excess amino acids produced by the digestion of protein-containing foods, or by the breakdown of protein materials of the body itself.

Carbon dioxide
Carbon dioxide is a waste product of respiration.

Water
Water is a waste product of respiration, it is also formed during other chemical reactions in the body, for example, condensations. Not all water eliminated from the body is true excretion, that is not all is the result of metabolic processes, some being taken in food or by drinking.

Nitrogenous waste

Nitrogenous waste excreted by an animal may be in the form of one of several different compounds, ammonia, urea, uric acid and urates or trimethylamine oxide.

Ammonia

Ammonia (NH_3) is a simple compound, very soluble in water but also highly toxic, therefore it needs copious quantities of water for its removal from the body.

Urea

Urea (NH_2CONH_2) is less toxic than ammonia but still requires a lot of water for its elimination from the body. Urea is formed from ammonia and carbon dioxide.

$$2NH_3 + CO_2 \dashrightarrow NH_2CONH_2 + H_2O$$

Some waste carbon dioxide from respiration is therefore excreted at the same time.

Uric acid and its salts, urates

Uric acid and urates are complex organic compounds. Uric acid is only slightly soluble in water and can be excreted in the form of crystals without water loss. Uric acid and urates are considerably less toxic than urea and ammonia.

Trimethylamine oxide

Trimethylamine oxide is soluble and non-toxic, it therefore requires little water for its elimination.

Water excretion and osmoregulation

In land animals water is lost by the respiratory surfaces which have to be kept moist and by the need to dissolve nitrogenous waste. In homoiothermic animals the evaporation of water is used as a means of controlling body temperature. The water required for these purposes can rarely be met by utilizing metabolic water alone, the animal relies on water taken in with food or by drinking. The kangaroo rat is unusual in being able to survive without drinking; by employing all possible water conserving methods it manages to survive on metabolic water alone. In land animals therefore, it becomes not a problem of water excretion but one of water conservation. Most have a waterproof skin to prevent evaporation from the surface of the body, (amphibians which use their skin as a respiratory surface cannot have this and are confined to a damp environment). The water taken into the body has to be balanced against output to keep the osmotic pressure of the body fluids within certain narrow limits; this is the process of osmo-

regulation.

Animals in fresh water, for example, freshwater fish, also take in water but by a different means. Mineral salts in the body result in the body fluids being hypertonic to the medium and water is unavoidably taken into the body by osmosis. Some way has to be found of eliminating it together with metabolic water, and use is made of it to flush away the nitrogenous waste. Many marine organisms have body fluids isotonic with sea water and do not have problems of osmoregulation, in fact most do not have any means of osmoregulation. The sea is a very stable environment but most marine organisms are confined to it and cannot venture into estuarine waters or beaches where there is fresh water influence. Some marine organisms, such as some species of crabs, have devices giving varying degrees of osmoregulation according to the salinity of the surrounding water, while others such as the lugworm, *Arenicola*, are able to withstand variations in the salt content of the environment without harm.

The marine bony fish are in an environment which is hypertonic to their body fluids, thus water is withdrawn from them by osmosis and has to be replaced by drinking sea water and eliminating the salt. The cartilaginous fish, such as the dogfish, retain a high level of waste nitrogenous matter in the blood to make it isotonic with sea water; it does not appear to be toxic to these fish.

Excretion and osmoregulation in different animals

In many animals the removal of nitrogenous waste is combined with the regulation of the water content of the body, in other words the control of the osmotic pressure of the body fluids. The functions of excretion and osmoregulation are often carried out by the same structures.

Amoeba
In *Amoeba* the animal is small enough for nitrogenous waste (probably ammonia) and carbon dioxide to diffuse out from the surface into the water, while the water which is unavoidably taken into the animal owing to the higher osmotic pressure of its contents, is expelled by means of the contractile vacuole. When this is a certain size it moves to the surface and discharges the water. In marine protozoans where the contents of the body are isotonic with the environment, the contractile vacuole is absent.

166

Turbellarians

In these non-parasitic platyhelminths, the functions of excretion and osmoregulation are combined and are carried out by the activity of the **flame cells**. Pores on the dorsal surface lead to two excretory canals which branch into ducts ultimately ending in flame cells. Each flame cell has an internal cavity continuous with the duct and contains a collection of long cilia that make flickering movements reminiscent of a flame. Waste products are secreted into the cavity and wafted outwards by the cilia. Carbon dioxide from respiration diffuses out over the surface of the body.

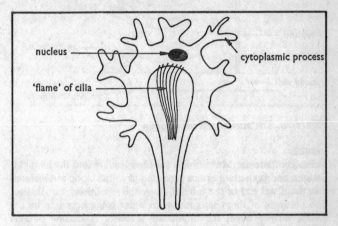

Figure 69. A flame cell

Earthworm

The excretory organs of the earthworm are the **nephridia**, paired structures found in all segments posterior to the fifth. A nephridium is a tubule which opens into the coelomic cavity by a ciliated **nephrostome** and to the exterior by a **nephridiopore**. In the coelomic cavity surrounding the gut muscles are **chlorogogen cells** capable of deaminating unwanted amino acids forming ammonium compounds and urea, some is secreted into the coelomic fluid. The beating of the cilia causes the coelomic fluid containing any excretory materials in solution to pass down the tubule, at the same time urea is extracted form the blood capillaries surrounding it. The wider part of the tubule near the nephridiopore probably absorbs water and therefore has an osmoregulatory function. Some carbon dioxide diffuses out of the surface capillaries and some is combined with calcium, forming particles of calcium carbonate in the calcareous glands, pouches leading to the gut in the oesophageal region.

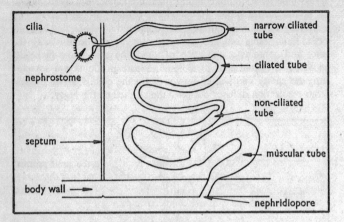

Figure 70. The earthworm nephridium

Insects

In insects there are **Malpighian tubules** leading into the hind gut. Sodium and potassium urates extracted from the blood are secreted into the distal end of the tubules where the conditions are alkaline. The presence of these salts results in water being drawn in by osmosis, further down the tubule the presence of carbon dioxide provides an acid medium, and uric acid together with sodium and potassium bicarbonates is formed. These bicarbonates and water are reabsorbed and sometimes leave uric acid in crystal form which passes into the hind gut and becomes mixed with the faeces, the two continuing through the rectum where more water is absorbed. The amount of water passed out varies in different insects. The ability of some species to conserve water to the extent of producing waste nitrogenous material in the form of uric acid crystals is one of the reasons for the success of insects capable of inhabiting very arid regions. The carbon dioxide produced by insects escapes through the cuticle.

Fish

Freshwater fish whose body fluids are hypertonic to the water outside will take in water by osmosis through the gills and lining of the mouth; this water is removed by filtration in the kidneys. The fish produce ammonia as a waste nitrogenous material. It is very soluble but highly toxic and the copious filtrate from the kidneys is utilized to flush it away. Freshwater fish have a problem in maintaining a balance of salts, most of the salts lost in the kidney filtrate are reabsorbed and in addition, the fish takes up salts from the water against the concentration gradient, by means of special **chloride secretory cells** in the gills. Saltwater bony fish have the opposite problem; the body fluid is hypotonic to the sea water and the fish is losing water all the time to the outside, the amount of filtrate from the kidneys is correspondingly small. To compensate for the liquid loss, the fish swallows sea water, salts are removed by the chloride secretory cells which are again moving salts against the concentration gradient, but this time in the *opposite direction* to that in the freshwater fish. In both cases, moving salts against the concentration gradient is an active process requiring energy. As little water is available for flushing away the waste nitrogenous matter, non toxic trimethylamine oxide is substituted for the highly poisonous ammonia of the freshwater fish. Carbon dioxide diffuses from the blood in the gills to the water outside.

Mammalian excretory organs

The kidneys excrete water, urea and salts; the lungs carbon dioxide and water from respiration; and the skin water, sodium chloride and a little urea.

Structure of the kidneys

The kidneys are both excretory and osmoregulatory organs. There are a pair of kidneys attached at the back of the abdominal cavity, each is supplied with blood by the renal artery, deoxygenated blood being removed by the renal vein. There is a tube, the ureter, carrying the final filtrate, the urine, from the kidney to the bladder for storage. The kidney itself consists of over a million nephrons, small filter units, and many blood capillaries held together by connective tissue and covered by a thin membrane. At each heart beat about a third of the blood pumped out passes through the kidneys. In longitudinal section the kidney can be seen to consist of an outer dark zone, the **cortex**; a middle paler zone, the **medulla**; and a central **pelvis** which leads to the **ureter**. Each **nephron** consists of a fine looped **uriniferous tubule** with one cup-shaped blind end in the cortex, the **Bowman's capsule**, closely surrounding a knot of capillaries, the **glomerulus**. The Bowman's capsule with its associated glomerulus is a **Malpighian body**. The distal end of the tubule joins a common collecting duct passing through the medulla to open into the pelvis. Each glomerulus is supplied with blood by

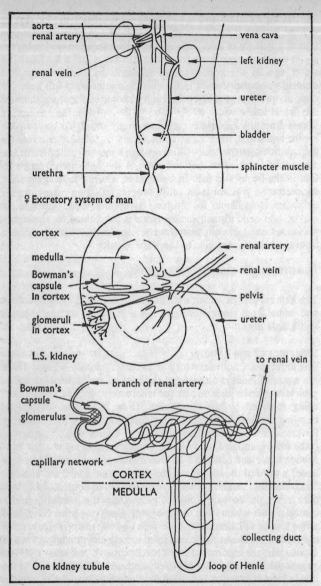

♀ Excretory system of man

L.S. kidney

One kidney tubule

Figure 71. Mammalian excretory system and kidney structure

an afferent vessel which is a branch of the renal artery; blood leaves the glomerulus by an efferent vessel of narrower bore which then forms a network of capillaries covering the tubule before joining the renal vein.

Function of the kidney

The function of the kidney is to remove waste products from the blood as it passes through the kidney and to regulate the amount of water in the blood. This is done by two processes, firstly by **ultrafiltration** (filtration under pressure) in which most of the materials carried by the plasma, with the exception of the larger plasma proteins, are forced out through the walls of the capillaries of the glomerulus and the membrane of the Bowman's capsule into the uriniferous tubule. Secondly by reabsorption of the useful materials including a lot of water, leaving urine, a solution of the waste products in water. Owing to the difference in internal diameter of the afferent and efferent blood vessels, the pressure in the glomerulus is high. Other contributory factors to this high pressure are the narrow coiled capillaries of the glomerulus which resist the flow of blood, and the fact that the efferent vessel forms a network of capillaries round the tubule before joining the renal vein. Blood at high pressure is therefore separated from the lumen of the tubule only by the thin capillary wall and the membrane of the Bowman's capsule, and liquid is forced through, becoming the glomerular filtrate. Electron microscopy studies show that the structure of the capillary walls of the glomerulus and the membrane of the Bowman's capsule are consistent with the theory that all the constituents of the plasma except the larger plasma proteins can be forced through under pressure. Evidence to confirm the importance of pressure is provided by the fact that a raised arterial pressure results in an increase in the production of urine.

The glomerular filtrate contains glucose, salts and urea dissolved in water, it averages $180 \, dm^3$ per day in man, and contains 1 kg of sodium chloride. Glucose is reabsorbed in the proximal portion of the tubule and salts in the distal portion. Water is absorbed in both parts. The amount of water and salts absorbed depends on the needs of the body at the time, the composition of the blood itself being the determining factor. Groups of cells in the brain are sensitive to the osmotic pressure of the blood, when this is too high a hormone is released into the blood stream causing more water to be reabsorbed (see page 201). Some of the water is absorbed by osmosis as the blood in the capillaries surrounding the tubule has come from the glomerulus and therefore has a high content of plasma proteins. The return of glucose and salts is against the concentration gradient and cannot come about by diffusion thus it must involve active transport. The cells lining the uriniferous tubule are covered with microvilli on the inner surface, they are particularly numerous at the proximal end where 70% of the water is absorbed. Near the surface in contact with the blood capillaries there are many mitochondria believed to supply energy for the active absorption of salts and glucose. The greater part of the loop formed by the tubule, the **loop of Henlé**, occurs in the medulla, here sodium chloride is concentrated causing water to be absorbed from the collecting ducts so that the urine produced is hypertonic to the blood. Only mammals among the vertebrates can produce a strongly hypertonic urine, a water conserving feature particularly marked in animals such as the kangaroo rat, mentioned earlier, which can produce urine several times more concentrated than sea water. Animals such as this living in very dry regions have a long loop of Henlé.

Counter-current multiplier hypothesis

As the glomerular filtrate travels up the ascending limb of the loop of Henlé, sodium ions are actively absorbed and transported to the descending limb where they are actively returned to build up the concentration of the filtrate. The concentration is therefore greater in the descending limb than in the ascending limb and it is at its most concentrated at the bend of the loop, becoming more dilute as it travels up the ascending limb. The region of high salt concentration is situated in the centre of the medulla where the strong osmotic concentration is also present in the tissue fluid and in the blood capillaries, the blood flowing through these so slowly that the concentration gradient is maintained. The collecting duct passes through the medulla before opening into the pelvis of the kidney and as the filtrate flows down, water is absorbed from it by osmosis. The effectiveness of the system can be judged from the fact that only about 1% of the glomerular filtrate is finally expelled as urine (see figure 72).

The lungs

The lungs are responsible for excreting carbon dioxide and water (see page 135).

The skin

In man the evaporation of water from the skin is the chief means of heat loss (see page 196). The quantity of sweat produced is very variable, in hot weather the amount increases and the production of

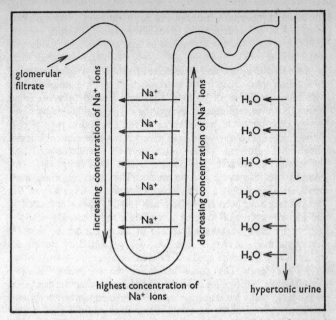

Figure 72. Diagram illustrating the counter-current multiplier hypothesis

urine decreases, while in cold weather the reverse is the case. The sweat glands are minor excretory organs, sweat contains a small amount of urea in its 1·5% of solids consisting largely of salt.

Behavioural ways of conserving water in animals

Many animals overcome some of the problems of water loss by seeking a damper environment, like earthworms and woodlice, or remaining in burrows during the heat of the day, a method adopted by the kangaroo rat. Others remain dormant during a dry season, this is a state of **aestivation** favoured by the lung fish and some amphibians which burrow into the mud at the bottom of ponds and swampy areas, remaining inactive while the water has dried up and reviving when the rains return.

Water conservation in plants

A **hydrophyte,** a plant living in water or wet places has no water conserving problems; a **mesophyte** has an adequate water supply, what is lost by transpiration is readily replaced. In drier regions land plants have the same problem as land animals, the problem of water conservation, however, they do have one advantage in that, in general, plant cells and tissues can tolerate a greater degree of desiccation than animal tissues. A plant of a dry habitat able to withstand conditions of prolonged drought is a **xerophyte**. Some plants, however, are able to escape the drying conditions by completing their life cycle in a remarkably short period of time after a shower, leaving seeds which have a very low water content but are capable of growing when water becomes available and the temperature is suitable. The Sahara Desert plant *Boerhaavia* can complete its life cycle in two weeks. The roots of some trees penetrate very deeply in their search for water, the roots of the tamarix tree have been known to reach 160 m. Other plants such as the saguaro cactus of Arizona spread their roots laterally near the surface in order to take advantage of every shower or dew. A xerophyte may survive in a region of low rainfall by storing up water during the short spells of rainfall, and keeping transpiration to a low level. The small leaves of the ice plant, *Mesembryanthemum*, store a lot of water, and there is water storage tissue in the large spiky leaves of the *Agave*, the American century plant, so called because of the many years that pass before it produces an inflorescence. *Euphorbias* and cacti store water in their stems, the leaves being much reduced mostly to spines to avoid transpiration, the function of photosynthesis being performed by the enlarged green stem. The roots of **epiphytes** growing on tree trunks have no contact with the soil, many trap water directly from the rain in their leaf axils; epiphytic orchids have roots hanging down in the air, the roots have enveloping sheaths of dead cells, the **velamen**, which can fill with water. Other xerophytes endure the desiccation, the amount of water that can be lost from the protoplasm before the dehydration becomes irreversible, depends on the particular plant species, the creosote bush (*Larrea divaricata*) may lose so much water by transpiration that the water content may fall to 50% of the dry weight, but nevertheless the plant will recover in the next shower. This is a very high water loss, the water content of mesophyte leaves would be 100 to 300% of the dry weight.

It has been established that at least some non-succulent xerophytes can transpire as readily as mesophytes when adequate water is available, but they differ from mesophytes in that they can endure periods of permanent wilting, that is a state in which the cells lose their turgidity, although there may be no obvious outward signs

174

such as drooping leaves and stems owing to the large amount of sclerenchyma these plants often contain. When the plant has wilted transpiration is at a very low level; this reduction in transpiration may be brought about in a number of different ways. The leaf surface may be small as in the cypresses or practically absent, as in broom, the leaves themselves may be inrolled as in some grasses. Other methods to reduce transpiration are associated with thick leathery leaves with reduced mesophyll tissue as in the olive, the thick waxy cuticle of holly, or sunken stomata where in the oleander they occur in groups in pits on the leaf. The leaves may be provided with hairs which are air filled, giving the plant a woolly appearance as in edelweiss, and perhaps protecting it from the sun. The orientation of the leaves themselves may protect them from the sun, as in the Australian acacias where the leaf surfaces are vertical. Deciduous plants solve the problem by shedding their leaves when water becomes scarce or the soil too cold for them to absorb it, others die back to leave a protective layer over buds at the soil surface. Many alpine plants grow crowded together in cushions, a growth form which helps to conserve moisture.

Certain plants have adapted to living in conditions where there is an influence of salt water, these are the **halophytes**. Plants of the mud flats may have to tolerate very difficult conditions when the water evaporates leaving a high salt content. The problem is overcome in two ways, the osmotic pressure of the root cells is high enough to enable water to enter by osmosis, and many plants such as the glassworts (*Salicornia*), store water to carry them over the periods when the osmotic pressure in their surroundings is too high to allow them to absorb water. A few plants do have the opposite problem of getting rid of excess water in conditions of high humidity; they exude liquid water, this is guttation (see page 157).

Key terms

Aestivation Dormancy during the dry season.
Chloride secretory cells Cells in the gills of fish moving salts between the blood and outside medium against the concentration gradient.
Deamination Removal of an amino (NH_2) group from a chemical compound.
Excretion Removal of waste products of metabolism from the body.
Flame cell Hollow cup-shaped cell with tuft of cilia having osmoregulatory and excretory functions.

Halophyte A plant able to survive in salt soil such as mud flats.

Hydrophyte An aquatic plant or plant of wet places.

Loop of Henlé Region of nephron concentrating sodium chloride in the kidney medulla resulting in rapid water absorption from collecting ducts, and thereby concentrating the urine.

Malpighian tubule Tubular excretory gland of insects.

Mesophyte A plant growing where the water supply is adequate.

Nephridium Tubular excretory and osmoregulatory organ present in many invertebrates.

Nephron An excretory and osmoregulatory unit in the vertebrate kidney consisting of a Malpighian body (Bowman's capsule with glomerulus) and a uriniferous tubule.

Osmoregulation Regulation of the osmotic pressure in an organism.

Ultrafiltration Filtration under pressure.

Xerophyte A plant of dry habitat able to withstand prolonged periods of drought.

Chapter 10
Co-ordination

Nervous and endocrine systems

The life of an animal is a struggle for survival, it needs to be able to respond appropriately to changes in the external environment and to be capable of making adjustments to changes in the internal environment. The first essential is a means of detecting these changes, and then a means of responding to them. The parts of the organism detecting the changes and the parts responding need to be linked in some way. There is a need for an effective communications system, this is supplied by a nervous system based on electrical signals, and an endocrine system based on chemical signals provided by hormones. A response by an animal to a change in the external environment is usually brought about rapidly by the nervous system, while the response to an internal change is more likely to occur over a period of time by the activity of the endocrine system. The two systems are however, closely linked and may operate together. Plants also need to make adjustments to the environment but as they have no necessity to move to seek food as animals have, most are fixed and responses to stimuli take place slowly by means of growth controlled by hormones.

In the majority of animals the nervous system consists of the **central nervous system** (which has been likened to a telephone exchange) and **peripheral nerves** linking it to **receptors** which receive information, and **effectors** which respond to it. The receptors consist of various types of sensory cells. The effectors are usually muscles or glands. Many are situated near the outside of the body where they readily detect changes in the external environment, while others lie inside the body monitoring changes taking place there.

Neurones

The nervous system is composed of neurones, nerve cells conducting signals or impulses. Neurones conducting impulses from receptors to the CNS are afferent or **sensory**, and those conducting impulses from the CNS to the effectors are efferent or **motor**. In the CNS there are intermediate neurones which connect up sensory and motor neurones. The cell bodies of the sensory neurones lie in the dorsal root ganglia near the spinal cord and the cell bodies of the motor neurones lie within the spinal cord.

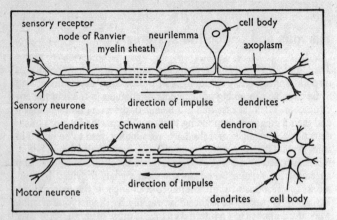

Figure 73. Sensory and motor neurones

The **cell body** has the usual cellular structure together with Nissl's granules made of RNA and concerned with protein synthesis. It has a number of processes called **dendrons**, one being extended to form the **axon**, all the processes ending in fine **dendrites**. An axon may be as much as a metre long, centrally it contains **axoplasm**, a continuation of the cell body and is bounded by the plasma membrane. This is surrounded by a **myelin sheath** interrupted at intervals by the **nodes of Ranvier**; it is composed of fatty material closely bounded by the thin **neurilemma** belonging to the **Schwann cells** which secrete the material of the myelin sheath enveloping the axon and dendrons. A large peripheral nerve is made up of several thousands of axons.

The nerve impulse

When an axon is not sending an impulse there is a difference of electrical potential between the inside and the outside of the membrane, the inside of the membrane is negatively charged and the outside is positively charged, the membrane is said to be polarized and there is a **resting potential**. When a neurone is stimulated and the impulse passes along the axon the charge is reversed for an instant, the inside of the membrane becomes positive and the outside negative, this is the **action potential**, and obviously it has involved depolarization. The action potential lasts for a millisecond before it reverts to the resting potential. The resting potential is associated with an excess of K^+ ions and various anions inside the axon, and Na^+ ions outside leaving the inside of the axon negatively charged. The Na^+ ions have been pumped out, a process found to be an active one, requiring energy. They cannot re-enter without some change in the permeability of the membrane, this change occurs when an impulse travels along the axon, the sodium pump stops and the Na^+ ions diffuse in rapidly, and K^+ ions diffuse out, causing a reversal of the potential, the inside is now positively charged, producing the action potential. These processes continue along the length of the axon, as the impulse travels along.

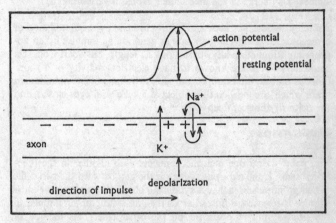

Figure 74. The passage of a nerve impulse

Impulses are generated in nerve cells by the stimulation of receptors. The strength of a stimulus must be above a certain minimum **threshold intensity** or no action potential is set up, but apart from that the size of the impulse is always the same from a given neurone, a more powerful stimulus does not produce a larger potential. After an impulse has passed through an axon another cannot follow it at once, some recovery time, the **refractory period** is needed for movement of ions to take place to restore the resting potential. The refractory period lasts about 1 to 3 milliseconds, this limits the frequency of impulses that can be transmitted to about 500 to 1000 per second. The rate of transmission depends on the cross sectional area of the axon and whether or not it is

medullated, that is, possesses a myelin sheath. Nerve fibres with a myelin sheath conduct impulses faster than those without. At the nodes of Ranvier the myelin sheath is missing and the membranes of the axon are exposed, elsewhere they are insulated by the fatty material of the myelin sheath. When an impulse passes along a medullated fibre the action potential jumps from node to node, the rate of transmission is therefore greatly increased. In vertebrates most axons are medullated and there is a more efficient nervous system. The reason for the cross sectional area of the axon to be of importance is not fully understood. Giant axons are found in cephalopods and much research work has been carried out on the nervous system of the squid. The rate of transmission of an impulse is certainly increased in a giant axon but does not reach that achieved by some of the medullated axons in vertebrates.

An impulse does not necessarily have to arise by the stimulation of a receptor, an axon can be made to generate an impulse by an appropriate stimulation anywhere along its length, but apart from this some nerve cells are known to have electrical activity of a spontaneous nature, for example, the alpha rhythms of the mammalian brain which occur when the subject is awake with eyes closed, and the delta rhythms of deep sleep.

The synapse

The point where one neurone connects with another in the functional sense is the **synapse,** which is the gap between the two cells. When an impulse reaches a synapse a chemical **transmitter substance** is released, diffuses across the gap setting up an impulse in the **post-synaptic neurone** on the other side. This method of transmission results in a delay of up to one millisecond but it prevents impulses going in the wrong direction. Impulses can pass along axons in either direction but only in one direction across the synapse. The chemical, usually acetylcholine, causes changes in the permeability of membranes, molecules of the substance become attached to the membrane of the post-synaptic neurone causing it to become depolarized at these points, sodium ions then flow in creating a positive charge, when this has reached a high enough level an action potential is created. Immediately after the liberation of acetylcholine and its effect on the post-synaptic neurone, it is destroyed by an enzyme, cholinesterase. From electron microscopy studies it is believed that the transmitter substance is contained in small vacuoles in the knob-like ends of the dendrites and that when an impulse arrives there a vacuole moves to the surface of the **syn-**

aptic knob and discharges its contents through the membrane into the gap. An impulse may be generated in a post-synaptic neurone as the result of the transmitter substance reaching it from a single knob; other neurones seem to need the activity of several synaptic knobs, presumably in this case the amount of transmitter substance from one synaptic knob is insufficient. The transmitting mechanism fails if too many impulses reach the synapse in a short period of time, it seems that the supply of transmitter substance becomes exhausted. A further characteristic of the synapse is that some synaptic knobs seem able to inhibit the generation of an impulse in the post-synaptic neurone by building up a greater negative charge within it.

Impulses then, cross synapses with varying degrees of ease or may in some instances be prevented from passing. Considering the very great number of synapses this introduces a versatility into the function of the nervous system, the flow of impulses does not have to be a uniform one throughout the system, the flow can take pathways appropriate to the situation at the time.

The neuromuscular junction
The neuromuscular junction, the point where the motor neurone comes in contact with a muscle fibre, is essentially similar to the synapse between neurones. Again the dendrites end in knob-like structures and at the point where each comes in contact with a muscle fibre the membrane of the latter is modified to form an **end plate**. Acetylcholine is released from vacuoles in the knob and it diffuses to the end plate which becomes depolarized. If the potential is high enough, that is if the charge builds up sufficiently, an action potential is generated in the muscle fibre.

Reflex actions

A **reflex action** is an automatic response by the body to a stimulus. The stimulation of receptors generates impulses in sensory neurones which are transmitted to the CNS, cross synapses to intermediate neurones in the grey matter and pass a second synaptic connection to motor neurones which terminate in effectors, usually muscles. The path taken by the impulse is the **reflex arc**. Examples of reflex actions are; withdrawing the hand from hot objects, blinking when something passes close to the eyes. Reflex actions have a protective function in that they assist in guarding the body from injury. In reflex actions involving the spinal cord, impulses passing along sensory neurones enter the dorsal root of the spinal cord, travel through intermediate neurones and leave by the ventral root in motor neurones, finally reaching muscles or glands. There are pathways for reflexes in all the spinal nerves and they are connected by longitudinal neurones in the white matter of the spinal cord, so that if it is appropriate to the situation other reflexes may be brought into action; for example, not merely removing the hand from something hot but moving bodily away. These longitudinal pathways also connect with the brain which is kept informed of the action.

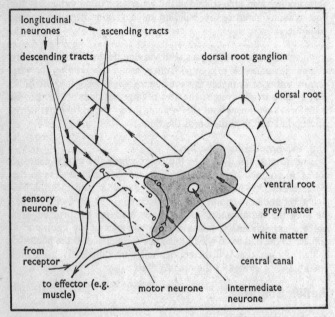

Figure 75. Part of a vertebrate spinal cord showing a reflex arc and position of longitudinal neurones

The vertebrate nervous system

The central nervous system

In the embryo a longitudinal tube of nervous tissue develops on the dorsal side. The anterior part enlarges and becomes divided into three regions; the **fore**, **mid** and **hind brains**. The fore brain later becomes divided into the **end brain** and the **'tween brain**. The end brain bears a pair of **olfactory lobes** anterior to the **cerebrum** which in the higher vertebrates becomes greatly enlarged forming the **cerebral hemispheres**. The 'tween brain bears the **pineal gland** dorsally and the **pituitary gland** on the ventral side. **Optic lobes** originate from the dorsal side of the mid brain. The **cerebellum** is formed from the anterior and dorsal portion of the hind brain and the **medulla oblongata** from the posterior and ventral portion. The medulla oblongata is continuous with the **spinal cord**. The whole structure is hollow and filled with **cerebrospinal fluid**; in the brain the fluid is in intercommunicating ventricles continuous with the central canal of the spinal cord. Cerebrospinal fluid is similar to lymph in that it is like blood plasma without the larger plasma proteins, but it has a lower protein content than lymph. The brain and spinal cord are covered by two **meninges**, protective membranes, the dura mater on the outside and the pia mater beneath, the two being separated by the arachnoid layer, a space filled with a delicate meshwork flooded with cerebrospinal fluid. Highly vascular membranes, the anterior and posterior **choroid plexus** develop in the dorsal surfaces of the 'tween brain and hind brain respectively. These membranes and the vascular pia mater convey oxygen and food materials to the nervous tissue. The brain is protected by the bony skull, and the spinal cord by the vertebrae, they bear holes through which the peripheral nerves pass.

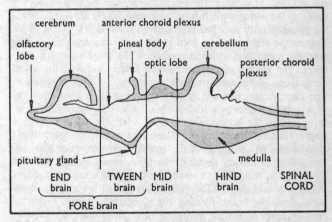

Figure 76. Diagram of a generalized vertebrate brain in L.S.

Peripheral nerves

The peripheral nerves are made up of the **spinal nerves** connected to the spinal cord and the **cranial nerves** connected to the brain.

183

There are 31 pairs of spinal nerves, each nerve being connected to the spinal cord by two roots, a dorsal root containing sensory fibres and a ventral root containing motor fibres, the two coming together a short distance from the spinal cord to form a mixed nerve. There are ten pairs of cranial nerves in the lower vertebrates and twelve pairs in mammals, they have a single junction with the brain, the dorsal and ventral roots are not joined and the pattern of one pair of nerves to each body segment has been obliterated by the development of the brain although it may still be discerned in the embryo. Some of the cranial nerves have sensory fibres only, others have motor fibres only, some larger ones are mixed. The peripheral nerves have a large number of branches connected to receptors and effectors, the cranial nerves serving the head and neck only, with the exception of the tenth cranial nerve, the vagus, which has branches in the thoracic and abdominal cavities.

The autonomic nervous system

Many of the vital activities of the body cannot be controlled voluntarily, for example, heart beat, peristalsis, secretion from salivary and sweat glands, and the functioning of the kidneys. Organs under voluntary control are connected by nerves directly to the CNS, while those not under voluntary control are connected to the CNS via ganglia. The peripheral ganglia and their associated nerves make up the **autonomic nervous system**. There are two sections, the **sympathetic** and **parasympathetic systems**. Nerve fibres connect the brain or spinal cord to the organ concerned, each fibre reaching a ganglion which is composed of a large number of synapses. The ganglia of the sympathetic system are near the spinal cord, those of the parasympathetic system lie within the effector. The two systems operate by different transmitter substances, the sympathetic system by noradrenaline, a chemical compound closely related to the hormone adrenaline, while the parasympathetic system utilizes acetylcholine. There are a pair of sympathetic ganglia one on each side of the vertebral column, each pair corresponding to a body segment; the fibres which emerge from the CNS via the ventral root and reach the ganglia, the pre-ganglionic fibres, are medullated. The ganglia are linked by a sympathetic nerve from the brain, forming the sympathetic chain. From the ganglia non-medullated post-ganglionic fibres pass to effectors either directly or through further ganglia. The parasympathetic system is made up of the tenth cranial nerve, the vagus, together with some other cranial and spinal nerves.

In general terms, the effects produced by the sympathetic system prepare the body to withstand stress, for example, it speeds up the action of the heart, constricts the arteries and slows peristalsis. The effects of the parasympathetic system are directly opposite, and their effect is dominant under normal non-stressful situations and so they help to create the internal conditions associated with the body in a restful state.

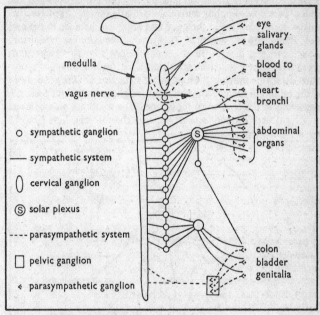

Figure 77. The autonomic nervous system

Vertebrate brain functions

The brain co-ordinates the activities of the body, it collects impulses coming in from receptors, many perhaps arriving from different receptors simultaneously, it integrates and interprets them, drawing on stored information if necessary, and sends out impulses to effectors. In lower vertebrates such as fish, different parts of the brain are clearly associated with particular functions whereas in mammals and especially in man the situation is very complex. In the fish the forebrain is concerned with smell, large olfactory lobes being present in fish such as the shark which use their very acute sense of smell to locate prey. The midbrain of the fish is associated with sight and the hind-brain with movement and the sense of pressure. Comparing figures 76 and 78 the enormous increase in the size of the forebrain of man can be seen at once. The hind brain which is an enlarged extension of the spinal cord is concerned with the regulation of involuntary activities such as heart beat and respiratory movements, it bears the origins of most of the cranial nerves. Anterior to the medulla is the cerebellum, an enlarged and folded part co-ordinating movements and posture, it receives impulses from receptors in the eyes and organs of balance in the ears and from proprioceptors. It makes fine precise voluntary movements possible. In the midbrain the optic lobes present in the lower vertebrates have almost disappeared in mammals, the **corpora quadrigemina** is the equivalent structure. On the ventral side of the midbrain there is an important ganglion, the red nucleus, it is important in the control of movement. The midbrain also contains important nervous connections between the fore and hind brains.

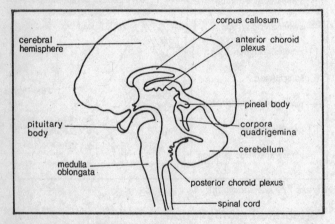

Figure 78. Structure of the human brain

The 'tween brain contains many ganglia, the dorsal and lateral parts of the 'tween brain form the thalamus, in it are contained major neurone connections between the forebrain and the spinal cord; the floor of the 'tween brain, the hypothalamus, controls body temperature, osmotic pressure, periods of sleep and activity and feeding. The nearby pituitary gland secretes several hormones important in osmoregulation, growth and development; this 'master gland' regulates the activity of other endocrine glands. In mammals the forebrain is greatly enlarged by the development of the cerebral hemispheres; the outer layer of the roof and side of the hemispheres form the cerebral cortex, made up of vast numbers of interconnecting nerve cells, it controls nearly all the voluntary activities and its existence in man probably makes the difference between an intelligent being and an insensitive vegetable-like creature. There are motor, sensory and association areas in the cortex; regions of the sensory areas are concerned with particular senses, and regions of the motor areas with specific muscles. The frontal lobes seem to be responsible for a person's individuality, his character, imagination and intelligence.

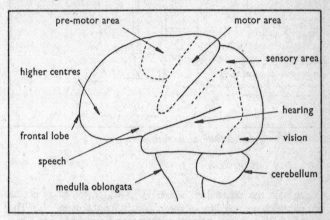

Figure 79. The functions of areas of the cortex in man

Nervous systems in lower animals

The coelenterates have a nerve net made up of neurones linked via synapses, there is nothing resembling a CNS, but simple reflexes are possible. These animals are radially symmetrical but most advanced animals are bilaterally symmetrical; this stage of development has been reached in the flatworms. Bilateral symmetry is associated with locomotion, the animal having a definite head end which reaches the new environment first and therefore there has been a tendency for receptors to develop there and also a brain to collect the information and send on impulses to other parts of the body. The development of a head during the process of evolution is **cephalization**. Flatworms show the beginnings of a brain in the anterior ganglionic mass and ladder-like nerve cord. In higher animals the receptors have become grouped into sense organs such as eyes and ears, and the brain has become progressively more complex to integrate and store information.

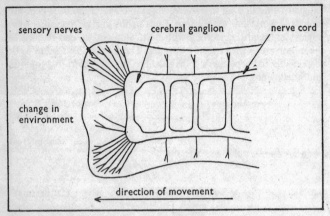

Figure 80. Cephalization in the flatworm

Sensory receptors

Changes in the external environment or within the body act as stimuli which are noted by receptors consisting of sensory cells. The sensory cells may occur singly or they may be grouped into sense organs. Sensory cells are of different types according to the nature of the stimulus to which they respond. Photoreceptors are sensitive to light, thermoreceptors respond to heat, chemoreceptors detect different substances in the water and air, and mechanoreceptors are sensitive to pressure, vibrations and muscle tension. All these receptors near the surface of the body are exteroreceptors. Internal receptors (interoreceptors) in, for example, the heart, gut, blood vessels and muscles register internal changes, these include the proprioceptors in muscles and joints which respond to movement and position of the body. There are also surface and internal receptors producing the sensation of pain. The basic mechanism is the same in all receptors, the stimulus produces small changes in potential which fire off nervous impulses for transmission to the CNS. All sensory cells have the same basic structure as other cells but in addition they have certain features related to the type of stimulation they receive. There are two main structural types of sensory cell; in primary receptors the fine end of the axon receives the stimulation and the remainder of the axon conducts the impulse generated, in secondary receptors a specially modified epithelial cell is stimulated and is in contact with the axon of a sensory neurone via a synapse. Receptors are highly sensitive, but in some cases increased sensitivity may be gained by a number of cells connecting with one neurone via synapses. This means that although the stimulation received by one sensitive cell may be insufficient to generate the action potential, a number of cells each receiving the same amount will together raise the potential of the neurone above the threshold value and it will fire an impulse (see page 178). Such is the state of affairs with the rods in the retina of the eye where sensory cells are grouped into elaborate sense organs, the behaviour of the individual sensory cells has not changed, the organ is largely concerned with the more efficient collection of stimuli.

The human eye

The eye has a tough white fibrous **sclerotic layer** on the outside which is transparent in the front forming the **cornea**. The back of the eye is lined by the **choroid**, it contains blood vessels and pigment; towards the front of the eye it forms the **ciliary body** and **iris**. The iris has two sets of muscles, circular and radial, controlling the diameter of the **pupil**. The ciliary body has muscles capable of producing tension on the **suspensory ligaments**, thus changing the shape and therefore the focal length of the **lens**, which consists of transparent cells in an elastic covering. The **retina** is composed of a pigmented layer lining the choroid as far as the iris, and a layer of light sensitive rods and cones. The space in front of the lens is filled with **aqueous humour** and the space behind with less fluid **vitreous humour**. When the eye is at rest it is accommodated to focus distant objects, but contraction of the circular ciliary muscles causes the tension on the suspensory ligament to be relaxed and the lens assumes a more rounded shape which brings nearer objects into focus. The ciliary and iris muscles are controlled by the autonomic nervous system.

Rods and **cones** are present in the region outside the fovea, with the exception of the periphery of the retina where rods alone are present. The rods are very sensitive to light and are associated with vision in conditions approaching darkness, they cannot distinguish colour and the image lacks sharpness and detail. They contain rhodopsin (visual purple) which degenerates in quite small amounts of light to opsin, a complex protein, and retinine, a derivative of vitamin A. It is probably the degeneration that brings about depolarization of the cell membrane and triggers off an impulse. In the dark, rhodopsin is regenerated but the reaction is much slower and this explains the time taken for the eye to adapt to dark conditions, also the fact that some forms of night blindness are due to a deficiency of vitamin A.

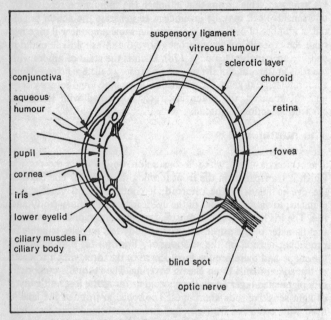

Figure 81. Structure of the human eye

The cones are responsible for colour vision. The highest concentration of cones occurs in the fovea on the optic axis, where rods are absent. In this region the colour sensitivity is most acute and the image is sharpest, especially in bright light. Many years ago the Young-Helmholtz theory postulated the existence of three colour sensitive mechanisms in the retina showing sensitivity to different wavelengths of light corresponding to blue, red and green. Mixtures of these three colours of light can be made to match any colour. Wald in the U.S.A. has since shown the existence of three types of cones with absorption in these three colour bands. Colour vision depends on the appropriate stimulation of one, two or all types of cone. The photochemical substance contained by the cones is iodopsin which is much more stable to light than rhodopsin and so a higher light intensity, such as daylight, is needed for the cones to function.

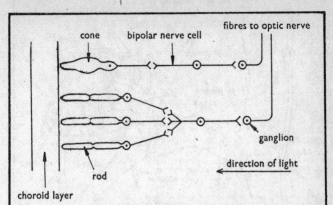

Figure 82. Rods and cones in the retina of the eye

The human ear

Structure

The ear is divided into an outer ear, middle ear and inner ear. The outer ear consists of the **pinna** and ear passage, the **external auditory meatus**, and is separated from the middle ear by the ear drum or **tympanic membrane**. The middle ear is an air-filled cavity connected to the throat by the **Eustachian tube**, and bridged by three small bones, the **maleus, incus** and **stapes**, held in position by muscles and ligaments. The stapes is held against the oval window, the **fenestra ovalis**, one of two membranes dividing the middle ear from the inner ear, the other being the round window, the **fenestra rotunda**. The inner ear is filled with **endolymph** and consists of the **membranous labyrinth** lying in a similar shaped space in the skull and separated from it by **perilymph** continuous with the cerebrospinal fluid. The membranous labyrinth comprizes the **cochlea** concerned with hearing, and the **semi-circular canals, saccule** and **utriculus** concerned with balance.

The cochlea is a tube, closed at the apex and coiled round a central core of bone. It is made up of three longitudinal sections separated by membranes, on one side is the vestibular canal connected with the oval window, on the other side is the tympanic canal connected

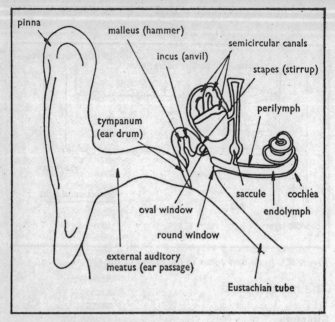

Figure 83. Structure of the human ear

with the round window, both contain perilymph and communicate at the apex of the cochlea. The central canal, containing endolymph, lying between the two. Reissner's membrane separates the vestibular canal from the central canal and the basilar membrane separates the central and tympanic canals. The **organs of Corti** concerned with the actual response to sound consist essentially of a projection, the tectorial membrane in the central canal in contact with the fine hair on sensory cells which together with their supporting cells occupy the space between it and the basilar membrane. At the bases of the sensory cells are nerve fibres that join the auditory nerve taking information to the brain.

Properties of sound

When the prongs of a tuning fork are struck they vibrate rapidly producing sound waves. The number of vibrations made in one second is the frequency. Each different note has a particular frequency, middle C on the piano has a frequency of 256 Hz. If the frequency is greater the note is higher, that is, it is a note of a higher pitch. A note one octave higher than a chosen note has double its

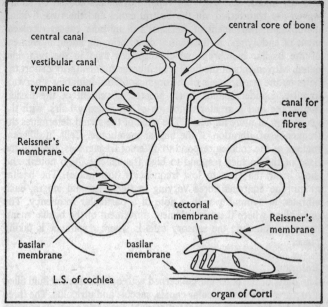

Figure 84. Structure of the cochlea and organ of Corti

frequency; if middle C is chosen, C one octave higher has a frequency of 512 Hz, C one octave below 128 Hz. If the tuning fork is struck more vigorously the note is the same, its frequency is unchanged but the prongs make a greater degree of movement, the vibrations are of greater amplitude and a louder sound is produced. Strings of a piano may vibrate in sympathy with sound from an outside source; a string will vibrate with the same frequency as the note picked up and will emit the same note, the string is said to be resonant.

The function of hearing

Sound waves enter the pinna and travel down the ear passage, the variations in air pressure due to the sound waves set the ear drum vibrating, the vibrations are carried across the middle ear by the bridge of bones and transferred to the oval window. The Eustachian tube equalizes the pressure on either side of the ear drum and prevents large variations in external pressure from damaging the drum. Inward movement of the oval window applies pressure to the perilymph, ultimately causing the round window to bulge outwards into the middle ear. The very rapid movements caused by sound waves are transferred via the central canal and the two dividing membranes. Movement of Reissner's membrane causes displacement of endolymph in the central canal bringing about movement of the basilar membrane which displaces fluid in the tympanic canal. Movements of the basilar membrane momentarily distort the hairs on the sensory cells of the organs of Corti initiating a nervous impulse. Louder sounds cause greater movement of the basilar membrane and a greater distortion of the sensory hairs, with the generation of more impulses. The pitch of the sound determines the frequency of vibration of the basilar membrane. Cells in different regions of the cochlea respond to different frequencies, those in the base of the cochlea respond to high frequencies (high notes), and those near the apex to low frequencies (low notes). The basilar membrane contains fibres varying in thickness and length, each vibrates in sympathy with a note of a particular frequency. The only place where there is sufficient movement of the basilar membrane to stimulate the sensory cells is where resonance is taking place.

Balance

The parts of the inner ear concerned with balance are the fluid filled structures, the semi-circular canals, saccule and utriculus. The three semi-circular canals are located at right angles to each other, each having a swelling, the ampulla, at one end. The ampullae, saccule and utriculus contain sensory cells; those in the ampullae bear hairs

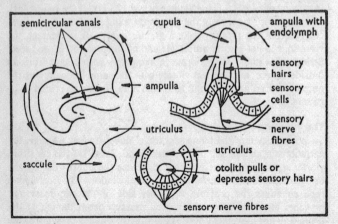

Figure 85. Organs of balance and posture in the ear

194

which are firmly fixed into a dome-shaped gelatinous body, the **cupula**. Any movement of the head will cause fluid to move in one of the semi-circular canals, this movement causes the cupula to be pushed over to one side pulling on the hairs of the sensory cells and triggering off a nervous impulse. In the fluid-filled saccule and utriculus there are sensory cells with their hair-like processes embedded in **otoliths**, aggregations of calcium carbonate granules. Different positions of the head result in varying degrees of tension or pressure on different sensory hairs and this determines the pattern of nervous impulses sent to the brain.

The skin

Structure
The skin consists of two main layers, the outer **epidermis** and the inner **dermis**. The epidermis is made up of three horizontal zones, that next to the dermis being the **Malpighian layer**, a single layer of actively dividing cells containing melanin granules responsible for the colour

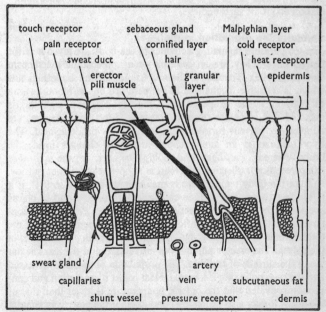

Figure 86. Structure of the skin

195

of the skin and giving a protection against ultra violet light. The cells produced by the Malpighian layer form the **granular layer** of living cells which in turn become the dead **cornified layer** as they are pushed to the outside. The dermis is a thicker layer containing **hair follicles, sweat glands,** blood capillaries and **receptors.** The sweat glands are coiled tubes lined with cells which absorb water from the surrounding blood capillaries and cells, secreting it into the sweat duct. The sweat contains some urea and lactic acid in addition to salt and water. The cells forming the hair are produced by the Malpighian layer, later when they become impregnated with keratin they die. The **sebaceous glands** produce oily material to keep the hair and skin supple and waterproof.

Functions

The skin is a tough, flexible and waterproof layer on the surface of the body; it protects the more delicate tissues beneath from injury, drying, invasion by bacteria and the harmful effects of ultra violet light. It bears sweat glands which provide a means of controlling body temperature, the sweat itself containing a small amount of waste material, making the skin a minor excretory organ. Sense organs in the skin collect information about the surroundings.

Temperature regulation in man

The temperature regulating activities of the body are given here for convenience. They are an example of a homeostatic mechanism (see page 199). There is a thermoreceptor in the hypothalamus which is sensitive to changes in temperature of the blood flowing through it. If the temperature of the blood is too high this is detected and steps are taken to lower it, if too low measures are adopted to prevent further heat loss, and to produce heat. The hypothalamus is an interoreceptor detecting changes inside the body whereas the heat and cold receptors in the skin are exteroreceptors collecting information about the conditions outside. In man the body temperature is maintained at about 36·9°C, if it is tending to rise the surface capillaries are dilated and in places special shunt vessels connecting arterioles and venules are constricted so that more blood flows near the surface of the skin; the total volume of blood may be increased by drawing on reserves in the spleen. The erector pili muscles are relaxed and the hairs lie flat along the surface of the skin. The production of sweat is increased and the metabolic rate is lowered. Heat is lost by radiation and convection provided that the outside temperature is lower than that of the body, it may also be lost by conduction if the body is in contact with a cooler surface. The evaporation of sweat causes a cooling of the skin which in turn cools the blood flowing through the capillaries. The position of the hairs prevents warm air being trapped close to the skin; even the fine hairs on human skin contribute to the temperature regulating mechanism. If the body temperature is falling too low the surface blood capillaries are constricted and shunt vessels dilated to divert blood from the surface, less blood is circulated, some being stored in the spleen. The erector-pili muscles contract pulling any hairs upright to trap warm air near the skin surface, their activity produces the 'gooseflesh' appearance. Less sweat is produced and shivering may occur, this is the involuntary contraction of skeletal muscles resulting in the production of heat. If the man moves to a warmer environment heat can be taken up by radiation, convection and conduction. The maintenance of the body within a narrow temperature range allows enzyme reactions to proceed at their optimum rate.

As the outside temperature falls, a point is reached, the low critical temperature, when physical methods of temperature control are insufficient alone and more thyroxine and adrenaline are released into the blood raising the metabolic rate (see page 202–3). Exposure to extreme cold may result in blood being withdrawn from the surface for so long that the cells die, a condition of frost bite to which the fingers and toes are particularly susceptible. If the body temperature falls, a point is reached when the temperature regulating mechanisms fail to operate, the surface capillaries dilate and give a feeling of warmth, the higher centres of the brain are 'numbed' so the man is unwilling to take voluntary exercise and is unaware of the danger. If the situation continues death will result. Alcohol may produce similar effects of dilation of surface capillaries together with lack of awareness of the danger in a cold environment. Conversely, a rising outside temperature will eventually overcome the temperature regulating mechanisms of the body, especially if the humidity is high and sweat evaporation is reduced. As the body temperature rises above this high critical point the metabolic rate increases, the chemical processes proceed at a faster rate (chemical reactions proceed at double the rate for a rise in temperature of 10°C), heat is produced which further increases the metabolic rate. This is an example of a **positive feedback mechanism**. As there is an impaired temperature regulating mechanism the body temperature continues to rise and will result in death if it remains above about 41°C for any length of time, this is a condition of heat stroke. The temperature range over which the normal temperature regulating mechanisms operate is the efficiency range.

Temperature regulation in other animals

One of the problems of homoiothermic animals is the conservation of heat, for although the condition of homoiothermy enables an animal to be active over a wide range of outside temperatures and to inhabit regions which would otherwise be too cold, maintaining the body temperature does entail a great deal of extra expenditure of energy, involving an increased consumption of food. Heat loss must therefore be kept to a minimum, this is achieved by a thick layer of hair in mammals, feathers in birds, or an oily blubber as in marine homoiotherms. The polar bear has a thick layer of sub-cutaneous fat as well for extra insulation, while the camel, an animal of hot climates and one resistant to dehydration, stores as much as 40 kg of fat as a food reserve but localizes it in a hump to overcome the problem of heat retention that would accompany its storage sub-cutaneously. The heat conserving layers make heat loss when necessary more difficult, especially in large animals; large ears richly supplied with blood capillaries are one way in which it may be achieved, as in the African elephant. Mammals having no sweat glands over the general body surface, such as dogs and cats and their relatives, lose heat by panting, this increases the rate of evaporation from the lungs and the blood flowing through the lungs, mouth and tongue is cooled. Birds also pant to lower the body temperature.

In winter, when the temperature of the environment falls, food may be in short supply just at a time when animals need to eat more to maintain the body temperature; some animals solve the problem by **hibernation**, a deep sleep in which the metabolic rate falls to a low level and the body temperature also falls. Birds may set out on **migration** to warmer climates, an activity probably initiated by lower temperatures.

The endocrine system in mammals

The endocrine system is also responsible for co-ordination, it is made up of a number of endocrine glands, glands without ducts, secreting potent chemical substances, **hormones**, directly into the blood. These hormones are carried round in the general blood circulation but influence only certain **target areas** which may be widely separated in the body. The effect of most hormones is to bring about a slow and gradual change over a period of time, in contrast to the rapid localized response engendered by the nervous system, thus hormones are suited to long term changes such as the control of growth and sexual maturity but they also have an important function in homeostasis.

Homeostasis

Homeostasis is the maintenance of a steady state in the internal environment of the organism, it requires energy. It is not a static condition but one in which the state of the body is controlled within narrow limits by the co-ordination of all the physiological processes. In mammals homeostatic mechanisms control, for example, body temperature, blood sugar level and osmotic pressure of body fluids. The liver has a number of important homeostatic functions, one, the regulation of blood sugar level is controlled by the hormone insulin. Some authorities use the term homeostasis in a wider sense to include the maintenance of a steady state in the external environment, so that the example concerning the control of populations (see page 291) would be regarded as one of homeostasis.

The mammalian liver

The liver is the largest organ in the body, it lies below the diaphragm and overlaps the stomach, it has a good blood supply brought by the hepatic artery and the hepatic portal vein, it returns blood to the heart in the hepatic vein. The liver has many important functions; it produces a number of essential substances, stores others, breaks down unwanted materials and plays a major role in the homeostatic control of the body, including the regulation of substances in the blood. It synthesizes important plasma proteins and bile, and it stores iron, vitamins A, B and D. Excess glucose is converted to glycogen for storage, any which cannot be accommodated in this way is made into fat and stored under the skin or around certain organs in the body. Old red blood cells are broken down and the iron retained while excess amino acids brought from the small intestine in the hepatic portal vein, are deaminated, that is the amino group (NH_2) is broken off, leaving a carbohydrate portion which can be utilized. The amino group forms ammonia which is a highly toxic substance so that it immediately undergoes a series of chemical reactions, the **ornithine cycle**, in which it is combined with carbon dioxide to form urea (NH_2CONH_2), this is then transported in the blood to the kidneys for excretion. The liver is able to split up many toxic materials for disposal and it deals with the destruction of hormones converting them to inactive com-

199

pounds for excretion by the kidneys while the reticulo-endothelial system in the liver is able to destroy foreign matter. The liver has a high metabolic rate and as it is a large highly vascular organ it is a centre of heat production and distribution.

Regulation of the blood sugar concentration by insulin

The blood sugar concentration in man varies between 0·08% and 0·16%, the highest level being found after a meal rich in carbohydrate. After digestion glucose is absorbed in the small intestine and taken by the hepatic portal vein to the liver, here it may be passed on into the general circulation, used by the liver cells in respiration or if present in large quantities, the excess is converted to glycogen and stored in the liver. When the maximum amount of glycogen has been stored any further excess of glucose is converted to fat and stored away from the liver. If the blood sugar falls at other times the liver converts stored glycogen to glucose and releases it into the blood stream, if necessary the fat reserves can also be mobilized. This regulation of blood sugar comes about in the following way; if the level is high the **islets of Langerhans**, groups of glandular cells in the **pancreas**, secrete the hormone **insulin** into the blood, it is carried to the liver which converts the excess glucose to glycogen, this brings about a fall in the blood sugar level so less insulin is secreted. If it falls below a certain level glycogen is converted to glucose.

Compare this with a response brought about by the nervous system. Each has a receptor; in this case the islets of Langerhans receive the information that the blood sugar level is too high, a message is sent off which reaches the liver, not by a nervous impulse but by the chemical substance insulin in the blood circulation; the liver is the effector which converts the excess glucose to glycogen. When the blood with lowered glucose content reaches the pancreas again the amount of insulin liberated is lowered accordingly. In this case the system involves the principle of **negative feedback**, that is, it is the rise in blood sugar itself which sets in motion a mechanism to bring about its own decrease and it is a low blood sugar which brings into action a mechanism for raising it, the deficiency of insulin favouring rapid conversion of glycogen to glucose. If the body produces too little insulin, the blood sugar rises to a high level resulting in sugar being lost in the urine, this is the condition of diabetes melitus which can be controlled by injections of insulin.

Regulation of the osmotic pressure of the blood by ADH

When an organism becomes dehydrated the concentration of the blood increases and this is detected by osmoreceptors in the hypothalamus, a region of the brain at the base of the pituitary gland. **Anti-diuretic hormone (ADH)** is then released from the pituitary gland into the blood stream and transported to the kidneys where the nephrons reabsorb more water and lower the concentration of the blood. If the blood becomes diluted as it would after drinking large quantities of water, the osmoregulators detect it and less hormone is released. This is another example of the negative feedback mechanism. Urine output varies between 0·35 to 15·0 cm³ per minute and ADH is the most important controlling factor.

The role of the pituitary gland

The pituitary gland situated below the hypothalamus of the fore brain is divided into anterior and posterior lobes by a cleft. The anterior lobe has two general functions; firstly the control of growth and metabolism and secondly the control of the sexual cycle. The control is carried out by six hormones, all protein in nature; **growth hormone (GH)**, other names pituitrin, somatotrophin; thyrotrophic hormone **(TSH)**, adrenocorticotrophic hormone **(ACTH)**, two **gonadotrophic hormones** and **prolactin** (lactogenic hormone). Trophic hormones or **trophins** are hormones acting on other endocrine glands, and as the pituitary gland produces a number of hormones of this type it is often called the master endocrine gland. The posterior lobe of the pituitary gland secretes; antidiuretic hormone **(ADH)**, **oxytocin** causing contraction of the muscles of the uterus during parturition, and **vasopressin** which constricts blood vessels thereby raising the blood pressure.

Excess growth hormone in the system before maturity results in gigantism, a man may reach 2·5 m in height. If increased production of hormone occurs after maturity the growth of the long bones is not possible but additional bone tissue is formed in the hands and feet, a condition known as acromegaly. Dwarfism is the result of too little growth hormone. Growth hormone appears to influence the condensation of amino acids into proteins. The thyrotrophic hormone controls the activity of the thyroid gland whose secretions regulate metabolism and adrenocorticotrophic hormone stimulates the cortex of the adrenal (suprarenal) glands to secrete a number of steroid hormones. The gonadotrophic hormones consist of follicle stimulating hormone (**FSH**) and luteinizing hormone (**LH**), the latter usually called interstitial cell stimulating hormone (**ICSH**) in the male. Prolactin is concerned with milk production in the female, following parturition. (For details of hormones regulating the sexual cycle see page 251.)

The thyroid gland

The thyroid gland consists of a two-lobed structure in the region of the larynx, it secretes the hormone, **thyroxine** which controls the metabolic rate. Thyroxine is a complex organic compound containing four iodine atoms in the molecule, the iodine being obtained from the food. A deficiency of thyroxine in youth results in cretinism, the individual fails to develop normally physically and mentally; in adults where growth is completed it causes sluggishness and a tendency to accumulate subcutaneous fat due to the low metabolic rate. The low production of thyroxine may be due to abnormal conditions of the thyroid gland itself or to a deficiency of iodine in the diet, in the latter case the problem can be overcome by, for example, the use of iodized table salt. Production of excess thyroxine leads to enlargement of the thyroid gland accompanied by a raised metabolic rate causing the sufferer to be

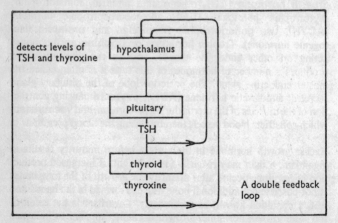

Figure 87. The feedboack mechanism controlling the level of thyroxine in the blood

engaged in restless activity and to lose weight, this is the condition of exophthalmic goitre. Under normal conditions an excess of thyroxine in the blood will cause the pituitary gland to secrete less thyrotrophic hormone, this in turn results in less thyroxine being produced. The lowered level stimulates the pituitary gland to release more TSH again. The hypothalamus detects the levels of both TSH and thyroxine.

The adrenal (suprarenal) glands

The adrenal glands lie on the anterior surface of the kidneys in man. The outer cortex and inner medulla of the glands have different origins in the embryo and they produce different hormones.

The adrenal cortex

The adrenal cortex comes under the influence of adrenocorticotrophic hormone (ACTH) from the pituitary gland. The adrenal cortex produces a number of hormones, chemically steroids which conserve sugar, control the mineral balance and regulate the breakdown of protein to carbohydrate. Some of the hormones are sex hormones which supplement those produced by the gonads. Two of the sugar conserving hormones are cortisone and hydrocortisone which promote the formation of glycogen from glucose in the liver.

The adrenal medulla

The adrenal medulla is activated directly by the nervous system, it produces the hormone **adrenaline**. Except under conditions of stress it is produced in a steady amount; under stress conditions however, it increases the heart rate and blood pressure, reduces the blood supply to the skin and gut by vasoconstriction and increases the blood supply to the brain, heart and skeletal muscles by vasodilation. It dilates the bronchioles and pupil of the eyes and raises the blood sugar level. These reactions prepare the body for an emergency; for this reason adrenaline is sometimes called the 'flight or fight' hormone. The increased adrenaline level ensures that more food and oxygen will reach the muscles ready for vigorous activity and that they will be cooled by the increased amount of sweat. Bleeding will be reduced if injury occurs. Adrenaline is almost identical with noradrenaline, the transmitter substance in the sympathetic nervous system, both adrenaline and the sympathetic nervous system bring about the same responses, this shows that the nervous and endocrine systems are closely related.

The gonads

In the male, **testosterone** helps to control sperm production and the secondary sexual characteristics such as deep voice and growth of facial and body hair. In the female **oestrogens** produced by the ovary promote the secondary sexual characteristics such as breast development, the onset of menstruation, enlargement of reproductive structures and deposition of subcutaneous fat. (For other hormones connected with the sexual cycle see page 251.)

Hormone control of metamorphosis

In insects the adult form is not attained while **juvenile hormone** is being secreted into the blood by cells in the brain. This hormone in conjunction with **moulting hormone** produced by a gland in the brain, causes a particular type of cuticle to be laid down which is characteristic of the immature stages of the insect. Not until production of juvenile hormone ceases will the insect develop into the adult form with the adult type of cuticle.

In the frog metamorphosis is controlled by thyroxine produced by the thyroid gland in the tadpole.

Behaviour

Behaviour is the sum total of an animal's activities. It is the result of the interplay of the animal's genetical constitution and its environment. Some behavioural activities are common to all members of the same species, for example, courtship display, while other aspects are peculiar to the individual.

Reflex action, kinesis and taxis

One form of behaviour is a **reflex action,** a short rapid response to a particular stimulus. An earthworm may emerge from its burrow on to the surface at night but it leaves the end of its tail gripping the entrance to the burrow, vibration of the ground makes it withdraw sharply. Many escape mechanisms in invertebrates are of this type. Sometimes an animal will orient itself in a particular position in relation to the stimulus, this orientation is perhaps the dividing line between a simple reflex and a behaviour pattern. Other animals will show accelerated random locomotion when subjected to an unpleasant stimulus from no particular direction, this type of behaviour, **kinesis,** serves the purpose of removing it from the influence of the stimulus. If the stimulus is directional the animal may move away from it if it is harmful or towards it if beneficial, this response is a **taxis**. *Chlamydomonas* (an alga) moves towards the light showing positive phototaxis; fertilization may occur as a result of an ovum producing a chemical substance which attracts a motile male gamete, the gamete shows positive chemotaxis. Many freshwater animals move against the current showing positive rheotaxis. Cercaria larvae of liverflukes exhibit negative geotaxis.

Genetical and environmental factors
Interesting experiments have been carried out to determine the relative importance of genetical factors and the influence of the environment in behaviour. Chaffinches kept so they do not hear the song of other members of their species never develop the full song, only the basic pattern. Mammals removed from the mother and other members of the species at birth and reared in isolation showed similar but simpler behaviour patterns particularly those associated with feeding and sex. It seems as if the pattern is there but needs a complete environment, one containing other members of the species, for it to develop fully.

Types of stimuli
Several types of stimuli are associated with behaviour. **Motivation** is the result of the internal state of the animal, it must be motivated or 'in the mood' or the releasing stimulus (releaser) will have no effect. The **releaser** is the external feature which brings about the response. Tinbergen has shown that young herring gull chicks will peck at models of the head and beak of the adult bird, hoping to make it regurgitate food, provided that there is red colouration on the beak, quite regardless of the shape and size of the model. Other experimentalists have shown that male robins will attack red card or wool to drive off a rival, even if the model shows no real resemblance to a robin. Hens will also try to incubate china eggs. These examples show a mechanical (or 'instinctive' – not a precise term) response, but under natural conditions the responses will be released at the right time bringing about a result which has survival value. One of the best known examples is the courtship and mating behaviour in the stickleback.

Breeding in the stickleback
In the spring hormonal changes in the male cause him to migrate upstream, when he reaches the breeding grounds he exhibits territorial behaviour, driving away other sticklebacks. He begins to change colouration, the ventral surface becoming bright red; during

this time he constructs out of water weeds a covered nest open at each end. When he sees a female laden with eggs he swims towards her in an unusual zig-zag fashion. The female then swims to the male displaying her swollen body, he turns and leads her to the nest. When the female has entered the nest the male gives her a few pokes with his snout to induce egg laying, she then leaves the nest and the male enters it spreading sperm over the eggs. After chasing her away he guards the nest and wafts water over the eggs with his pectoral fins, in this way they are kept supplied with oxygen. After hatching he protects the young for a short while, keeping them together. Tinbergen has shown that it is the swollen belly of the female that elicits the response of the zig-zag dance, his red belly is the stimulus which causes her to follow him; in each case a model will do equally well. The poking causes her to lay her eggs but any gentle poking will do the trick, while the presence of the eggs causes the fanning, if these are removed the fanning will stop.

Learning

Learning is a change in behaviour resulting from previous experience. Learning is not restricted to intelligent animals, lower animals whose behaviour is mainly mechanical or instinctive are capable of learning. **Habituation** is one form of learning, if an animal is constantly subjected to the same stimulus it may fail to respond after a time, this prevents it being totally occupied with one activity, thereby failing to perform other vital activities.

Associative learning

The animal remembers (not necessarily consciously) the result of an action and its behaviour is modified in accordance with it. Pavlov's experiments with dogs provide a well known example of a **conditioned reflex**, a form of **associative learning**. Pavlov was aware that the sight or smell of food caused the dogs to produce a flow of saliva. In an experiment he rang a bell after producing the food and repeated this for some days. In time the dog salivated at the sound of the bell alone, the dog had learned to associate the bell with the food.

Trial and error learning

Many experiments have been carried out to investigate the ability of an animal to learn. In general the animal is obliged to make a choice, the 'right' choice being rewarded, usually with food. Even animals like earthworms and flatworms learn simple things but the memory is only retained for a short time. Higher animals such as rats will soon learn their way through a maze if food is available at the end. They will also learn which one of several levers to pull if one results in an issue of food. Other experiments are based on the 'wrong' choice being accompanied by an electric shock, the animal soon learns to avoid it.

Imprinting

The first thing a young animal sees is usually its mother, it imprints on the mother and follows her everywhere, an important factor in its protection. There are interesting cases of a young animal imprinting on a human and accepting it as 'mother'.

Intelligence

Intelligence may be defined as reasoning or the ability to solve a problem not encountered before. It reaches its highest level in man.

Co-ordination in plants

In plants there is nothing comparable with the nervous system in animals, but there are plant hormones similar to animal hormones in that they are organic compounds produced by the plant, low concentrations promoting or inhibiting growth usually in target areas away from the site of their production. They differ from animal hormones in that they are produced by unspecialized cells whereas animal hormones are secreted by glands.

Auxins

'Auxin' was the first plant hormone to be discovered, but it has become clear that it is not a single substance but several substances collectively called auxins, the most common is indoleacetic acid (IAA). Auxins are concerned with growth and tropisms; they promote the elongation of roots and growth of adventitious roots, and they bring about stem elongation with the suppression of the development of lateral buds. They initiate fruit formation when the flowers have not been pollinated, and in conjunction with other hormones promote secondary growth, the formation of the abscission layer before leaf fall and wound healing. Their action stimulates cell elongation and with cytokinins they induce cell division.

Cytokinins

Cytokinins are found in regions of rapid growth. In association with auxins they promote cell division, the presence of the two types of hormones appears to be essential. The first hormone of this type to be isolated was named kinetin.

Gibberellins

Gibberellins are also concerned with growth but not with tropisms (see page 210). Although they inhibit the growth of the main root and adventitious roots they cause the elongation of the main stem and stimulate the growth of lateral buds. They initiate the production of indoleacetic acid and probably because of this they are also capable of bringing about fruit formation without previous pollination. They promote cell elongation and cell division. Gibberellins will cause elongation of the stems of dwarf varieties of some plants, particularly maize and peas, this has led to the suggestion that as dwarfness is inherited, dwarf plants may lack the means of making gibberellins. Gibberellins were first isolated from unusually tall rice seedlings which were found to be infected with a fungus *Gibberella fujikuroi*.

Phytochrome

Phytochrome is a substance which absorbs light of particular wavelengths. It occurs in two interconvertible forms r-phytochrome and fr-phytochrome, the former being the inactive form and the latter the active one. There is some evidence that the active form causes production of a hormone which induces flowering; such a hormone, given the name of florigen, has not been isolated.

Evidence for the existence of a growth hormone

Experiment 1

Oat or wheat grains are germinated and allowed to grow until the coleoptiles are about 2 cm long, they are kept in the dark or in red light to which they are insensitive. About 2 mm at the tip of each coleoptile is sliced off. In one third of the batch (A) the tip is replaced with a layer of some impermeable material such as perspex or aluminium foil between it and the stump; in another third of the seedlings (B) the tip is replaced with a piece of agar jelly between it and the stump, the remainder (C) receives no further treatment. Later it is found that the group with the agar jelly has continued to grow, the others have not. It appears that the tip of the coleoptile must produce some substance capable of diffusing through the agar in B, but which is stopped by the impermeable barrier in A. Batch A shows that it is not drying of the decapitated shoot that prevents further growth.

Experiment 2

In another batch of similar seedlings a cut is made on one side of the coleoptile about 2 mm from the top and a piece of aluminium foil inserted. The coleoptile ceases to grow on that side but continues to grow on the other side so that the shoot bends. This provides further evidence that a growth hormone diffuses down from the tip.

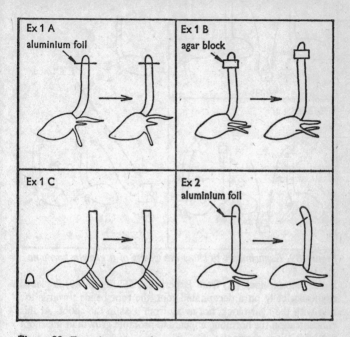

Figure 88. Experiments to show the presence of a growth hormone

Experiment 3

The tips of coleoptiles are cut off as before and each is placed on an agar block and left for one hour. In one third of the batch (A) the agar block is then placed symmetrically on a newly decapitated shoot. In another third of the batch (B) the agar block is placed asymmetrically. In the remainder (C) the agar block is placed on a larger block of agar for one hour and a portion of the larger block placed asymmetrically on a newly decapitated shoot. In A the shoot grows straight up, in B and C it shows a curvature, the greater curvature is shown by B where the agar blocks contained about twice the concentration of growth hormone. The degree of curvature appears to be directly related to the amount of growth hormone present.

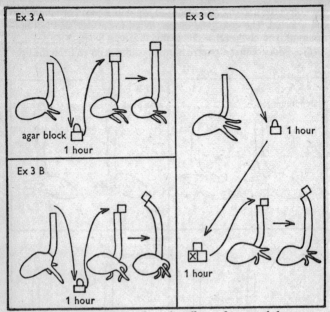

Figure 89. Experiments to show the effects of a growth hormone

If the second block (X) from Experiment 3C (figure 89) is placed asymmetrically on a decapitated root, the root bends towards the side with the agar block, not away from it as in the shoot. At this concentration the hormone appears to promote growth in the shoot but inhibit it in the root.

The hormone concerned in these experiments is one of the group of auxins, the most common being indoleacetic acid (IAA). Early work on auxins was carried out by Went, a Dutch botanist, in the 1920s. Since IAA has been isolated it has been possible to determine its effect by applying it to the plant directly, in varying concentrations, mixed in a base substance such as lanolin. The effects have been consistent with those already obtained.

Tropisms and auxins

A **tropism** is a growth movement made by a plant in response to a unilateral stimulus, the direction of growth being related to the direction of the stimulus. A tropism may be a response to light (phototropism), gravity (geotropism), water (hydrotropism), certain chemicals in the soil (chemotropism), or touch (thigmotropism). If the movement is towards the stimulus it is a positive tropism, if away it is a negative one.

Geotropism

Shoots are negatively geotropic and roots positively geotropic. This can be explained if it is supposed that if a seedling is placed in a horizontal position in the dark, auxin accumulates on the lower side. In the shoot the increased concentration on the lower side will cause the shoot to grow upwards, but in the root the increased concentration on the lower side will inhibit growth and the root will grow downwards.

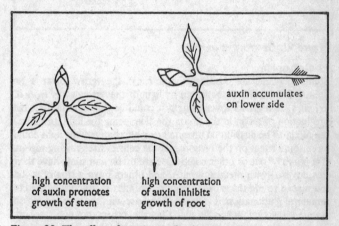

Figure 90. The effect of gravity on the direction of growth of a shoot and a root

Geotropism can be demonstrated by using a clinostat. Soaked bean seeds which have grown short straight radicles are pinned to the cork disc with the roots horizontal. The plastic cover is placed over them to conserve moisture and the apparatus is set going, the disc revolving about four times an hour. After about two days it will be found that the roots have continued to grow horizontally, each side of the root having been exposed equally to the stimulus of gravity. A control is set up with the clinostat not in motion, in this the roots grow straight downwards. The effect of gravity on a shoot is more easily shown by fixing a potted plant in a horizontal position to a clinostat.

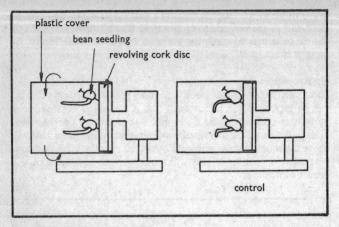

Figure 91. Geotropism in roots

Phototropism

Stems of plants are positively phototropic, they grow towards the light, roots are either unaffected by light or they grow away from it. When a stem grows towards light it could be that light inhibits the production of auxin in the tip on the side facing the light, or causes the auxin to be distributed unequally, or alternatively the light could have some effect on the response of the cells in the growing region. If a batch of oat or other coleoptiles are taken and some have their tips covered with metal foil caps, and others have a ring of metal foil placed round the growing region, and they are then subjected to unilateral illumination, it is found that those with the growing region covered respond normally and that the others do not respond. Therefore the alternative suggestion to explain the influence of light cannot be true. It can be shown that if the tips of coleoptiles are cut off and each placed on an agar block divided vertically by metal foil, then the tip illuminated from one side, more auxin will collect in the agar block corresponding to the dark side. It can also be shown that the total amount of auxin produced is about the same whether the plant is in the dark or in the light. Therefore light appears to influence the distribution of auxin and not its production.

The photoreceptor mechanism

Light affects many activities of plants but before a plant can respond to it some kind of photoreceptor mechanism must be involved. A photoreceptor substance, phytochrome, a conjugated protein blue in colour, was isolated about 1960. It exists in two interconvertible forms, one r-phytochrome (P_r) absorbs red light and has its absorption maximum at 660 to 666 nm, the other fr-phytochrome (P_{fr}) absorbs far red light and has its absorption maximum at 725 to 730 nm. When one form of the phytochrome absorbs light of the appropriate wavelength it is converted into the other form, while in the dark P_{fr} is slowly changed back to P_r.

P_{fr} is an active form which initiates enzyme action, P_r is inactive. The mode of action of P_{fr} is not known, but possibly the absorption of light and the initiation of enzyme activity leads to the production of a growth hormone.

Seed germination

A few seeds need light before they will germinate, the effective wavelength is in the red band about 660 nm; this will convert inactive P_r to active P_{fr} activating the enzymes. Far red light inhibits germination, P_{fr} is converted to inactive P_r.

Flowering

Plants will not flower until a certain minimum of vegetative growth has been made. In addition some plants require other conditions, for example, henbane (*Hyoscyamus niger*) will not flower at all unless subjected to a low temperature for a sufficiently long period, a process known as **vernalization.** Winter varieties of cereals can be spring sown and brought to maturity in one season if vernalized, without vernalization spring sown winter varieties would not flower in the same year but continue to put on vegetative growth. The flowering of some plants is influenced by the relative length of the day and night, a phenomenon known as **photoperiodism,** thus there are short day plants, such as *Poinsettia* which flower only when the period of daylight in 24 hours is below a certain critical length; and long day plants which flower only when the period of daylight in 24 hours exceeds a certain critical length; many summer flowering annuals belong to this group. The actual critical length of the daylight period varies in different plants in both these groups. There are also day neutral plants which are not influenced in their flowering by the length of the period of illumination, e.g. tomato. There is plenty of evidence to show that phytochrome is involved in the processes controlling

213

flowering; the stimulus of light is received by the leaves, this can be shown by covering the plant with the exception of a few leaves, the usual flowering response will still take place. It is possible that the activity of P_{fr} initiates enzyme activity leading to the production of a hormone which reaches the stem apices.

Nastic movements

A **nastic** movement is one made by the plant in response to a non-directional stimulus such as temperature, light intensity and humidity. Opening and closing of flowers and leaves are examples of nastic movements. In some cases the movement may be a result of growth, in others sudden changes in turgor pressure may bring about the response. Sudden movements in leaves or leaflets are due to changes in turgor pressure of the cells of special structures, **pulvini**, at the bases of the leaves or leaflets; when they are fully turgid the leaf is kept rigid, when flaccid the weight of the leaf causes it to droop. These movements appear to be concerned with protecting the delicate inner parts of flowers and perhaps preventing too great a fall in temperature in flowers and leaves.

Commercial uses of plant hormones

Most of the so-called hormone substances in use commercially are in fact produced synthetically, many are active substances closely related to the natural hormone but not identical with it. One is the weedkiller 2,4-dichlorophenoxyacetic acid (2,4-D), when sprayed on to lawns containing broad leaved weeds, a greater amount reaches these than the narrow upright leaved grasses, and as it has the effect of increasing respiration it results in the death of the weeds. Various substances such as naphthalene acetic acid (NAA) encourage rooting and are sold as rooting compounds. In California, gibberellic acid is used to spray grapes which then develop into fruits without pollination and are seedless. It has the further effect of causing the main axis of a bunch of grapes to elongate so that the fruits become separated and are less likely to suffer from fungal diseases. Besides making use of substances which promote growth, there are hormone-like substances which retard it; one is known as CCC, it reduces the stem length in cereals and conveys an advantage in that the crop is less likely to be flattened during heavy rain.

Key terms

Autonomic nervous system Concerned with activities of the body not under voluntary control, e.g. heart beat, peristalsis. Consists of sympathetic and parasympathetic systems.

Conditioned reflex action A reflex action in which the original stimulus has been replaced by another of a different type, the response being unchanged.

Effector A structure in an organism which responds, directly or indirectly, to a stimulus.

Hibernation Dormancy during the winter accompanied by a greatly lowered metabolism.

Homeostasis The maintenance of a steady state in the internal environment.

Innate behaviour Inborn tendency to perform certain apparently rational activities.

Instinct Not a precise term but usually taken to mean innate behaviour.

Intelligence Ability to reason and to solve a problem not encountered before.

Kinesis Accelerated random locomotion by an animal in response to an unpleasant stimulus which is non-directional. The speed or frequency of turning, but not the direction, depending on the strength of the stimulus.

Learning A change in behaviour resulting from previous experience.

Motivational stimulus In behaviour, one bringing about an internal state in an animal which enables it to respond to a releasing stimulus.

Nastic movement A response by a plant to a non-directional stimulus.

Parasympathetic nervous system Part of the autonomic nervous system, dominates sympathetic system in non-stressful situations, creates internal conditions associated with the body at rest.

Receptor That part of an organism receiving a stimulus.

Reflex action A short unvarying and immediate response by an animal to a particular stimulus.

Releasing stimulus (releaser) In behaviour, the external feature acting as a stimulus which brings about a response in a motivated animal.

Stimulus any change in the environment producing a response from an animal or plant.

Sympathetic nervous system Part of the autonomic nervous system, its effects prepare the body to withstand stress.

Taxis Movement of an organism towards or away from a directional stimulus.

Transmitter substance Chemical substance released at a synapse in response to a nervous impulse and diffusing across the gap causing an impulse to be initiated in the neurone on the other side.

Tropism A response by a plant to a unidirectional stimulus, by means of growth.

Vernalization A period of low temperature experienced by plants which affects developmental processes, one is the initiation of flowering.

Chapter 11
Movement, Support and Locomotion

Muscles and glands are important effectors, that is structures which respond to a stimulus; these are under the control of the nervous system, but there are other effectors which are not controlled in this way such as the nematoblasts (stinging cells) of *Hydra* which respond when stimulated directly.

Muscle structure and function

Vertebrate muscle is of three types; **striated**, voluntary or skeletal; **unstriated**, smooth, involuntary or visceral; and **cardiac**.

Striated muscle

A muscle is composed of large numbers of muscle fibres varying in length from 1 to 40 mm and held together by connective tissue. Each muscle fibre consists of sarcoplasm surrounded by a membrane the sarcolemma. Within the sarcoplasm are many large nuclei but the fibre is multinucleate and is not divided into separate cells. Under the microscope the fibres show transverse striations made up of dark and light bands, and longitudinal threads called **myofibrils**. Electron microscopy studies reveal the structure of the myofibrils, each has transverse dark and light bands, the adjacent myofibrils being aligned so that the bands appear continuous across the muscle fibre. The dark and light bands are called the A and I bands, respectively. In the centre of the light bands is a dark line, the Z band, and a clearer region in the dark band is the H band. A length of myofibril between Z bands is a sarcomere. The explanation for this appearance is also revealed by the electron microscope which shows that the myofibril is composed of thick and thin longitudinal filaments. Thick filaments occur in the dark zones, while in the light zones there are thin filaments which extend into the dark zones. The thick filaments are connected together by the M membrane and the thin filaments by the Z membrane. Therefore there are three regions, one consisting of thick filaments only, one of thin filaments only, and the third of thick and thin filaments together, giving the characteristic banding. The thick filaments have been found to be composed of the protein **myosin**, and the thin filaments of the protein **actin**. A further discovery is the existence of bridges connecting the two types of filaments in the regions where they overlap. These bridges project outwards from the thick filament at intervals of about 6·0 nm, they are spirally arranged each spiral consisting of a set of six bridges occupying about a 40 nm length of filament. Each bridge is connected to one of six thin filaments arranged round a thick filament.

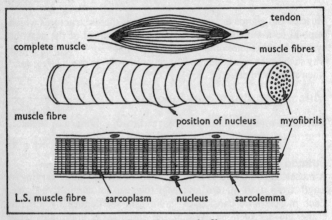

Figure 92. A whole muscle and a muscle fibre

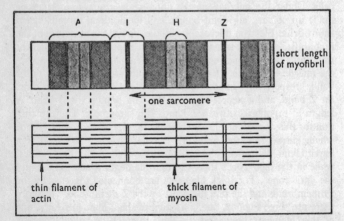

Figure 93. The banding pattern in a myofibril and the corresponding arrangement of myosin and actin filaments

The mechanism of contraction

Huxley and Hanson suggested that during muscle contraction the thick and thin filaments slide further between each other. If true this would change the banding pattern, the I and H bands becoming shorter and the darker regions of the A band, longer, although the length of the A band as a whole would be unchanged. The sarcomere, the Z to Z length, would shorten. Examination of muscle fibres and myofibrils in the relaxed (extended) and contracted states confirm these predictions.

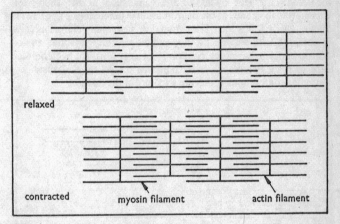

Figure 94. The arrangement of myosin and actin filaments in relaxed and contracted muscle

There is some evidence from electron microscopy and X-ray analysis to show that when a muscle contracts each bridge becomes attached to a thin filament, the myosin and actin combining to form actomyosin, the bridge then contracts. The combined effect of a number of bridges acting similarly being to pull the thin filament along and between the thick ones, the bridges then become detached and re-attach themselves further along the thin filament, the process being repeated many times resulting in contraction of the muscle.

Under natural conditions muscle fibres contract only when they receive impulses from a motor neurone via the end plates, each neurone having a large number of end plates going to different muscle fibres. The reactions of a muscle can be-studied outside the body, a leg muscle of a frog is commonly used. A single electric

219

shock or impulse results in a swift twitch of the muscle. If two shocks are given one after the other two separate twitches result, but shortening the time between the shocks leads eventually to only one contraction being visible, this is known as summation. A series of impulses if delivered sufficiently rapidly result in a sustained or **tetanic contraction**, this is the way that a skeletal muscle functions naturally, contracting as a result of a series of high frequency impulses reaching it from a nerve, relaxing as these cease, usually as a result of a voluntary decision. In time a tetanic contraction will fade and disappear owing to the exhaustion of the supply of transmitter substance at the neuromuscular junction (see page 181). Single muscle fibres have been shown to have many characteristics in common with nerve cells, they exhibit a resting potential, an action potential and a refractory period (see page 178). The bacterial disease of man, tetanus, owes its name to the severe and sustained muscular contractions which are a feature of the disease.

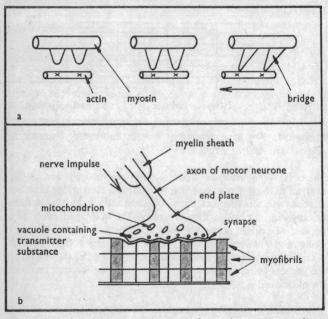

Figure 95. a. Suggested mechanism of muscle contraction b. A motor nerve end plate

From the rate at which muscles contract and the rate at which energy is liberated from contracting muscles in the form of heat, calculations have been made indicating that each bridge would have to complete its cycle of activity between 100 to 500 times a second and that each cycle would require the energy provided by the splitting of one molecule of ATP. Not surprisingly, large numbers of mitochondria are found between the myofibrils. ATP provides the energy for the combination of myosin and actin, and the presence of calcium ions also appears to be essential. Only small amounts of ATP are stored in muscle, but additional energy is stored in the chemical compound, creatine phosphate. When the energy stored in the ATP is used it is replaced from the store of creatine phosphate which is itself kept replenished by the respiratory breakdown of glycogen. A high demand for energy results in glycogen being broken down anaerobically with the formation of lactic acid, its accumulation causing muscle fatigue. An accelerated breathing rate will provide extra oxygen to convert some of the lactic acid to water and carbon dioxide, but at the end of the activity there is likely to be lactic acid remaining, the amount of oxygen required to dispose of it is the oxygen debt.

Unstriated muscle

This type of muscle is composed of spindle shaped cells with very fine myofibrils, it is found in the walls of the gut and blood vessels often in two separate layers, one circular and one longitudinal. Unstriated muscle is controlled by the autonomic nervous system, contraction taking place more slowly than in striated muscle and it

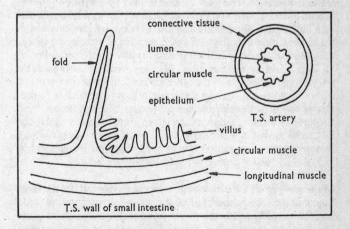

Figure 96. Unstriated muscle in gut and blood vessel

does not become fatigued.

Cardiac muscle

Cardiac muscle is found only in the wall of the heart. It consists of finely striated fibres with cross connections. It contracts rhythmically but the contraction is not initiated by the nervous system but by the SAN which is the pacemaker (see page 152).

Bones, joints and muscles

In many animals locomotion is achieved by means of muscles attached to a skeleton, this may be an **endoskeleton** as in vertebrates or an **exoskeleton** as in arthropods. Many invertebrates without skeletons have muscles working against fluid under pressure, a **hydrostatic skeleton**. In land-living vertebrates the skeleton consists of the **axial** portion made up of the skull, ribs and vertebral column, and the **appendicular** portion consisting of the limbs and the limb girdles. It provides support, protection for vital structures as in the protection of the heart and lungs by the ribs, and it supplies anchorage points for muscles to bring about movement at joints. Moveable joints are of two types, **hinge** with movement in one plane, and **ball and socket** with more universal movement; there are also **fixed** joints such as those in the skull. At moveable joints the ends of the bones are encased in a **ligament capsule**, the articulating surfaces being covered by a layer of smooth **cartilage**. The joint capsule is lined by a **synovial membrane** secreting **synovial fluid** which acts both as a lubricant and as a buffer fluid. Muscles are attached to bones by **tendons**, tough tissue consisting of collagen fibres. The point of attachment nearer the centre of the body is the origin of the muscle, the second point of attachment is the insertion. Muscles work in **antagonistic pairs**, while one contracts the other relaxes. The muscular system is highly complex but may be divided into groups according to particular function. Considering the movement of a leg; flexors bend the knee and ankle, extensors straighten them, rotators enable the foot to be moved in a circular motion, a protractor moves the limb forward, a retractor moves it backward, a levator (abductor) lifts it to the side and a depressor (adductor) lowers it.

In the arthropods the cuticle acts as an exoskeleton. It has the same functions as the endoskeleton of vertebrates, it supports, protects and forms points of attachment for muscles. Movement takes place by means of antagonistic pairs of muscles operating across a moveable joint.

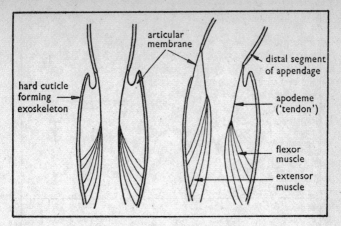

Figure 97. Skeleton, joint and muscles in an arthropod

Levers

In a lever, movement takes place about an axis or pivot called the **fulcrum**, as the result of two forces, the **load** and the **effort**. The effort is the force required to hold the load in equilibrium. In the body the effort is supplied by muscles. In **first order levers** the load and the effort are on opposite sides of the fulcrum and any movement of the effort brings about a movement of the load also, but in the opposite direction. When the fulcrum is centrally placed the load and the effort are equal but when the fulcrum is nearer the effort a greater effort is required to hold the load in equilibrium, but the movement made by the effort is less than that made by the load. In man, the head is balanced on the spine, the spine is the fulcrum, the facial portion of the head is the load and the effort is supplied by the neck muscles. When the head is held upright little effort is needed to maintain it in this position, but when the head is bent a greater effort is needed by the neck muscles to return it to the upright position. The movement of the head on the spine is an example of a first order lever.

In a **second order lever**, the load is inserted between the fulcrum and the effort. In this case movement of the effort results in the load moving in the same direction; the effort is less than the load but its movement is greater than that of the load. Raising the body on the toes is an example of a lever of this type; the load is the body mass, the fulcrum the ball of the foot and the effort is supplied by the muscles of the calf of the leg.

223

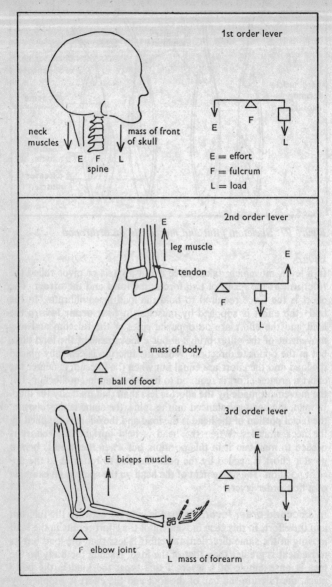

Figure 98. First, second and third order levers in man

224

In a **third order lever**, the effort is exerted between the fulcrum and the load, the effort and the load moving in the same direction, the effort is greater than the load but the distance moved is less than the load. Many levers in the body are of this type, a small contraction of the muscle producing a relatively large movement. Bending of the forearm is a good example of a third order lever.

Locomotion in water

Fish

Water provides support but resists the movement of structures through it. The resistance encountered by an object is lessened by streamlining, an adaptation found in fish and other large water animals. The dogfish is propelled forward by side to side swishing of the tail which bears a large caudal fin; the movement is brought about by contraction of muscle blocks, **myotomes**, on alternate sides of the body. Contractions pass posteriorly in a wave the thrust increasing towards the tail, the most flexible part. As a wave of contraction passes down the right side the tail sweeps to the right

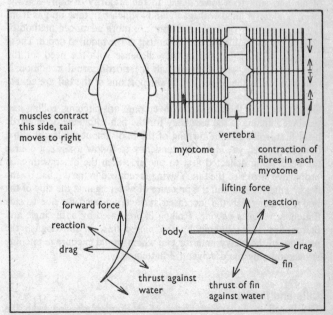

Figure 99. Locomotion in the dogfish

pushing against the water. This force produces a reaction, an equal and opposite force which has a forward component propelling the fish, and a lateral component the drag. The dogfish is heavier than water but remains afloat as long as it continues swimming. This is achieved in two ways, the anterior end is supported by the upward force resulting from the fact that the pectoral fins are held at an angle to the body, the drag which also results is overcome by the propulsive force of the tail. The end of the spine is slightly upturned and the tail is **heterocercal**, that is the lower part of the caudal fin is larger than the upper part. As the tail moves to the side in a swimming stroke the flexible lower portion of the tail trails behind, that is it is not vertical in the water, the thrusting of the fin against the water results in upward and lateral forces; the upthrust keeps the posterior end of the fish afloat while swimming and the lateral drag is cancelled out by pressure of the water against the anterior end.

In bony fish there is an air filled **swim bladder** to provide buoyancy. In some species, such as the goldfish, the fish itself can swim to the surface and take in air to improve buoyancy, or expel bubbles of air and sink to a lower level. In the majority of bony fish the swim bladder is lined with gas glands which can take up gas from the swim bladder or expel gas into it, a more advanced method of adjustment to enable the fish to remain at the required depth. These methods of adjusting the density dispense with the need for the heterocercal tail, and in bony fish the **homocercal** condition is found in which the upper and lower portions of the tail are equal.

Other problems the fish has to overcome are pitching, rolling and yawing. Pitching is the tendency for the fish to plunge downwards head first, rolling is the turning of the body about the longitudinal horizontal axis, yawing is the tendency to follow a zig-zag course the head being deflected first to one side then the other with each propulsive stroke of the tail. Yawing is reduced in the dogfish by the heavy anterior end and the pressure of water against the side of the body. In bony fish the increased surface achieved by side to side flattening reduces yawing. Rolling is prevented by both single and paired fins, and pitching by the paired fins. In the dogfish the problem of the heavy anterior end which would encourage pitching is overcome by the dorsiventral flattening.

Cilia and flagella
The flagellum undergoes waves of motion progressing from the base to the distal end exerting forces which can be compared with

226

those of the tail of a fish. Cilia do not move in this way, they work like oars in a rowing boat, each stroke propelling the organism forward, but unlike oars they bend as they return to the starting position in order to reduce drag.

Pseudopodia
Movement by pseudopodia is discussed on page 17.

Locomotion on land

The axial skeleton and myotomes are important in the movement of vertebrates living in water, but in land animals the limbs, limb girdles and their associated muscles have become increasingly important for both support and locomotion. Land animals have evolved the **pentadactyl limb** to compensate for the lack of buoyancy provided by the water. In fish the pelvic girdle is not directly connected to the vertebral column but in tetrapods, four limbed land vertebrates, the thrust of the limbs against the ground must be communicated to the body to produce locomotion. The pelvic girdle is firmly fused to the spine to support the weight and transmit force from the legs to the body, but the pectoral girdle is not attached directly to the spine instead it is bound by muscles, a system which is less effective in transmitting force from the fore limbs to the body. The vertebral column is subjected to entirely different stresses from those in a fish, it has become a weight supporting bridge and is no longer a delicate flexible structure composed of uniform vertebrae but is a sturdier structure composed of five types of vertebrae. Early land animals, amphibians, had difficulty supporting the body mass on limbs which splayed out at the sides; they moved like a newt, the movement of the limbs being accompanied by lateral undulations of the body, while at rest the ventral surface touched the ground. During evolution the limbs came to be more directly under the body so that the weight could be supported by them, the limb bones lengthened enabling the animal to travel further with each step.

In walking there is little movement of the backbone. During the power stroke the foot presses downwards and backwards on the ground, the resulting equal and opposite force is composed of a vertical force which lifts the body and a horizontal force which propels it forward. The relative proportions of the vertical and horizontal forces depends on the angle of the limb when pressing on the ground; when the limb is vertical the resulting force is entirely upwards but as the axis of the limb deviates progressively from the

227

vertical there is an increasing component of horizontal force. The movement of the lever system of the leg is the result of the alternate contraction and relaxation of the appropriate sets of muscles. In the recovery stroke the leg is lifted clear of the ground, carried forward and extended. When a muscle is stretched proprioceptors send impulses to the spinal cord and information is relayed to the brain which will have an overall pattern of this activity, the contraction and relaxation of many sets of muscles is co-ordinated and the legs move in the correct sequence. The sequence of movement, for example, left front, right hind, right front, left hind, ensures that as only one leg is lifted from the ground at a time the remaining three form a tripod with the centre of gravity of the animal lying within it. When the animal trots the sequence is speeded up and a leg is raised before the preceding one in the sequence touches the ground, momentarily the body is supported by two diagonally opposite legs. Increased speed results in a gallop in which the sequence is entirely changed, for example; left front, right front, left hind, right hind as in the horse, or left front, right front, right hind, left hind, as in the dog. In a gallop fore limbs may be raised off the ground before the hind limbs have touched down and in very fast running animals this may be accompanied by arching and straightening of the backbone. Aquatic mammals have a similar movement, they lash the tail up and down not laterally as in the fish.

Locomotion in air

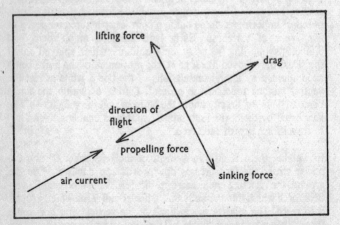

Figure 100. Forces involved in the movement of a bird through the air

Birds, bats and insects are the only animals to be successful in the air. During the active flight of a bird the wing beat is produced by the contraction of the depressor muscles which pull the wings down, followed by the contraction of the levator muscles which lift them, the downstroke taking place more slowly than the upstroke. The movements result in air flowing over the wings which behave as **aerofoils**. If there are upward air currents the bird is able to glide with motionless outstretched wings, in either case the air flowing over the wings results in their being subjected to an upward lifting force at right angles to the general direction of the flow of air. This lifting force is opposed by gravitational forces, one component of this being a sinking force, the other component propels the bird obliquely downwards and is itself opposed by the drag force. The lifting force and the drag force together are the components of the aerodynamic force.

Support in plants

Most stems are vertical and need support. A number of factors combine to resist the tendency to bend caused by the force of the wind. If a non-woody stem is split longitudinally the two halves bend away from each other owing to the fact that the inner turgid cells are no longer confined within the epidermis but are free to expand. Vascular bundles containing thick walled xylem vessels and sometimes further supplied with fibres provide substantial support; in the stem of a dicotyledon they are arranged in a ring round the periphery, this arrangement giving the most resistance to bending. Roots are subjected to longitudinal rather than lateral forces and they have the support of the soil; here the central core of strengthening tissue provided by the xylem and sometimes by additional fibres, provides the ideal structure to withstand the forces.

Key terms

Actin Protein forming thin filaments in the myofibrils of striated muscle.
Aerofoil A structure so shaped that it offers the minimum of resistance to the medium through which it is travelling with the maximum of lifting force and the minimum of drag.
Heterocercal (tail) Caudal fin of cartilaginous fish in which the ventral part is larger than the dorsal part.
Homocercal (tail) Caudal fin of bony fish in which the dorsal and ventral parts are equal.
Lever System in which movement takes place about a pivot

(fulcrum) as the result of two forces, the load and the effort. The effort is the force required to hold the load in equilibrium.

Myofibril Longitudinal thread in muscle fibre.

Myosin Protein forming thick filaments in the myofibrils of striated muscle.

Pentadactyl limb Limb with five digits found in amphibians, reptiles, birds and mammals.

Sliding hypothesis (of muscle action) Huxley and Hanson suggested that during muscle contraction the thick filaments of myosin and the thin filaments of actin slide further between each other.

Tetanus (tetanic contraction) Sustained muscle contraction.

Tetrapod Four-legged land vertebrate.

Chapter 12
Growth and Reproduction

Growth

True growth involves the production of more protoplasm and is best expressed as an increase in dry mass; increase in size or mass may otherwise be due to water absorption. Many marine organisms such as lobsters and seaweeds have unlimited growth which continues throughout the life of the organism. The land environment is more demanding and living things reach a maximum size.

Measuring growth
Measuring the increase in dry mass over a period of time involves beginning the experiment with a large number of individuals and removing a portion at intervals for drying. Obviously the method is most generally applicable to plants and other criteria such as height or mass may have to be used for animals.

Growth curve
If the measurements obtained for mass or height or other suitable measurements are plotted against time, a growth curve is obtained having the characteristic form shown in figure 101a. This is a **nor-**

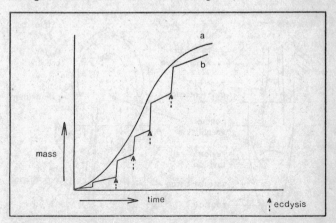

Figure 101. a. Normal growth curve b. Growth in an arthropod

mal growth curve and is found in most organisms with the exception of arthropods, where growth takes place in stages. From time to time the creature moults, growth then taking place rapidly before the new cuticle hardens. In most organisms growth starts slowly, increases to a maximum rate, sometimes called the grand period of growth, before reaching a stage when no further growth takes place.

Growth in plants

In plants growth takes place in certain regions called meristems. Meristems are found at the **stem apex** and in the **root tip** just behind the root cap. Growth in girth takes place by divisions of the **cambium,** meristematic cells located between the xylem and phloem in the vascular bundles. A longitudinal section of a root tip or stem apex shows three zones. At the tip is a zone of **cell division** characterized by rather cubical cells with large nuclei or cells undergoing mitotic division, behind this a zone of **vacuolation** showing small vacuoles joining further back to form the large central vacuole, beyond that a zone of **differentiation** where the cells are becoming changed into specialized types of cells. In the root tip the root cap protects the meristem, this mass of loose cells breaks down to form a slimy substance which aids the passage of the root through the soil and is itself constantly renewed from the inner side by divisions of the meristem. In the stem the meristem forms leaf primordia on either side, they grow protecting the meristem and forming the apical bud which consists of young leaves each with an axillary bud. These buds have cells at the tip capable of dividing

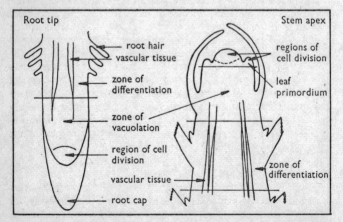

Figure 102. Growing regions of stem and root in a flowering plant

and producing lateral branches.

Secondary thickening

In the stem of a dicotyledon a single layer of cambium cells occurs between the xylem and phloem. When growth in girth takes place the cambium joins up between the vascular bundles forming the **interfascicular cambium** and giving rise to a cylinder of cambial cells. Tangential divisions of the cells of the cambium produce new cells which become differentiated into **secondary xylem** on the inside and **secondary phloem** on the outside, with more xylem than phloem being produced. In between the vascular bundles some cambial cells produce parenchyma leading to the formation of **medullary rays**, these allow for lateral transport of water and mineral salts. Continued divisions result in the cambium and phloem being pushed outwards, radial divisions of the cells of the cambium increasing the diameter of the cylinder. The xylem vessels formed in the early part of the growing season are large as a good supply of water is necessary at this time but as the season proceeds the xylem vessels become smaller until finally growth ceases in the autumn. In the following spring growth starts again and large vessels are produced; being adjacent to the small vessels of the previous year they give the impression of a ring, the **annual ring**. The number of annual rings gives the age of the tree, the distance between them the amount of growth which took place in any one year, this in turn gives some information about the climatic conditions at the time, a wide ring indicating a good growing season. The increasing girth of the stem renders the original epidermis inadequate and a layer of cells inside the epidermis becomes meristematic, this secondary meristem is the **cork cambium** or phellogen. The cork cambium divides tangentially giving rise to cork cells on the outside and secondary cortex or phelloderm on the inside. Like all secondary tissues the cork cells and phelloderm cells are arranged in radial rows. The impervious cork layer would cut off the air supply to the stem if it were not for the fact that at intervals round the stem the cork cambium actively produces loosely packed parenchyma cells, a group of them burst through to the outside forming a **lenticel**. The cork, cork cambium and phelloderm make up the layer known as the periderm.

Growth in animals

Growth in animals is not confined to localized areas but occurs generally although not at the same rate in all parts of the body; for example, the head of a new born baby occupies about one third of its length whereas in an adult this has become about one seventh.

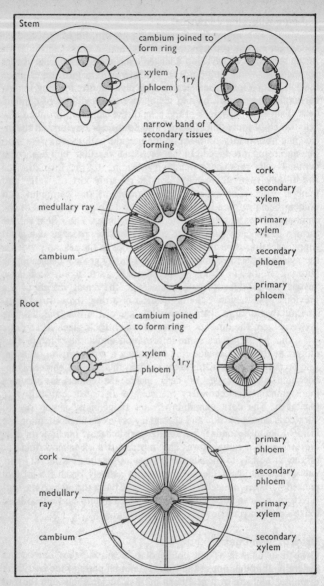

Figure 103. *Secondary thickening in a stem and a root*

Factors affecting growth

There are two major factors affecting growth, hereditary and environmental. The genotype of an individual largely determines the hormone balance and size within certain limits. The actual size attained is the result of environmental factors. Nutrition is an important factor, malnutrition in animals leads to stunted growth and lack of the necessary mineral salts will prevent a plant reaching its full potential. Light is essential for the growth of green plants but not for animals although some mammals are able to synthesize vitamin D in sunlight. Temperature affects growth, an increase in temperature bringing about accelerated growth in plants and shortening the life span of homoiothermic animals. The role of hormones in growth is discussed in Chapter 10.

Mitosis

Mitosis is the type of cell division which occurs during an organism's growth. The cell has a fixed number of chromosomes and division takes place in such a way that the daughter cells have the same number of chromosomes with identical characteristics to those of the parent cell. Mitosis is a continuous process but it is convenient to regard it as being divided into four stages; **prophase, metaphase, anaphase** and **telophase.** In prophase the chromosomes appear as double threads, two chromatids, joined together at the centromere, they become shorter and thicker and move towards the periphery of the nucleus. The nuclear membrane disappears, the centriole if present divides and each half moves to the opposite side of the nucleus, spindle fibres start to form and the nucleolus disappears. During metaphase the chromosomes migrate to the equator of the cell and the centromeres become attached to the spindle fibres, the centromeres divide and the chromatids pull apart commencing in the region of the centromere. In anaphase the chromatids migrate to opposite poles of the cell. During telophase the chromatids reach the poles, the nuclear membrane and the nucleolus are re-formed, the spindle fibres disappear and the cell begins to divide into two. The chromatids, now the new chromosomes finally become thread like and there are two new daughter cells which return to the resting state, interphase.

Reproduction

There are two methods of reproduction, sexual and asexual. Sexual reproduction involves the fusion of haploid nuclei, usually those of reproductive cells, gametes, derived from two different individuals.

235

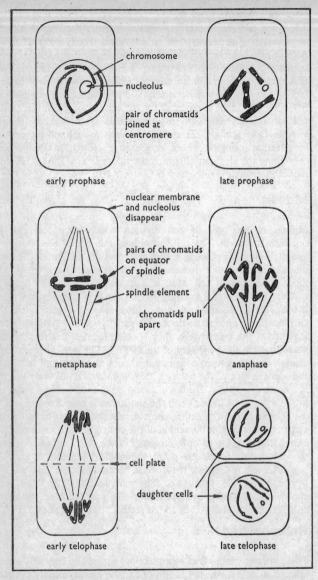

early prophase

chromosome

nucleolus

pair of chromatids joined at centromere

late prophase

nuclear membrane and nucleolus disappear

pairs of chromatids on equator of spindle

spindle element

chromatids pull apart

metaphase

anaphase

cell plate

daughter cells

early telophase

late telophase

Figure 104. Stages in mitosis

236

The fusion is fertilization and the resulting cell, the zygote, grows into a new individual. Many primitive organisms produce similar gametes, isogametes, or slightly dissimilar ones, anisogametes; however there is an advantage in having one immobile gamete with stored food and a smaller active gamete, markedly dissimilar cells which have evolved into egg and sperm. If nuclei of different genetical make-up are to fuse, the nuclei must come from different individuals; in higher organisms the individuals will be of different sexes, unlike structurally and physiologically. In lower organisms, for example, fungi, there are plus and minus strains structurally identical but having physiological differences. The fusion of gametes of different genotypes results in offspring with genetical variations. Asexual reproduction involves only one individual, there are no gametes and the offspring are identical. The production of individuals with different genotypes provides a pathway along which evolution can proceed.

Asexual reproduction

Bacteria and many unicellular organisms reproduce by **binary fission,** the organism splitting into two parts. Bacteria can divide about every twenty minutes so building a large population very rapidly. Animals like *Hydra* reproduce by **budding**, an outgrowth like a miniature adult appearing at the side which is nipped off to form a separate individual. **Spores** are formed by many organisms both animal and plant, for example, protozoa, fungi, mosses, ferns and some bacteria; they are of many different types produced in different ways and may be widely distributed by a variety of means giving rapid increase in the population. There are many examples of asexual or **vegetative reproduction** in the flowering plants, the reproductive structures often contain stored food and remain in the ground over the winter growing into a new plant in the following year, these structures are perennating organs. There are bulbs with food stored in scale leaves as in the tulip, or in leaf bases as in the daffodil; corms like the crocus with food in a short swollen stem; stem tubers as in the potato, the food being stored in a few terminal nodes and internodes of lateral underground branches. Runners like those of the strawberry have no food store. In addition to these natural methods, gardeners take cuttings and make graftings to increase the stock. A group of asexually produced plants obviously has the same genetical composition and is called a **clone**.

Meiosis

Meiosis occurs at some stage in the life cycle of all organisms

237

reproducing sexually. At fertilization each gamete contributes the haploid number of chromosomes resulting in a diploid zygote which develops into a new organism. Later the process of meiosis at gamete formation halves the number of chromosomes. Meiosis consists of **two rounds of divisions**, each conveniently divided into four stages as in mitosis. In the first round of divisions the homologous chromosomes, that is those corresponding chromosomes derived from each parent, become separated randomly into different cells; in the second round of divisions the chromatids are separated.

In prophase 1 the nucleolus disappears and the centrioles if present arrange themselves at opposite sides of the nucleus. Homologous chromosomes lie side by side forming a **bivalent**, later when they tend to move apart they usually remain in contact at points called **chiasmata**. Each bivalent forms between one and eight chiasmata and they may be formed between any two of the four chromatids.

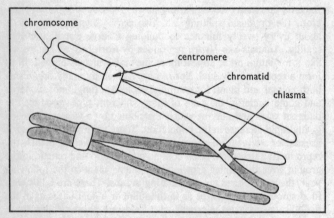

Figure 105. Chiasma formation and crossing over

As the bivalents tend to move apart and the chromosomes, composed of a pair of chromatids, contract, the presence of chiasmata cause them to form characteristic shapes. The chromatids may break at a chiasma and rejoin in such a way that a portion of one changes place with a portion of the other, this brings about an exchange of genetic material and is termed **crossing over**. During metaphase 1 the bivalents move to the equator of the spindle, homologous chromosomes lying on opposite sides of the equator,

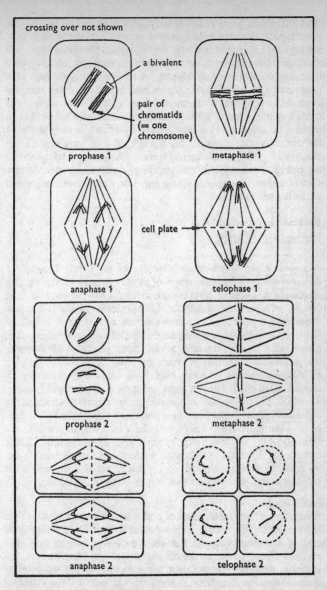

Figure 106. Stages in meiosis

239

the centromeres being attached to spindle fibres. In anaphase 1 the homologous chromosomes made up of a pair of chromatids containing any exchanged material received during crossing over, pull apart and travel towards opposite poles, the chromatids diverging from one another. During telophase 1 the chromosomes reach the poles and the cell divides. Sometimes there is a brief rest, interphase, or prophase of the second round of divisions may begin at once. Superficially the divisions of the second round are similar to mitosis, in prophase 11 a new spindle is formed, in metaphase 11 the chromosomes move to the equator, during anaphase 11 the chromatids pull apart and move towards the poles, in telophase 11 the cell divides separating the groups of chromatids, now the new chromosomes. The spindle disappears, the nuclear membrane and nucleolus are re-formed.

Sexual reproduction in flowering plants

A flower is the reproductive structure of the plant. Typically a flower consists of an outer whorl of **sepals** forming the **calyx**, this surrounds a whorl of **petals** collectively called the **corolla**. The two whorls together constitute the **perianth**. Inside is the **androecium**, a collection of **stamens** each consisting of a stalk or **filament** and an **anther** composed of pollen sacs containing pollen grains, each bearing the male nuclei. In the centre of the flower is the **gynaecium** of one or more **carpels**, each consisting of a **stigma**, a **style** and an **ovary** containing one or more **ovules** each bearing an egg cell. There is great variation in the size and shape of flowers and in the number of the various floral parts; sometimes the sepals and petals are similar these parts then being called collectively, the perianth. The flower may be radially symmetrical, **actinomorphic**, or bilaterally symmetrical, **zygomorphic**. Some flowers are dioecious or unisexual, stamens and carpels being found in separate flowers instead of the more usual monoecious or bisexual state with stamens and carpels in the same flower.

Pollination

Pollination is the transference of pollen grains from a stamen to a stigma. When this occurs within the same flower it is self pollination. Cross pollination is the transference of pollen from the stamens of one flower to the stigma of another. Some flowers, for example, some members of the Compositae will be self pollinated if cross pollination fails. Most flowers are adapted to either insect or wind pollination although birds, bats and water are also agents for carrying pollen.

Insect pollinated flowers
Insect pollinated or **entomophilous** flowers are conspicuous, they have coloured or white petals or perianth segments and where the flowers are small they may be grouped together in an inflorescence; they contain nectar and are often scented. The stamens and carpels are enclosed within the flower, the pollen grains being comparatively large and often sculptured and sticky. The flower may be so formed as to provide a landing stage for the insect and may bear markings or hairs, a honey guide, which attract attention. Often the flower favours pollination by a particular kind of insect.

Wind pollinated flowers
Grasses and most catkin bearing trees are wind pollinated or **anemophilous**. Catkins disperse their pollen before the leaves are on the trees thus avoiding waste. Grasses usually have a large number of flowers in a head or spike at the top of a tall stem where use may be made of air currents to disperse the pollen. Individual

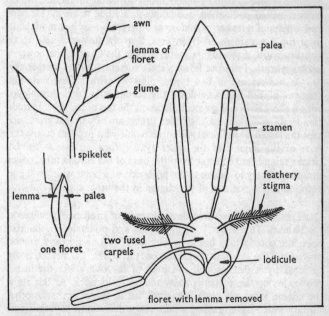

Figure 107. Flower structure of oat (Avena)

16   241

flowers are inconspicuous, brown or greenish in colour and lacking in scent and nectar, they are grouped in spikelets which are separated from each other by modified leaves called glumes. Each small flower or floret is protected by two bracts, the larger lemma which may bear an awn and the inner palea. The androecium consists of three stamens and the gynaecium of two fused carpels. When the flower is mature it opens and the stamens which have long thin filaments hang out of the flower dispersing large quantities of dry light pollen. The stigmas are large and feathery and have a sticky surface to which the drifting grains adhere. Small lumps at the base of the floral parts, called lodicules are believed to represent much reduced perianth segments. Pollen grains have characteristic shapes and markings providing a means of identification, they are resistant structures and their presence in peat deposits at different depths provides much information about past vegetation.

Pollination mechanisms

The biological aim of sexual reproduction is to introduce genetic variation, this is achieved by the fusion of gametes from different sources. There are many mechanisms to avoid or reduce the incidence of self pollination, one common method is for the stamens and stigma of a flower to mature at different times; it is more common for the stamens to ripen first, then the flower is said to be **protandrous**, if the stigma matures as in the figwort, the flower is **protogynous**. Primrose flowers show the condition of **heterostyly**, the flowers are of two types; pin-eyed with a long style and stamens placed half way down the corolla tube, and thrum-eyed with a short style and stamens placed at the top of the tube. In addition to these differences, the pollen grains are of different sizes such that the pollen size of one type corresponds with papillae on the surface of the stigma of the other type. When an insect visits a primrose and sucks nectar from the base of the corolla tube, pollen grains are likely to adhere to the proboscis at a point which will correspond to the position of the stigma in the other type of flower.

Dead nettles (*Lamium*) provide an example of an efficient pollination mechanism. The flower is zygomorphic and pollinated by bumble bees; the corolla tube has a landing stage on one side and a hood protecting the internal structures on the other, the nectar being secreted by a disc around the base of the ovary. As the insect probes for nectar, pollen is showered on to its back. At this stage the stigma lobes are closed together but as the insect visits other flowers which have reached a later stage the opened stigmatic surface will pick up pollen from the insect's back.

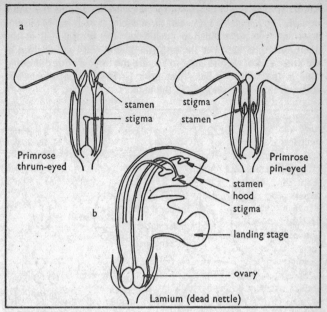

Figure 108. a. Heterostyly in the primrose b. Flower structure in dead nettle (Lamium)

In orchids there is only one stamen consisting of two pollen masses or **pollinia** situated in a pouch at the entrance to the spur where the nectar is located. When the appropriate insect visits the flower the pollinia become detached and stick in a vertical position to the insect's head, in a very short time the pollinia bend over into a horizontal position perfectly placed to stick directly on to the stigmatic surface of another orchid flower.

Development of the embryo sac
Each ovule has a stalk, the **funicle,** which is attached to the ovary wall at the placenta. Inner and outer **integuments** of the ovule protect the inner **nucellus,** they do not completely enclose it but leave a hole, the **micropyle.** In the interior of the ovule the embryo sac develops a megaspore mother cell which divides by meiosis producing four haploid megaspores, only one develops the other three degenerate. The developing cell enlarges rapidly to form the **embryo sac,** the nucleus dividing three times by mitosis giving eight nuclei, four arrange themselves at each end of the embryo sac,

one from each group migrating to the centre to become the **polar nuclei**. The remaining groups of three nuclei at each end of the embryo sac become divided by cell walls the central cell at the micropylar end becomes the **egg**, the lateral cells, **synergids**; at the other end of the the embryo sac are the three **antipodal cells**. This is the state of affairs just prior to fertilization; meanwhile pollen grains are developing in the anthers.

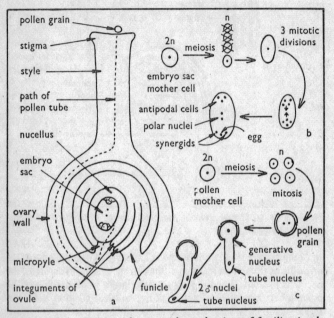

Figure 109. a. Ovary with one ovule at the time of fertilization b. Development of embryo sac c. Development of pollen grain

Development of the pollen grain

Pollen grains are produced from pollen mother cells in the pollen sacs of the anther, each undergoes meiosis producing four haploid pollen grains. Inside the grain the nucleus divides by mitosis to form two haploid nuclei, one the **generative nucleus**, the second the **tube nucleus**. This is the state of affairs at the time the pollen grains are released. The stigma of the flower produces a sticky secretion to which the pollen grains adhere and which appears to stimulate them to germinate, each grows a pollen tube down the style to the ovary, the tube nucleus being at the tip of the pollen

244

tube. During this process the generative nucleus divides by mitosis into **two male nuclei**. The pollen tube enters the micropyle, reaches the embryo sac and bursts, the tube nucleus degenerates, one male nucleus fuses with the egg nucleus forming a **zygote**, the other male nucleus fuses with the polar nuclei to form a triploid nucleus, the **primary endosperm nucleus**.

Affinity with other groups of plants

In the angiosperms there is extreme reduction of the gametophyte generation. It will be remembered that in *Selaginella* (see page 50) there are microspores and megaspores, the microspores on germination divide into two cells, one represents a vegetative cell of the gametophyte while the other develops into a single antheridium enclosing haploid sperm. In the pollen grain, essentially a microspore, there are two cells, a generative cell and a tube cell, the former divides forming two haploid male nuclei. In *Selaginella* the megaspore on germination never escapes from the megaspore wall, it forms a small amount of vegetative tissue and archegonia, each with an egg cell. In the angiosperms, the ovule has evolved from a megasporangium by the addition of integuments; at one stage four megaspores are formed, only one surviving, this develops into the embryo sac which may be compared with the female gametophyte. The nucleus divides three times to form eight nuclei, one becomes the egg cell, the synergids can be regarded as non-functional eggs, the others probably represent vegetative cells of the female gametophyte. Thus the flowering plant is the highly developed diploid sporophyte generation, its pollen grains being microspores and its embryo sacs megaspores. The gametophyte generation is so reduced that the spores on development give rise to little more than sex cells. The double fertilization, however, of one sperm nucleus with an egg and a second sperm nucleus with the polar nuclei is a feature found only in angiosperms.

Development of the seed

The zygote divides forming a chain of cells, the **suspensor** and **pro-embryo**, the pro-embryo is the cell furthest from the micropyle, it develops into the **embryo**. The embryo becomes differentiated into **radicle, plumule** and one or two **cotyledons**. The triploid endosperm nucleus divides repeatedly forming a mass of endosperm which supplies food for the developing embryo. The fertilized ovule becomes a seed; the growing embryo together with the endosperm coming to occupy the space inside the integuments, these in turn become the protective outer testa and inner tegmen. In the mature seed the endosperm may remain as a separate food store, this is an **endospermic seed** such as the castor oil, or the food store constituting the endosperm may be transferred to the cotyledons, this is a **non-endospermic seed** such as the broad bean.

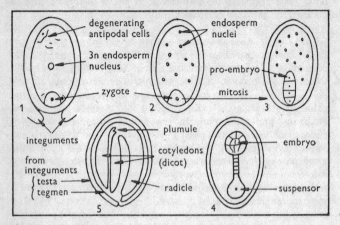

Figure 110. Development of the angiosperm seed

Fruit and seed dispersal

Fruits and seeds are dispersed by wind, water or animals, or they may aid their own dispersal by some explosive mechanism which throws out the seeds. The balsam fruit disperses its own seeds in this way. Fruits may be winged, such as ash or have a parachute of hairs, as in the dandelion, aiding wind dispersal. Hooked fruits like cleavers or agrimony catch on to the bodies of animals. The coconut with its thick layer of fibres enclosed in a waterproof covering is transported by sea while brightly coloured fruits attract birds and some mammals, the seeds passing through the gut undigested.

Seed germination

Many seeds require a period of **dormancy** before they will germinate. Seeds vary greatly in the length of time they remain viable, lotus seeds from peat deposits believed to be 1,000 years old have been germinated successfully, but this is exceptional. Seeds require water, oxygen and a suitable temperature for germination, some also require heating or chilling or light. Many fruits contain germination inhibitors which prevent the seeds from developing while still within the fruit. On germination the seed absorbs at least its own weight in water, the water activates the enzymes which hydrolyse the stored food forming soluble products which can be translocated to the growing regions of the embryo. The testa is ruptured and the radicle emerges followed by the plumule. There are two types of germination, **epigeal** as in the sunflower in which the cotyledons come above the ground, turn green and carry out photosynthesis, and **hypogeal** germination as in the broad bean and maize in which the cotyledons remain below the ground, the first foliage leaves being developed from the plumule.

Sexual reproduction in animals

In fish large numbers of eggs are produced and fertilized externally as eggs and sperm meet in the water. Many eggs, however, remain unfertilized and there is a high mortality rate among developing eggs and young. Amphibians return to the water to breed, fertilization again being external and the eggs unprotected. Land vertebrates have had to overcome the problem of protecting gametes and fertilized eggs from desiccation; this has been solved by internal fertilization followed by the provision of a shell for the egg, a leathery one in reptiles and a chalky one in birds. Eggs are provided with yolk to supply food for the developing embryo. Birds show parental care in protecting and feeding their young, a stage of advancement which is further developed in the mammals where following internal fertilization the embryo is retained inside the body of the female not being born until it reaches an advanced stage of development, this birth of live young is **vivipary**. After birth the young are fed on milk from mammary glands and have a long period of parental protection. With the greater certainty of successful rearing to adult life the number of possible young has dropped from millions in a single spawning in the fish to a maximum of about one child a year in humans which would produce an exceptionally large family, even allowing for the limited number of child-bearing years. In many mammals there are breeding seasons, commonly one a year in spring or summer, in others two breeding seasons. During these seasons which are of varying length the female may be in oestrus, when ovulation occurs, only once or several times. The human female, in common with rats, mice and cows has no particular breeding season.

Reproduction in man

The male urinogenital system
The **testes** are made up of **seminiferous tubules** and lie outside

the abdominal cavity in the **scrotal sacs** where the temperature is slightly lower and more favourable for sperm production. The tubules where the sperm are formed lead into the **vasa efferentia** then into the **epididymis** which lies outside the testis, and from there into the **vas deferens**. During **coitus** the vas deferens contract forcing sperm along the **urethra**, where they mingle with secretions from the **seminal vesicles** and **prostate glands**. They then pass through the erected **penis** to be projected into the top of the vagina of the female, during the process of ejaculation. The secretions provide a medium in which the sperm become fully active, swimming by undulations of the tail.

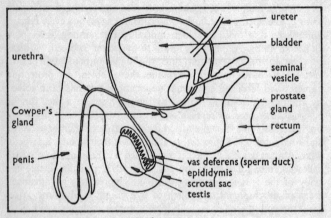

Figure 111. Male urinogenital system

Spermatogenesis, sperm production, takes place in the seminiferous tubules, it begins in the germinal epithelium on the outside of the tubules and as cell divisions proceed the mature spermatozoa end up next to the lumen of the tubule. Repeated mitotic divisions of the diploid epithelial cells produce diploid spermatogonia which grow into primary spermatocytes, each undergoes meiosis, the first division resulting in two haploid secondary spermatocytes and the second division four haploid spermatids. The spermatids become differentiated into spermatozoa, their tails projecting into the lumen of the tube into which they are finally released. Sperm production begins at puberty at about 14 years of age and may continue until about 70. The anterior pituitary gland secretes the gonadotrophic hormone FSH which stimulates spermatogenesis, and ICSH, called LH in the female, which stimulates the production of testosterone (see page 204).

The female urinogenital system

There are two **ovaries** at the back of the abdominal cavity, close to each is the funnel shaped end of the **oviduct** which leads to the muscular **uterus**. At its junction with the **vagina** which leads to the outside, the uterus has a ring of muscle, the **cervix**.

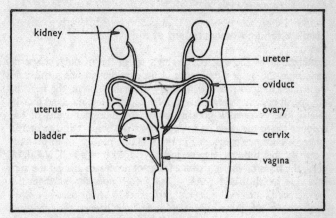

Figure 112. Female urinogenital system

Oogenesis, egg production, is basically similar to spermatogenesis, it begins in the germinal epithelium covering the outside of the ovary where cells divide mitotically to produce diploid oogonia. Of the group of oogonia produced by each cell only one develops, it grows considerably forming a large primary oocyte. Each oocyte undergoes meiosis the first division resulting in a haploid secondary oocyte and a small haploid first polar body, the second meiotic division produces a haploid ovum and a small haploid second polar body. The first polar body often does not divide again. During the process each oogonium moves deeper into the ovary, it is surrounded by cells of the germinal epithelium, the whole structure forming a primary follicle. Several hundreds of thousands of these follicles are produced but only a few hundred complete their development during the child-bearing years of the female. A mature **Graafian follicle** has a wall several layers thick enclosing the **ovum** and liquid, as it matures it rises to the surface of the ovary again and discharges its contents, the empty follicle then develops into a **corpus luteum** which persists only if fertilization occurs. Fertilization can occur only round about the time of ovulation, this period is called **oestrus**, it is part of the oestrus or sexual cycle. An ovum is discharged about every 28 days from an alternate ovary and it travels down the oviduct to the uterus, its fate depending on whether or not it is fertilized. If fertilization occurs this normally takes place in the upper regions of the oviduct, an un-fertilized egg passes through the uterus and out through the vagina. Ovulation begins at puberty at about the age of 12 and continues until the menopause at 45 to 50.

Fertilization and development of the foetus

Fertilization of the egg occurs high up in the oviduct, a sperm penetrates the outer membranes of the egg, the vitelline membrane then thickening to prevent the entry of further sperm, the head of the sperm becomes detached from the tail and the male and female nuclei fuse. Waves of contraction of the muscular walls of the oviduct move the dividing zygote down the oviduct to the uterus where it becomes embedded in the wall, the process of **implantation**. By this time the zygote has developed into a hollow ball of cells, the **blastocyst**, it grows a fringe of processes around the sur-face, the **trophoblastic villi**, these absorb nourishment from the uterine wall. The developing embryo comes to be enclosed in **extra-embryonic membranes**; the inner membrane, the **amnion** encloses the embryo in **amniotic fluid** which protects it acting as a buffer fluid, the outer membrane is the **chorion**, the two mem-branes being separated by the **extra-embryonic coelom** con-tinuous with the coelom in the embryo. An outgrowth from the gut, the **allantois**, grows between the two membranes into the extra-embryonic coelom. The chorion and allantois become the **placen-ta**. **Chorionic villi** which develop blood capillaries project into the wall of the uterus, and oxygen, food and waste products are exchanged across the thin capillary walls. As development proceeds the placenta enlarges, the **yolk sac** becomes smaller and the am-niotic cavity enlarges so that it comes to fill the uterus, the amnion and chorion coming together, the foetus being attached to the placenta by the allantois which becomes the **umbilical cord**. The cord contains an umbilical artery which collects oxygen and food materials diffusing from the maternal circulation at the placenta, and an umbilical vein which takes carbon dioxide and waste nitrogenous materials back. In the foetus the lung circuit is not in use and the blood is shunted through a hole, the **foramen ovale**, between the auricles, and also through the **ductus arteriosus** which links the pulmonary artery and the aorta. The **gestation**

period begins when the egg is fertilized and ends at birth, **parturition**, a period of nine months in man. During the gestation period the uterus increases greatly in size, reaching about 500 times its normal volume, the wall becomes correspondingly thickened and supplied with blood. The process of parturition takes place in three stages, firstly dilation of the cervix, secondly the expelling of the foetus by powerful contractions of the uterine muscles, and thirdly the expelling of the placenta.

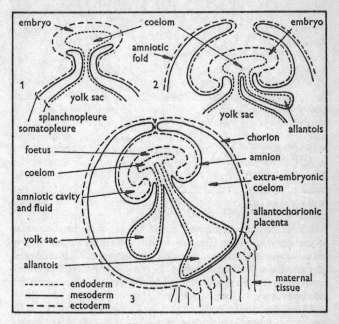

Figure 113. Formation of the extra-embryonic membranes

The role of hormones in the oestrus cycle

In the female, FSH released from the anterior pituitary gland into the blood stream stimulates the growth of a Graafian follicle containing an ovum, and the production of oestrogen from the ovary. The production of oestrogen increases steadily for about fourteen days, it causes the wall of the uterus to thicken, and the release of FSH to be suppressed; at its maximum it triggers off the release of

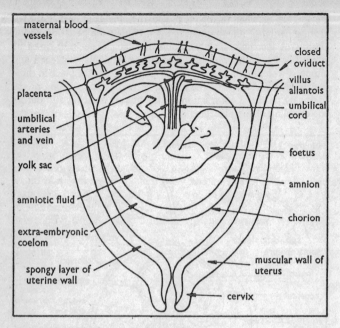

Figure 114. The foetus at six months

LH from the anterior pituitary gland. LH brings about the release of the ovum from the Graafian follicle, the empty follicle turning into the corpus luteum secreting progesterone. This hormone prepares the wall of the uterus for the reception of a fertilized ovum, it also suppresses the production of FSH which in turn lowers the oestrogen level. As the progesterone level rises it inhibits the release of LH which results in the cessation of progesterone secretion by the corpus luteum which degenerates. At this stage of the events **menstruation** takes place. The fall in the progesterone level causes FSH to be released again. If fertilization takes place the corpus luteum does not degenerate but continues to produce progesterone, this by its suppressive action on FSH prevents the development of a Graafian follicle. A low level of oestrogen continues to be produced by the ovary and this together with progesterone brings about the development of the uterus and mammary glands. After a few months the placenta itself takes over the job of secreting these two hormones. At **parturition** the supply of progesterone declines and oxytocin is released from the posterior pituitary gland, this causes the muscles of the uterus to contract, oestrogen appears to sensitize the uterine muscles to oxytocin and the change in the hormone balance triggers off the release of prolactin from the anterior pituitary gland, this hormone stimulates milk production (see also page 202).

Embryology in Amphioxus

Amphioxus is a primitive chordate, its development illustrates the fundamentals of chordate embryology. Differences in higher chordates arise from the presence of varying amounts of yolk which alter the cleavage pattern and by the involvement of extra-embryonic membranes in birds and mammals. Following **fertilization** of the egg the zygote develops by **cleavage** into a number of cells called **blastomeres,** followed by gastrulation, the organization of the new cells into layers, and then by the formation of various organs and systems. Cleavage takes place by successive mitotic divisions, each in a plane at right angles to the preceding one. In time a hollow ball of cells, the **blastula** is formed, invagination now takes place at one end forming a cup-shaped structure, the

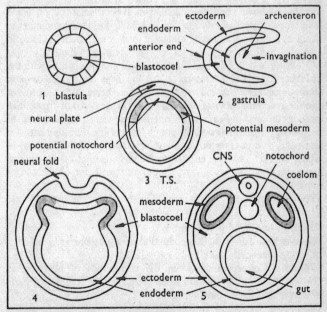

Figure 115. Development in Amphioxus

gastrula, which comes to be two layered, the original cavity being obliterated. The outer layer, the **ectoderm,** gives rise to the skin, the inner layer, the **endoderm,** forming the lining of the gut; the new cavity, **archenteron,** formed by the invagination becomes the gut. The embryo lengthens and another opening is made to the exterior which becomes the mouth. Cells of the ectoderm forming the **neural plate** sink inwards, folds on either side growing up and fusing over the top of the neural tube which becomes the **CNS.** The **notochord** (forerunner of the vertebral column) is formed from cells of the endoderm immediately below the neural plate. The **mesoderm** forms from lateral invaginations of the archenteron and becomes interposed between the ectoderm and endoderm. These three layers, ectoderm, mesoderm and endoderm are the **germ layers,** the **coelom** being a cavity within the mesoderm. Organs are formed from the mesoderm.

Parthenogenesis

Parthenogenesis is the development of an egg, without fertilization, into a new individual. It can be induced artificially in some cases but little is known about the mechanism. It occurs naturally in some invertebrates, particularly insects. In aphids during the summer the wingless females produce diploid eggs by mitosis, instead of haploid eggs by meiosis, they are of course identical genetically; this process leads to rapid build-up in numbers and dispenses with the necessity for males at this stage. In hive bees the drones develop from unfertilized haploid eggs, the queen being able to prevent sperms reaching some of the eggs after mating. Adult frogs have been produced by artificial parthenogenesis. Both types of parthenogenesis also occur in plants, that is the development of a haploid egg without fertilization and development of a diploid egg in which meiosis has been omitted in the development of the embryo sac.

Key terms

Anemophily Wind pollination.
Asexual reproduction Reproduction without gametes, producing offspring genetically alike.
Chiasma Connection between the chromatids of homologous chromosomes during meiosis when crossing over occurs and parts of chromosomes are exchanged.
Cleavage Repeated mitotic divisions of an egg following fertilization.

Ecdysis Shedding of the cuticle in arthropods. Moulting.

Embryo sac Structure in ovule of a flowering plant representing the female gametophyte and derived from a megaspore by mitotic divisions of the nucleus, one becoming the egg.

Entomophily Insect pollination.

Epigeal (germination) Seed germination in which the cotyledons come above ground and form the first green leaves.

Fertilization The fusion of two haploid nuclei, one from each gamete in sexual reproduction.

Fruit A ripened ovary containing one or more seeds.

Gastrulation Movement of cells during the development of an animal embryo at the end of cleavage.

Growth An increase in dry mass.

Hypogeal (germination) Seed germination in which the cotyledons remain below ground the first green leaves being derived from the plumule.

Meiosis Process in which a diploid cell undergoes two successive divisions forming four haploid cells.

Meristem Region of active cell division in plants.

Mitosis The division of a cell to produce two daughter cells with an identical complement of chromosomes.

Oestrus cycle Sexual or reproductive cycle in sexually mature non-pregnant female mammals.

Ovule Structure found in seed plants derived from a megasporangium by the addition of integuments.

Parthenogenesis The development of an egg without fertilization.

Pollination The transference of pollen from stamen to stigma.

Seed Fertilized ovule after development consisting of embryo, food store, and protective coat (testa) derived from integuments.

Sexual reproduction Reproduction involving the fusion of haploid nuclei giving possibility of genetic variation in the offspring.

Chapter 13
Genetics

Genetics is the study of heredity. The first scientific study of heredity was carried out by the Austrian monk **Gregor Mendel** (1822 to 1884).

Monohybrid inheritance

Monohybrid inheritance is the inheritance of one pair of contrasting characters. Mendel worked with the garden pea *Pisum sativum*. He first chose pure breeding tall plants and pure breeding dwarf plants and crossed them by taking stamens from one type and dusting the pollen on to the stigma of the other type. The ripened seeds were collected and sown and all these plants of the first filial generation (F_1) grew tall. Flowers of the F_1 generation were self pollinated and the resulting seeds sown, these plants of the second filial generation (F_2) produced tall and dwarf plants in the proportion of approximately 3 : 1. Mendel wrote of 'factors' for the characters or traits of tallness and dwarfness, in modern terms they are **genes**. Dwarfness disappeared in the F_1, the gene for tallness in this species is **dominant**, that for dwarfness **recessive**. The original pure breeding tall plants and the tall plants of the F_1 look similar, they have the same **phenotype**, but that they are not genetically similar is shown by the fact that the original tall plants produce only tall plants when the flowers are selfed whereas tall plants of the F_1 produce a mixture of tall and dwarf when selfed, the tall plants are of different **genotype**. Tall plants of the original parent stock contain two similar genes for tallness (T and T), they are **homozygous**, tall plants of the F_1 contain two dissimilar genes, one for tallness and one for dwarfness (T and t), they are **heterozygous**. These two varieties of genes controlling size are **alleles**.

Mendel's First Law
In modern terms Mendel's First Law or Law of Segregation states that when two pure bred individuals showing a pair of contrasting characters are crossed, the characters pass unchanged through the F_1 and segregate out in definite proportions in the F_2. Segregation may be defined as the separation of characters in the offspring of hybrid individuals.

The use of symbols

When using symbols to represent genes it is usual to write the dominant gene with a capital letter and the recessive gene with a small letter, the letter itself being the initial letter of the character (see figure 116).

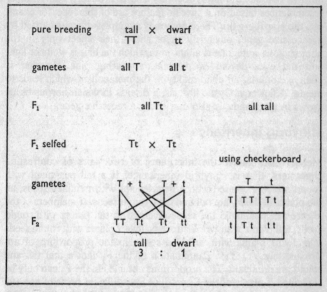

Figure 116. Mendel's experiments on the inheritance of height in peas. (Monohybrid inheritance)

Distinguishing between homozygote and heterozygote

When the homozygous tall pea plants are self pollinated they produce only tall plants whereas the heterozygous tall plants produce tall and dwarf in the ratio of 3 : 1, but the usual way the problem is solved in animals is to cross the organism with the homozygous recessive.

TT × tt   all Tt in F_1 all tall

Tt × tt   gametes

	T	t
t	Tt	tt
t	Tt	tt

F_1 tall : short 1 : 1

Monohybrid inheritance in man

There is a wide range of characters each inherited by a single dominant gene which may make an appearance in man. One is white
forelock, another brachydactyly (short fingers), a third a type of
dwarfism (chondrodystrophy) in which the head and trunk are of
normal size but the limbs are very short. Probably many family
resemblances based on a specific feature are of this type, for example, the Hapsburg lip. There are many examples of traits carried by
a recessive gene, obviously these show their effect only in the
homozygous state, one is albinism in which the hair is white or light
and the eyes devoid of pigment, appearing pink. Another is
phenylketonuria, an abnormality in the metabolism which leads to
mental deficiency. Cystic fibrosis, a disease in which fibrous tissue
grows in the glands, is also carried by a recessive gene.

Dihybrid inheritance

Mendel also studied the inheritance of two pairs of contrasting
characters, that is, dihybrid inheritance. If a tall pea plant with
round seeds is crossed with a dwarf plant with wrinkled seeds, all
the plants in the F_1 are tall and have round seeds. If members of the
F_1 are self pollinated the seeds give rise to tall plants with round
seeds, tall plants with wrinkled seeds, dwarf plants with round seeds
and dwarf plants with wrinkled seeds, in the proportions of approximately $9:3:3:1$. Examination of the F_1 shows that tall and
round are dominant. The proportions obtained in the F_2 can only be
explained if plants of the F_1 produce four different types of gamete,
those carrying genes for tall and round (TR), tall and wrinkled (Tr),
dwarf and round (tR), dwarf and wrinkled (tr). Remembering that
there will be four kinds of pollen grains and four kinds of eggs and
that fusion between them is a matter of chance, there are 16 possible combinations of gametes as shown in the chequerboard in figure
117. A count of the squares should make it clear how the
$9:3:3:1$ ratio arises.

Mendel's Second Law

Mendel's Second Law or Law of Independent Assortment states
that when two pure bred individuals showing two or more pairs of
contrasting characters are crossed the characters segregate out independently in the F_2 generation.

Mendel knew nothing of meiosis but it can now be seen that his
laws can be explained by meiosis if the genes for one pair of
homologous chromosomes and the genes for a second pair of

characters lie on another pair of homologous chromosomes.

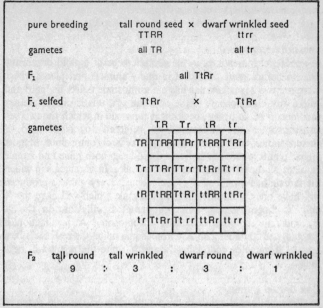

Figure 117. Mendel's experiments on the inheritance of two pairs of contrasting characters in peas (Dihybrid inheritance)

The basis of heredity

Linkage

There are cases when Mendel's Second Law does not appear to be true, the genes do not segregate and assort independently. The first exception was found by Bateson and Punnett in 1906, they crossed races of sweet peas, one with purple flowers and long pollen grains with a second having red flowers and round pollen, purple flowers and long pollen grains being dominant. They did not obtain the expected 9 : 3 : 3 : 1 ratio but found the combination of characters present in the parents appeared more frequently than expected. Morgan found the same problem in 1910 when working with the fruit fly *Drosophila*. It appears that some characters tend to remain in the same combinations and are transmitted together, it is now known that this is because they are on the same chromosome, they are linked and the phenomenon is linkage. This does not mean they can never become separated but that this occurs less frequently. The genes separate during meiosis if it so happens that a chiasma forms between them (see page 238).

Sex determination

In general chromosomes in the somatic cells of diploid organisms exist in homologous pairs, but in many animals and plants where there are two sexes, one sex has a chromosome unlike its 'pair' and unlike any chromosome in the opposite sex, this is one of the sex chromosomes. In many species it is the male in which the two sex chromosomes are different and referred to as X and Y chromosomes, the female having a pair of X chromosomes. In most higher plants where one individual produces both male and female gametes all the chromosomes occur in pairs. In organisms in which the female has a pair of X chromosomes, every gamete produced will have one X chromosome; in the male which will have the X and Y chromosomes, half the gametes will contain the X chromosome the other half the Y chromosome. At fertilization, if the gametes containing an X chromosome unite, the result will be a female, if gametes containing X and Y unite the result will be a male.

Sex linked genes

In *Drosophila*, red eye is dominant to white. If the wild red-eyed type is crossed with a white-eyed the results depend on whether the cross is of a white male with a red female or a red male with a white female; in other words the results depend on the sex of the parent in which the character is introduced, a phenomenon not encountered previously. If a white male is crossed with a red female the offspring are red-eyed and there are equal proportions of male and female. If a red male is crossed with a white female the offspring consist of red-eyed females and white-eyed males in equal proportion. The results can be explained if the genes for eye colour are carried on the X chromosome and not on the Y chromosome, as shown in figure 118.

A more complex situation arises in cats where the gene for coat colour is carried on the X chromosome. If fusion occurs between two gametes each carrying the X chromosome, but one with a gene for black coat and the other with a gene for ginger coat, the result is an offspring with a tortoiseshell coat and as the two X chromosomes will result in a female, tortoiseshell cats are always female, a male of this type is unknown (see figure 119 also Dominance page 263).

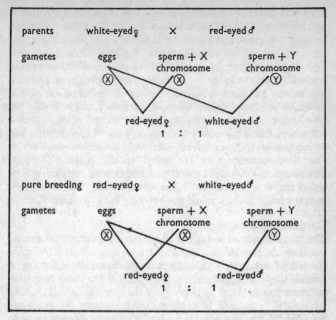

Figure 118. Sex linkage involving eye colour in Drosophila

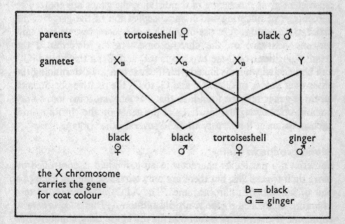

Figure 119. Sex linkage involving coat colour in cats

These principles of sex linkage apply to other organisms. A similar situation arises with colour blindness in man. If a colour blind man marries a normal woman all the children are normal, if a colour blind woman marries a normal man all the sons will be colour blind and all the daughters normal; these daughters, however, are carriers and will be able to transmit colour blindness to their sons. The gene for colour blindness is carried on the X chromosome and is recessive to normal colour vision, it will only manifest itself when the X chromosome carrying the gene for normal colour vision is absent, that is in the male which has only one X chromosome and in the homozygous recessive female. Most sex linked genes are on the X chromosome, so sex linked usually means X linked. Haemophilia, a disease in which the blood clotting mechanism is inadequate, is a serious sex-linked disease which affected several Royal families in Europe and can be traced back to Queen Victoria.

Chromosome maps

The phenomenon of linkage in which genes for certain characters occur on the same chromosome affords an opportunity to discover the relative positions of these genes on the chromosome, for during meiosis they will sometimes become separated due to the formation of a chiasma followed by breakage of the chromatids and crossing over. It is reasonable to suppose that the nearer the genes are together the less likelihood there is of a chiasma forming between them and of the genes becoming separated; thus the determination of the percentage of offspring which show separation of the characters gives a measure of the distance the genes are apart. The percentage of offspring which show separation of the genes is the **cross-over value**. A cross-over value of 1% represents one unit (or one Morgan) on the chromosome. Having determined the relative positions of these two genes (G_1 and G_2) a third gene (G_3) can be selected which is linked with the first two; by determining the cross-over values of G_1 to G_3 and G_2 to G_3 the relative positions of all three genes may be found. In this way chromosome maps may be built up showing the locations of the genes on the chromosome, such maps exist for *Drosophila* and several other organisms.

Blood groups in man

Sometimes a particular character in an individual is controlled by more than two alleles, but there are only two sites, one on each of a pair of homologous chromosomes. The ABO blood group system in man is controlled by the **multiple alleles** A, B and O. Where A is present the antigen A is found in the red blood cells, similarly B is responsible for the production of the B antigen, O results in no antigen being produced (see page 147). Obviously only two alleles will be present in any individual and the following combinations are possible; AA, AB, BB, BO, AB, OO. A and B have the same degree of dominance, they are **co-dominants**, but both are dominant to O. Persons with AA or AO belong to the blood group A, those with BB or BO belong to blood group B, where the alleles A and B are present the person is of blood group AB, and persons with OO belong to blood group O. The blood groups are inherited according to Mendel's laws.

Dominance

The characteristics studies by Mendel showed the phenomenon of complete dominance, and the occurrence of co-dominance has been mentioned in connection with the blood groups in man. There are, however, all degrees of dominance; for example, a cross between red and white antirrhinums results in pink flowered members of the F_1, the red showing only **partial dominance**. Similarly crossing red short horned cattle with white produces roan in the F_1, the coat being made up of a mixture of red and white hairs.

In man a rare inherited condition may be present in which the red blood cells are crescent shaped and contain an abnormal haemoglobin, the so-called sickle cell in which the oxygen carrying capacity is greatly reduced giving rise to the generally fatal sickle cell anaemia. Of more common occurrence is the condition in which about 35% of the red blood cells are abnormal with an accompanying slight anaemia. These conditions are known among African tribes, and in southern India, Greece and Italy. It can be explained if it is assumed that the fatal sickle cell anaemia is associated with the homozygous condition, the other being found in the heterozygote in which the gene for normal blood is not completely dominant to the sickle cell type. An interesting correlation has been found between the sickle cell condition and the resistance to malaria. Individuals heterozygous for sickle cell are more resistant to malaria than normal individuals or those homozygous for sickle cell, therefore in areas where malaria is rife there will be a selection pressure in favour of the heterozygotes.

Lethal combinations of genes

The seeds of some cereal plants sometimes produce seedlings which are white and spindly and soon die because they lack essential chlorophyll. If the seeds from such plants are sown and the green seedlings and white seedlings are counted the numbers approximate to the 3 : 1 ratio. An explanation would be that the parent plant was heterozygous having a gene for chlorophyll production which was dominant and a recessive gene for its absence: when selfed one quarter of the seedlings would be homozygous for absence of chlorophyll, obviously a lethal condition. In this example the effect of the lethal combination can be seen, but in animals a lethal combination of genes is often manifested by the death of the embryos so that the expected ratios from certain matings are not obtained. In house mice the yellow variety is never found in the homozygous condition; matings between yellow mice produce yellow offspring and black, brown or grey offspring in the ratio of 2 : 1. If a yellow mouse is mated with a non-yellow about half the offspring are yellow and half non-yellow, a ratio to be expected if the yellow parent was heterozygous. Matings between yellow mice give smaller litters and dead embryos amounting to about one quarter of the total number of offspring have been found in the body of the female, it seems that the homozygous yellow die at an early stage of development.

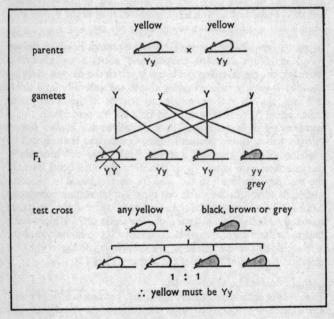

Figure 120. A lethal combination of genes in mice

The expression and interaction of genes
There are cases in which genes belonging to different pairs of alleles,

when present in the same organism, produce a particular character even though they are inherited independently in the Mendelian manner. The first example of this kind was discovered during experiments on the inheritance of the form of the comb in fowls. Common varieties of poultry have a characteristic comb shape which breeds true. The shapes are described as rose, pea, and single comb. Crosses between rose and single showed rose to be dominant, the F_1 generation being all rose comb and the F_2 producing rose and single in the ratio of 3 : 1. Crosses between pea and single showed pea to be dominant and the F_2 showed the simple 3 : 1 ratio of pea to single. In crosses between rose and pea, however, the F_1 generation showed a new form of comb described as walnut, and when members of the F_1 were crossed all four types of comb appeared in the ratio of 9 walnut : 3 rose : 3 pea : 1 single. This is the ratio to be expected in the F_2 from a dihybrid cross where two different characters in the parents are considered. The results can be explained by the interaction of two pairs of alleles, say Rr and Pp. When R and P are present together the result is a walnut comb, R alone gives rise to a rose comb, P alone to a pea comb, while the

parents rose × pea
RRpp rrPP

gametes Rp rP

F_1 RrPp

RrPp × RrPp

gametes ♂ → RP Rp rP rp
♀ ↓

F_2

♀ \ ♂	RP	Rp	rP	rp
RP	RRPP walnut	RRPp walnut	RrPP walnut	RrPp walnut
Rp	RRPp walnut	RRpp rose	RrPp walnut	Rrpp rose
rP	RrPP walnut	RrPp walnut	rrPP pea	rrPp pea
rp	RrPp walnut	Rrpp rose	rrPp pea	rrpp single

Figure 121. Gene interaction in comb form inheritance in fowls

recessive r and p together produce a single comb.

The chemical nature of a gene

Genes determine the characteristics of an individual, and characteristics are handed on to the next generation, therefore genes must be capable of carrying information and they must have some means of replication. Search began for a chemical substance which could carry information and be able to replicate itself; in 1944 nucleic acid was suggested as being such a substance. **Deoxyribonucleic acid** is found in the nucleus of cells and **ribonucleic acid** mainly in the cytoplasm. Nucleic acid consists of **nucleotides** which are themselves composed of **phosphoric acid, a 5-carbon (pentose) sugar** and an **organic base** (see page 61). The manner in which these components are assembled in DNA was a mystery until Watson and Crick put forward their hypothesis in 1953 that DNA consists of two parallel chains coiled to form a **double helix,** the two chains being linked at intervals which correspond to a nucleotide, one complete turn of the helix being completed for every length of ten nucleotides. Watson and Crick suggested that the side chains are made up of alternate phosphate and sugar groups, the links being composed of organic bases arranged in such a way that they point inwards and link up, adenine (A) with thymine (T) and cytosine (C) with guanine (G) (see figures 122 and 22). The sequence in which these bases occur along the chain is different in different species and varies among individuals of

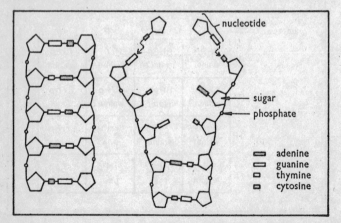

Figure 122. A short length of DNA and its replication

the same species. It is this particular sequence which carries with it coded instructions determining the organism's development. Although only four different bases are involved, a nucleic acid molecule may contain several million nucleotides giving an almost infinite number of possible combinations.

The replication of DNA

The suggested structure for DNA makes it easy to see how DNA could replicate, all that is required is the presence of free nucleotides and the breaking of the weak bonds between the bases in the DNA, the free nucleotides could then take up appropriate positions on the broken links making a complete new double helix from the half on each side, rather like unzipping a zip fastener and supplying a new half zip of the appropriate shape to each half of the original. Kornberg has shown that if DNA is added to a solution containing free nucleotides and the necessary enzyme, additional DNA is formed containing the same relative proportions of the different bases as in the original DNA; this provides supporting evidence that replication has occurred but does not indicate how it takes place.

Meselsohn and Stahl carried out experiments in which bacteria were grown on a medium containing a heavy isotope of nitrogen ^{15}N in place of the normal ^{14}N until all the DNA had become labelled with the heavy nitrogen. They were then fed on a medium with normal nitrogen and samples were taken at intervals. DNA

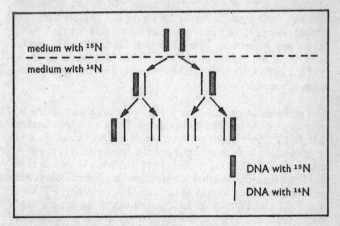

Figure 123. Meselsohn and Stahl's experiment

with ^{15}N is heavier then DNA with ^{14}N and the two can be separated by a high speed centrifuge. In the first generation there was only one kind of DNA and its density was midway between the figures expected if the DNA contained all ^{14}N or all ^{15}N, showing that it contained equal amounts of each. In the second generation there were two kinds of DNA, one containing only ^{14}N and the other identical with that found in the first generation, that is containing equal amounts of ^{14}N and ^{15}N. These experiments confirm the **zip fastener hypothesis** of DNA replication (see figure 123).

Protein synthesis

There is experimental evidence to show that genes control the production of enzymes. Enzymes are responsible for the chemical reactions in a cell which collectively make up the cell's metabolism and they are themselves protein in nature. Therefore it seems reasonable to suppose that in some way DNA controls protein synthesis.

Proteins are made up of amino acids, there may be several hundreds in a single molecule, the amino acids themselves, of which there are over twenty types, being arranged in a precise sequence in the protein molecule. There are only four different bases in the DNA molecule, therefore more than one must be involved in the synthesis of an amino acid or only four different amino acids would be formed. The involvement of two bases arranged in all the possible 16 combinations would enable 16 different amino acids to be synthesized, still not enough. Three bases give the possibility of 64 different arrangements, far in excess of the requirements. The arrangement of three bases then could form a code for the production of any amino acid. This is known as the **triplet code** and the sequence of three bases which forms a code for a particular amino acid is a **codon**. The codon is written using the initial letters of the bases concerned.

The synthesis of protein takes place in the cytoplasm of the cell whereas DNA is confined to the nucleus. There is evidence to show that DNA brings about the synthesis of RNA (ribonucleic acid) which escapes from the nucleus into the cytoplasm, it is known as **messenger RNA**. RNA is similar to DNA but it is a single chain and it contains the 5-carbon sugar, ribose, in place of deoxyribose and the base uracil instead of thymine. The messenger RNA will bear the coded instructions for the synthesis of one protein which may contain 250 amino acids and each will involve a code of three bases, so a length of DNA corresponding to 750 bases must have been involved in the synthesis of the messenger RNA. This length will also correspond to the length of the gene responsible for the synthesis of this particular protein. It has been suggested that the DNA 'unzips' in the region of one gene and that individual nucleotides which are components of RNA assemble themselves opposite one of the exposed DNA strands, cytosine joining with guanine and adenine with uracil. Once formed it becomes detached and leaves the nucleus, in character it will have the same sequence of bases as one of the strands of the DNA apart from the fact that uracil has replaced thymine. In the cytoplasm the RNA becomes attached to a **ribosome** and it is here that the assembly of the amino acids into a protein takes place.

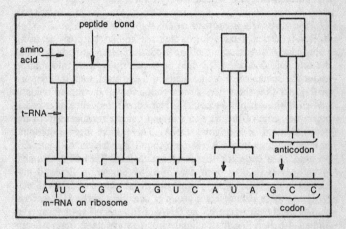

Figure 124. Diagram to show amino acids being assembled into polypeptides at a ribosome

In the cytoplasm are relatively short molecules of nucleic acid known as **transfer RNA,** they consist of about 70 nucleotides and there is one kind of transfer RNA for each kind of amino acid. It has been suggested that a transfer RNA molecule has three un-paired bases at one end forming an **anticodon** which is capable of connecting up with a codon, three bases on the messenger RNA where the sequence is right. The other end of the transfer RNA becomes attached to its particular amino acid. In this way transfer RNA molecules will link up with their appropriate amino acids then attach themselves to the messenger RNA at points which corres-pond to their codon, thus the amino acids will line up in the correct order corresponding to the coded sequence in the messenger RNA. **Peptide bonds** then link neighbouring amino acids to form polypeptides which peel off the line of transfer RNA molecules. The transfer RNA molecules then become detached fror ᵗʰe messenger RNA.

Electron microscopy studies have revealed that ribosomes occur in groups of up to 50 connected by a strand of RNA, the group being called a polysome. It has been suggested that a procession of ribosomes travel along a messenger RNA strand, each synthesizing a polypeptide chain. Briefly then, the DNA contains information in code which is copied on to messenger RNA and carried to the cytoplasm where it is translated.

Working out the structure of DNA

If DNA carries a code for proteins it should be possible using knowledge of the structure of the proteins to learn something about the original code. First it would be necessary to have information about the sequence of amino acids in the protein, then making use of the fact that the letters of the codon for all the amino acids is known (although not necessarily their correct sequence) it is possible to go some of the way to working out the arrangement of the nucleotides in the original DNA. There have been additional problems, for example, it has been found that triplets of bases can be used as a code for the same amino acid. Two new chemical techniques have now been developed by Sanger in England and Gilbert in the U.S.A. for working out the structure of DNA directly. Using these techniques a group of scientists in the U.S.A. have elucidated the structure of the DNA of the animal virus known as Simian 40. It is the first animal virus to have its structure determined and the DNA molecule has been found to contain 5226 nucleotides. Virus particles consist of a strand of DNA within a protein coat; when the virus infects a cell the viral DNA enters the cell causing it to manufacture proteins for the virus. In the case of Simian 40, the virus prompts the cell to synthesize four proteins, three of which are used to make protein coats for new virus particles while the fourth upsets the normal functioning of the cell.

Key terms

Alleles Contrasting forms of a gene situated on comparable regions of homologous chromosomes.
Anticodon A sequence of three bases capable of linking with a codon found on transfer RNA.

Chromosome Thread-like structure consisting of DNA and protein found in the nucleus of a cell.

Codon A sequence of three bases forming a code for a specific amino acid found on messenger RNA.

Dihybrid inheritance Inheritance of two pairs of contrasting characters.

DNA Deoxyribonucleic acid, inherited material carrying coded instructions for the organism's development.

Dominant (gene) The one with most influence in a pair of alleles.

F_1 (First filial generation) The first generation from a cross.

F_2 (Second filial generation) The generation produced by crossing members of the F_1.

Gene Part of a chromosome responsible for a particular character in an organism.

Genotype The genetic constitution of an organism.

Heterozygote Organism with two contrasting genes for the same character.

Homozygote Organism with two similar genes for the same character.

Lethal genes Combination of genes causing death of an organism.

Linkage The occurrence of genes on the same chromosome.

Locus Position on a chromosome occupied by a gene.

Monohybrid inheritance Inheritance of one pair of contrasting characters.

Multiple alleles A number of alternate forms of a gene.

Phenotype The characters shown by an organism.

Recessive (gene) The one with least influence in a pair of alleles.

RNA Ribonucleic acid, inherited material in some viruses, but mainly concerned in translating DNA code into proteins.

Triplet code Sequence of three bases in DNA forming a code for an amino acid.

Chapter 14
Evolution

The **theory of organic evolution** is that present species of plants and animals have developed from earlier forms by natural selection over a long period of time. This is in contrast to the theory of special creation, that is the belief in the literal truth of the biblical account of the Book of Genesis. The ideas put forward by **Darwin** and **Wallace** in 1858 in their paper 'A Theory of Evolution by Natural Selection', and in the following year by Darwin in his book 'On the Origin of Species by means of Natural Selection', caused prolonged controversy. Darwin presented evidence in support of evolution having taken place and put forward a hypothesis for the mechanism of evolution. Since Darwin's time much additional supporting evidence has accumulated.

Evidence in support of evolution

Geographical evidence
Wallace made a survey of the world's mammals and birds and he showed that the percentage of endemic species was twice as great in South America, Africa and Australia as it was in North America, Europe and Asia. He attributed the difference to geographical isolation. It has been suggested that modern mammals arose in Asia and migrated across Europe, and North America across what is now the Bering Strait, and from the Northern Hemisphere to South America, Africa and Australia during distant geological times when it is known that land bridges existed. Australia then became isolated in the Cretaceous period and later the Atlantic broke through forming the Straits of Gibraltar cutting one connection with Africa. As South America has the largest number of endemic species it seems likely that the continent was cut off for a long period, for once the group of animals was isolated it evolved independently into forms suited to a variety of habitats, and it would be expected that the group isolated for the longest period would show the greatest differences from other groups.

Darwin visited the Galapagos Islands in 1835 during his long voyage on the Beagle. These volcanic islands show the result of geographical isolation for their fauna is unique; there are giant iguanas, giant tortoises (now sadly greatly depleted in numbers) and 13 species of finches which Darwin found of absorbing interest. The finches show a variety of adaptations to exploit all possible sources of food on the islands; stout beaks for seed crushing, curved beaks for fruit eaters, slender beaks for insect eaters and so on. On the mainland the one species of finch is a seed eater, other food sources being exploited by other species of birds. Isolation need not be solely due to separation of land masses or the formation of new islands but may be due to natural barriers such as deserts or mountain ranges.

Anatomical evidence

The structural similarities between certain groups of animals or plants suggest a common ancestry. **Comparative anatomy** is the study of structural similarities and differences upon which relationships may be based and possible lines of evolution indicated. Structures which are basically similar are said to be **homologous**, the **pentadactyl limb** is one of the best examples of homology, it is found in amphibians, reptiles, birds and mammals and has undergone a variety of modifications, for example, to become adapted for different kinds of locomotion, as in the leg of a horse, the flipper of a whale and the wing of a bird, or for manipulation as in man or for digging as in the mole. The evolution of all these different forms from the basic pentadactyl limb is an example of **adaptive radiation**. Darwin's finches are an excellent example of adaptive radiation, other examples are shown by the mouthparts of insects, from the chewing form as in the locust to the sucking form of the butterfly or bee, or the piercing and sucking apparatus of the mosquito. These adaptive radiations result in organisms able to exploit a variety of food materials and fill available ecological niches; this gradual spreading out of the organisms is **divergent evolution**.

The presence of **vestigial structures** may indicate the relationship of an organism to a group and indicate a common ancestor, as in the whale which has the remains of a pelvic girdle but no hind limb. The possession of apparently similar structures needs careful investigation before the organisms to which they belong are pronounced as related, for structures which perform the same task are likely to be similar in some respects, for example, the legs of arthropods and mammals have a similar function but their construction is very different; they are examples of **analogous** not homologous structures and they show **convergent evolution**. An even more striking example of convergent evolution is shown by the

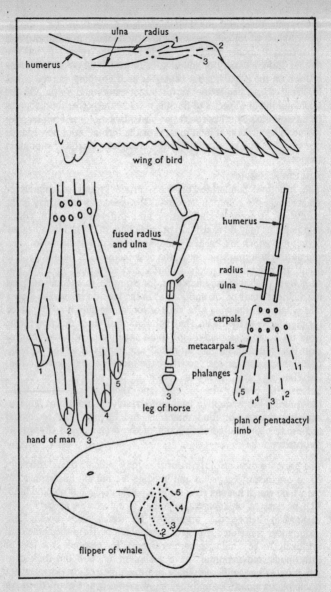

Figure 125. Homologous pentadactyl limbs in vertebrates

eye of a mammal and an octopus, structures which are very similar but have been shown to have evolved in quite a different way. Where it can be shown that one anatomical arrangement has obviously been derived from another it is an indication of evolutionary affinity, in some cases a whole series can be built up as in the case of the heart and arterial arches in vertebrates. However, no one piece of evidence should be considered in isolation for a study of the homologous series of hearts and arterial arches in vertebrates although clearly indicating the evolutionary pathway

$$fish \rightarrow amphibians \rightarrow reptiles \rightarrow birds$$

also shows a closer affinity between mammals and amphibians than between mammals and reptiles, which contradicts the fossil record. As the fossil record represents animals living at the time it has to be assumed that the reptiles from which mammals are believed to have evolved had a different blood circulation from that found today, in fact more like modern amphibians.

Taxonomic evidence
Taxonomy is the study of classification. Organisms are usually classified on the basis of homologous features with due consideration being given to any other relevant evidence, such a natural classification will inevitably reveal evolutionary affinities or phylogenetic relationships. The classification of animals is more satisfactory than that of plants where the origins of higher plants and the relationships between them are more obscure. By constructing a natural classification an evolutionary tree is being expressed at the same time.

Embryological evidence
Sometimes phylogenetic relationships are not obvious from examination of the adult organism, but they may be exhibited by the embryos or larval stages, for example, the sea squirt is only shown to belong to the chordates by the presence of a notochord and other chordate features in the larval stage. Similarly adult annelids and molluscs are most unlike but both have trochophore larvae, small organisms with a belt of cilia and other characteristic features indicating that the phyla had common ancestry. Vertebrate embryos are similar in their early stages, showing the presence of a tail and gill clefts.

Biochemical evidence
The basic similarity in the structure of cells and in their biochemistry points back to a common ancestry; the similarity of the steps of the process of respiration, for example, is striking.

Nucleic acids are common to all living organisms and the carbohydrate, cellulose, is found in most plants. The presence of a particular chemical substance may be taken as indicative of a relationship which may be confirmed by other evidence. For example the physiologically active alkaloids, complex bases containing nitrogen are confined to a few orders of dicotyledons, sometimes a particular alkaloid is found in only one order or even genus. Each one of a number of distinct species of *Aconitum* contains a particular alkaloid but they are all closely related chemical compounds. Thus a study of an organism's biochemistry is a useful aid in establishing a phylogenetic relationship. In animals, the four blood pigments show an interesting distribution. Three including haemoglobin contain iron in the molecule, the fourth, haemocyanin, contains copper and is found in many molluscs and crustaceans. Haemoglobin is present in all vertebrates and some invertebrates, of the other two iron-containing pigments one is confined to polychaete worms and the other to some minor invertebrate groups. Wilson and Sarich have determined the sequence of amino acids in haemoglobin and have shown that it is the same in man and the chimpanzee and that it differs by two amino acids in man and the gorilla, and by twelve amino acids in man and monkey, this strongly suggests that man and chimpanzee had a common ancestor more recently than man and gorilla or man and monkey.

Serological studies or precipitin tests give useful information about possible affinities between organisms if it is assumed that related organisms are more likely to have similar blood proteins, and that the more unlike the proteins are the more distant is likely to be the relationship. If, for example, human serum is injected into a rabbit the animal produces antibodies against it in the plasma, these antibodies when mixed with human serum will produce a precipitate. The reaction of these antibodies with the serum of other animals can then be studied and compared with their reaction with human serum. A similar degree of precipitation would indicate that the proteins of the blood serum were closely related to those of man, the less precipitate formed the more distant the relationship. Tests carried out in this way by Nuttall indicate that the blood of man is most closely related to the chimpanzee, a result in line with other evidence. However, serological tests alone should not be regarded as conclusive evidence.

More than half of our evolutionary history concerns microorganisms and our knowledge of evolutionary pathways in these distant times is very scanty indeed, any knowledge we are likely to gain will probably come from the field of molecular biology. Work on the molecular structure of several proteins including ferrodoxin and cytochrome c, from a variety of different micro-organisms has been carried out by Schwartz and Dayhoff (1978). Based on the assumption that closely related macromolecules come from closely related species they have produced a suggested reconstruction of the early evolution of micro-organisms.

Evidence from comparative parasitology

Baer and Clay have shown that comparative parasitology can be used to show affinity between different hosts. Parasites, particularly endoparasites live in a habitat where conditions are constant and therefore any evolutionary change will take place slowly, the host however is exposed to changing conditions in the environment which are likely to result in evolution proceeding at a faster rate. This means that parasites can still show close affinities while their hosts show evolutionary divergence. The tapeworm *Bertiella studeri* is a parasite of man, apes and New World monkeys who it seems must have all derived from the same ancestral stock. The body louse *Pedicularis* which parasitizes man is found on only one other host, the chimpanzee.

Fossil evidence

Palaentology, the study of fossils, has provided the only direct evidence that evolution has taken place and it has enabled information to be gained about the structure of a large variety of animals and plants which lived at some time during the last 550 million years. Fossils can be formed in a number of ways, the most common is that the organic matter has been replaced by mineral material, usually only the harder parts becoming fossilized as the softer parts decay too quickly. Bones and shells are the commonest fossils but wood and accumulations of plant debris, such as that which collects where the flow of water in a stream is impeded, may become petrified, that is silica replaces the original structure in such a way that details of cellular structure can be observed. In other cases a complete organism may be buried in mud and decay leaving a mould which may become filled with other material. Other common fossils are impressions of structures such as leaves, stems and scales which have been trapped in layers of deposit and have decayed leaving an outline and perhaps an imprint of some prominent features. Less commonly, insects have been found preserved in amber, the fossilized resin of ancient pine trees; carcasses of an elephant, mammoth and woolly rhinoceros with intact internal organs and fur have been recovered from the frozen wastes of

Siberia. Lastly, the acid and anaerobic conditions existing in peat deposits result in decay proceeding only very slowly, so that the plant remains of which it is composed remain identifiable. Considerable information about past vegetation has been built up by examination of plant fragments and pollen grains from different peat deposits and different depths in the deposits.

When fossils occur in sedimentary rock, clearly, excluding any geological upheavals, those found near the top of the deposits are the most recent, and it has been possible in the case of some animals, notably the horse, to trace the evolution of the modern animal from early ancestors. The early ancestor of the horse was a small animal now named *Hyracotherium* which lived about 50 million years ago in North America; unlike the modern horse it had well developed toes, the fossil record shows that it gradually increased in size and that the third digit became longer and stouter while the others became reduced, until we have the modern horse standing four times as high and walking literally on tip-toe. Such a series of fossils as that showing the evolution of the horse does not in itself tell us anything about the length of time this process has taken or the age of the different fossil stages but with the help of other information Simpson calculated that the modern horse was the culmination of evolution over 60 million years and 15 million generations.

Dating the rocks Nearly all known elements exist in several **isotopic forms**, that is atoms having the same atomic number (same number of protons) but different atomic masses (different numbers of neutrons). Calcium, for example, has eight isotopes with different atomic masses. The atomic mass of an element is given as an average of the relative masses of all the isotopes of that element. Many elements have isotopes which are unstable, they are **radioactive** and decay until they reach a stable form. Radioactive isotopes give out different kinds of rays; when a uranium atom of atomic mass 238 gives out an **alpha ray** it loses two protons and two neutrons and becomes an atom of thorium with a different atomic number and mass. The thorium atom then gives off a **beta ray** which results in one neutron changing into a proton; this process of **decay** continues with alpha and beta rays being given off until eventually non-radioactive lead is formed. It takes 4510 million years for half of any given quantity of uranium 238 to change into thorium and other members of the series, thus it is said that the **half-life** of uranium 238 is $4 \cdot 51 \times 10^9$ years. With the passage of time therefore, rocks with uranium become less radioac-

	PERIOD	BEGAN (MILLIONS OF YEARS.)	ANIMAL	PLANTS
Cainozoic	Recent	1	modern mammals man	flowering plants dominant
Cainozoic	Pleistocene			
Cainozoic	Pliocene			
Cainozoic	Miocene			
Cainozoic	Oligocene		birds and placental mammals	
Cainozoic	Eocene			
Mesozoic	Cretaceous	70 / 135	extinction of dinosaurs and ammonites	beginning of dominance of flowering plants
Mesozoic	Jurassic		reptiles dinosaurs } dominant first birds and mammals	
Mesozoic	Triassic	220	first dinosaurs	conifers dominant
Palaeozoic	Permian	300	reptiles	
Palaeozoic	Carboniferous	350	first reptiles amphibians	pteridophytes dominant
Palaeozoic	Devonian	400	first amphibians bony fish	first trees
Palaeozoic	Silurian		first land arthropods	first land plants
Palaeozoic	Ordovician	500	first vertebrates brachiopods and cephalopods dominant	
Palaeozoic	Cambrian	600	all invertebrate phyla trilobites and brachiopods dominant	algae
Palaeozoic	Pre-cambrian			blue-green algae and bacteria

Figure 126. Geological periods and major groups of organisms

tive and accumulate more lead, so we have a means of estimating the age of the rock. More convenient from the point of view of dating fossils is the decay of a radioactive potassium isotope to argon, potassium being a common element in rocks, or for more recent fossils which have some remaining organic matter, the decay of radioactive ^{14}C with a half-life of 5000 years.

Some organisms have remained almost unchanged throughout tens of millions of years, others show steady changes and once the age of these various stages is known their presence in other rocks is an aid to dating. The molluscs known as **ammonites** are very common fossils and their suture pattern shows progressive complexity from the Devonian period to the Jurassic so they are useful in dating upper Palaeozoic and Mesozoic rocks. Similarly the **trilobites** are useful for dating rocks of the lower Palaeozoic period. Occasionally living animals and plants are discovered which were known previously only as fossils and were thought to be extinct. Such is the case with the coelacanth, a primitive fish, fossils of which date from the Devonian period 300 million years ago, and are found little changed up to Cretaceous times. A living specimen was caught off the South African coast in 1938 and since then a few other specimens have been found. Coelacanths are the only known survivors of a group closely related to the lobe-finned fish which are believed to have contained ancestors of land vertebrates. Another living fossil is the maidenhair tree (*Ginkgo biloba*), native to parts of China; from fossilized remains in Jurassic, Cretaceous and Tertiary rocks it seems to have been abundant during these times.

The evidence of artificial selection
Most of the domestic animals and the crop plants in existence have been bred by man from carefully selected stock, for example, new varieties of cereal have been bred with increased yield, greater resistance to disease, stronger stems or other desirable qualities. Cattle have been bred for increased milk yield or muscle for meat production. Similarly there are breeds of dog suitable as guard dogs, guide dogs, gun dogs and so on, together with many breeds popular as pets. Many of these breeds would never survive in the wild. If all this can be done by man it provides evidence that it could have taken place in nature.

The mechanism of evolution

Darwin and Wallace are responsible for the theory of evolution by natural selection, they believed that natural selection takes place in the following way:—

1. More offspring are born than survive, therefore there must be **competition for survival**.

2. Offspring show variations and some will be more suited to survive than others and these will be the ones likely to produce offspring. **(The survival of the fittest)**

3. Variations will be passed on to the offspring and in time there will be an accumulation of favourable variations such that there will be a divergence from the original stock producing new forms. **(The origin of species)**

Darwin v. Lamarck

Lamarck in contrast to Darwin believed that variations were acquired during the lifetime of the individual and passed on to the offspring. To illustrate the difference between the theories of Darwin and Lamarck the example provided by the giraffe is usually quoted. In the course of evolution the fossil record shows that the neck of the giraffe has got progressively longer. Lamarck would have explained that in the competition for food the giraffe stretched its neck to browse leaves from higher branches and that this slightly increased neck length was passed on to its offspring, the same process being repeated generation after generation. Darwin would have said that giraffes are born with slight variations in neck length among them and that those with longest necks would have an advantage in the struggle for food and would therefore tend to survive to pass this advantage on to their offspring whereas the giraffes with shorter necks would tend to die out.

Variation

Variations which occur in a population may be due to diet or other environmental factors or they may be due to genetic differences or both. Variations are of two types, **continuous** and **discontinuous**, the former show an even gradation in a population, in the latter individuals will fall into two or more distinct groups as with Mendel's tall and dwarf peas. Height in man is an example of a continuous variation; if height is measured in an adult human population and a histogram constructed by counting the number of individuals whose height falls within a chosen range, each range decided upon being equal, it will show a curve of **normal distribution** (Gaussian curve). This does not mean that a character showing a normal distribution is necessarily controlled by the environment completely. In the case of a discontinuous variation the distinct groups may differ in a gene as with the peas in Mendel's experiment, but in the tall group and in the dwarf group there was a variation in height which showed continuous variation. Other genes or differences in environment may account for this variation. Height in man is known to be partly genetically controlled, the range of heights shown by the Tutsi and Pygmies of central Africa which scarcely overlap, indicate this. A character which is partly genetically controlled and shows continuous variation is believed to be controlled by many genes, each contributing to the character, it is said to be **polygenetic**.

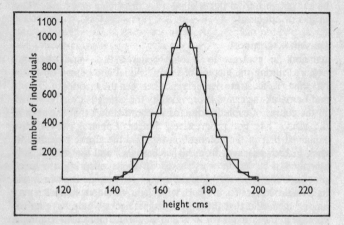

Figure 127. Histogram of height in an adult human population

Variation in organisms comes about as a result of a number of different gametes being produced at meiosis. The number of possible gametes is 2^n where n is the haploid number. At fertilization the number of possible combinations is $(2^n)^2$. Thus with a haploid number of only five the number of possible combinations of gametes is 1024. Added to this there is the possibility of crossing over giving an opportunity for the separation of genes occurring on the same chromosome. However these processes merely reshuffle existing genes.

Mutations

Occasionally an offspring arises having a characteristic quite different from its ancestors, if this new character is capable of being transmitted to future generations it shows that it is the result of change in the genetic material known as a mutation. An individual bearing the new character is a **mutant**. Mutations are responsible for the conditions of haemophilia and chondrodystrophy in man (see pages 258 and 262), the white-eyed type of *Drosophila* and other variants, many trees with copper coloured leaves or weeping forms of growth and various new leaf forms and flower colours such as the striking red sunflower found in Colorado in 1910 which proved to have red colour as a Mendelian dominant. The frequency of mutation varies in different species and in different genes even in the same chromosome, but on average mutations may arise in one or two gametes per 100,000. Most mutations are harmful and are eliminated. If the new gene is dominant and confers an advantage natural selection will operate in its favour and it will spread and in the course of time bring about evolutionary change. Most mutants are, however, recessive and even if potentially advantageous will not be manifested except if brought together in the homozygote, a rare event, so if the gene is not totally lost it can only be expected to spread slowly.

Mutations may be due to **gene changes** or to **chromosome changes**. During meiosis various incidents may occur resulting in chromosome changes; a section of chromosome may become lost (deletion) or turned round (inversion) or become attached to another chromosome (translocation) or may replicate itself (duplication). The sequence of genes in the chromosome will therefore become changed, some of the new arrangements may prove to benefit the organism. Sometimes a gamete may be produced minus one chromosome. homologous pairs having failed to separate at meiosis. Various clinical conditions in man are associated with an extra chromosome, for example, mongolism. If homologous chromosomes fail to separate altogether some gametes may form with the diploid number of chromosomes. Fusion with a haploid gamete will result in a triploid organism. Tetraploids and **polyploids** are known and may be induced artificially by colchicine and other chemicals which interfere with spindle formation. Polyploidy is mainly confined to plants, such plants are usually larger and stronger. **Allopolyploids** are fertile hybrids of two plant species in which the chromosome number has doubled as in the vigorous rice grass *Spartina townsendii* first found in Southampton Water in 1870 and now widespread and invasive. Gene mutations may occur by a change in the sequence of nucleotides in DNA, giving rise to the production of different protein which may have far reaching effects. The change in the sequence may occur by the loss of a nucleotide (deletion), gaining of a nucleotide (insertion), the wrong nucleotide getting into position (substitution) or a change round in the normal sequence (inversion).

Natural selection in action

Industrial melanism

The peppered moth *Biston betularia* is normally pale and speckled but **melanic forms**, dark in colour, were first reported from the Midlands in 1850. The existence of more than one form is polymorphism. Kettlewell investigated the distribution of the light and dark forms in Britain and found that the melanic form had almost replaced the pale form in industrial areas where there was a high incidence of smoke and soot pollution, whereas in the west of the country and in Ireland the pale form was common and the melanic form rare. The moths settle on the trunks of trees where they are preyed upon by insectivorous birds, in sooty areas the melanic form has the advantage in being less conspicuous than the pale form, whereas in the unpolluted areas the pale form is less easily seen against the pale lichen covered tree trunks but the melanic form is conspicuous.

The banded snail

The banded snail *Cephaea nemoralis* occurs in a number of coloured forms, basically yellowish or brownish, and it may be plain or banded. The distribution is such that the ground colour of the snail shell matches the background of vegetation; the plain shells tend to be found in a uniform habitat, the banded forms in mixed habitats such as hedgerows. The mixed population is maintained largely by the activity of thrushes which feed upon the snails, banded snails are more readily seen against a uniform background and tend to be selected, while plain shells are more visible in a varied background than the banded form. In addition it was found that brownish snails tended to be captured in the summer as they showed up against the greener background, while yellowish forms were most clearly seen at other times of the year.

Mimicry

There are instances in which convergent evolution has resulted in unrelated species resembling each other, if some advantage is thus gained it is said to be mimicry. Wasps are dangerous to many animals and they are conspicuously coloured and patterned exhibiting **'warning colouration'**. If a harmless insect resembles the wasp it is less likely to be attacked and therefore has more chance of survival. To achieve this protection it must be found in the same area and have a similar behaviour pattern. The protection works so long as the number of mimics does not exceed the number of models, otherwise the mimics begin to be eaten. The African robber fly, *Hyperechia*, is a large fly which preys upon carpenter bees, *Xylocopa*, the flies so closely resemble the carpenter bees that they can mix with them killing and eating some and laying eggs near the burrow; when the larvae hatch they move into the burrow and feed upon the larvae of the carpenter bees. There are several species of robber fly each species preying upon and closely resembling a particular species of carpenter bee. This close resemblance clearly confers advantage to the fly and must come about by natural selection. Such a degree of resemblance is exceptional; here it is a case of the predator deceiving the prey more usually it is the prey itself deceiving its enemies by resemblance to a more dangerous species. For example, the African egg-eating snake (*Dasypeltis*) varies in colour matching various venomous snakes in different areas between Egypt and the Cape.

Population genetics and the origin of species

Any species tends to exist in units among which interbreeding takes place, these genetic units are known as **demes**. All the different genes in a deme make up its **gene pool**. As the result of inter-breeding there will be a general movement of genes, **gene flow**, within the deme but the overall picture will be unchanged producing a state of **genetic equilibrium** in which the **gene frequency**, that is the frequency of a gene in relation to its alleles, is unchanged. Evolution will only take place if something happens to disturb the equilibrium, this may come in the form of mutations, interbreeding at the boundaries with members of other demes, environmental change or **genetic drift**, that is the fall in frequency of a gene which might occur if individuals carrying the gene failed to reproduce; or a combination of these factors. Once a change has taken place natural selection will ensure that evolution proceeds. Mostly, on the boundaries of a deme there is likely to be some inter-breeding and migration of individuals from other demes which will ensure a common pool of genes such that interbreeding may continue to occur. If a deme should become isolated for any reason any new genes will continue to accumulate within it and selection will result in new genotypes unlike those in the main stock. After a long period of isolation the genotypes will become very different from the common gene pool of the species and should interbreeding take place between a member of the isolated deme and a member of the original stock the offspring may well be sterile. Further isolation will in time result in even interbreeding being impossible, – a new species has arisen.

Biological control

It sometimes happens that a population of organisms builds up becoming a threat to the interests of man in some way. The cultivation of a particular crop plant may result in the build up of pests which attack it. In some cases it has been possible to control the numbers by biological means; a well known example is that of the coconut moth *Levuana iridescens* whose larvae feed upon the leaves of the coconut tree and gradually defoliate them. In the Fiji Islands coconuts were cultivated on all the islands except one where the coconut moth was established. In 1925 the moth showed signs of spreading to other islands and measures had to be taken to prevent the ruin of a valuable crop. A search was made for the natural enemies of the coconut moth but the moth could not be found elsewhere. However, a fly *Ptychomyia remota* was found to parasitize a moth with similar feeding habits, infected larvae were imported and the laboratory-reared flies were found to parasitize coconut moth larvae. The flies were released at intervals and controlled the coconut moth in one year. The flies have not, in turn, become a pest, a potential danger which has been realized in some attempts at biological control.

Key terms

Adaptive radiation The evolution from common stock of divergent forms adapted to different modes of life.
Allopolyploidy A polyploid organism which has received one or more sets of chromosomes from two different species.
Comparative anatomy The study of structural similarities and differences.
Convergent evolution Evolution resulting in the appearance of superficially similar structures in organisms of different ancestry.
Deme Population of similar individuals forming a genetically isolated or almost isolated group.
Divergent evolution The evolution of different forms from common stock.
Endemic (species) One confined to a particular region, e.g. country, continent.
Gene flow Movement of genes within a population as a result of interbreeding.
Gene frequency The frequency of occurrence of a gene in relation to its alleles.
Gene pool The sum total of all the different genes in a deme.
Genetic drift The fall in frequency of occurrence of a gene.

Homology The occurrence of a fundamental similarity of structure in all or part of different organisms.

Melanism The occurrence of melanic or dark forms.

Mimicry Resemblance between unrelated species of animals which confers an advantage to one.

Mutant A gene which has undergone mutation or an individual bearing such a new gene.

Mutation A change in the genetic material.

Natural selection Mechanism of evolutionary change suggested by Darwin.

Organic evolution The development of the present fauna and flora from earlier forms by natural selection over a long period of time.

Palaeontology The study of fossils.

Phylogeny Evolutionary history.

Polyploid Organism, usually a plant, bearing three or more times the normal haploid number of chromosomes.

Serology The study of antigen-antibody reactions.

Taxonomy The study of classification.

Chapter 15
The Environment

Soil

Soil is the superficial outer layer of the Earth's crust, created by weathering and matured by vegetation. All natural soils are stratified, formed of superimposed layers extending from the surface to the subsoil or rock beneath. An examination of the vertical walls of a pit dug down to the subsoil shows a **soil profile** composed of the complete series of layers; the major divisions shown by the profile are **horizons** which are themselves divisible into **zones**. It is the uppermost horizon, the A horizon, which is of the most interest to the biologist, in addition to rock particles it contains humus, living organisms, water and air. The climate, perhaps surprisingly, is the major factor responsible for soil type, particular types of soil are characteristic of particular climates. In a given climate quite different rocks tend to produce a similar type of soil and conversely in different climates the same kind of rock will tend to produce different soils. The distribution of the major plant communities in the world (e.g. coniferous forest, mixed deciduous forest, grassland, tropical rain forest etc.) is determined primarily by climate and therefore they may in turn be related to soil type. The vegetation itself will produce its own effect on the soil in time.

The two most important climatic factors in determining soil type are rainfall and temperature. Heavy rainfall will wash away the smaller particles and deposit them elsewhere as alluvium, or percolate through the soil washing down finer particles and soluble materials as it goes, leaving the upper surface leached (deficient in mineral salts) and coarser textured. Low rainfall will bring minimal change. High temperatures speed up all chemical reactions in the soil and increase evaporation so that there is less water to percolate through. The ratio of precipitation (rainfall) to evaporation is an important index of climate and has profound effects on the type of vegetation. Where the ratio is high the soil is leached and finer particles washed away; where the ratio is low there is little effect of this kind, and where evaporation exceeds rainfall, water containing mineral salts is drawn up through the soil by capillarity.

Mineral matter
Mineral matter in soil consists of particles of **weathered rock**, and

weathered sediments such as clays and sands originally derived from hard rocks by weathering followed by subjection to washing away, deposition and weathering again. Mineral particles 2 to 0·2 mm diameter are designated coarse sand, those in the 0·2 to 0·02 mm diameter are fine sand, silt particles 0·02 to 0·002 mm, and clay consisting of particles less than 0·002 mm in diameter. Mineral matter will be made up of particles in all groups but the nature of the soil is described as coarse sand, fine sand, silt or clay according to which fraction predominates. A good mixture in which plants will grow well is a **loam**. Soil formed by weathering of limestone is very different. The calcium carbonate of which it is largely composed is soluble in weak carbonic acid, formed when rain dissolves carbon dioxide in the air, leaving little almost insoluble material which forms the mineral fraction of other types of soils. This mineral fraction is only decomposed slowly under acid or alkaline conditions giving a variety of mineral salts. Calcium ions in the soil have the property of causing very fine particles to collect together giving a good crumb structure. A good supply of basic ions is essential if the soil is to be capable of supporting a wide variety of plant life, even if the overall reaction of the soil is acid. Most soils in Britain except those derived from limestone are acid.

Most species of plants grow or grow best within a certain **pH** range, for the majority this includes pH7 the neutral point. Some will not tolerate alkaline conditions, these are the **calcifuge** plants of which species of *Sphagnum* moss provide good examples. Other species, the **calcicoles**, are usually found on alkaline soils, for example, dogwood (*Cornus sanguinea*), wayfaring tree (*Viburnum lantana*) and spindle tree (*Euonymus europaeus*). In general the pH value of a soil is the best single indicator of the type of vegetation likely to thrive in it.

Humus

A mature soil contains a quantity of organic material in varying stages of decay arising from plant debris such as fallen leaves, roots and twigs. The decay is brought about by bacteria or fungi often aided by the action of earthworms, and results finally in the liberation of materials which contributed to the building up of the structure initially, such as carbon dioxide, water, nitrates and other mineral salts. Thus, plants and the animal life which feeds upon them merely 'borrow' these materials for their lifetime and the time taken for them to decay. Materials are continuously being recycled, the examples of the **carbon and nitrogen cycles** being most familiar. When organic debris decays rapidly, which takes place if there is an adequate supply of water, oxygen, basic ions and a suitable temperature, a soil favourable to the growth of a variety of plants will result. When conditions exist causing organic matter to decay slowly, the soil is very acid and only acid loving species such as heaths (*Ericaceae*) and sedges grow. This type of raw humus is known as mor, the slow decay takes place by the activity of fungi rather than bacteria and earthworms are absent. Where the ground is waterlogged there will be a deficiency of oxygen and decay is very slow resulting in the accumulation of plant debris forming peat. Mors and bogs are formed where conditions are very acid, fens if the water has drained from limestone and is therefore alkaline. Humus in the soil has water holding properties, it may lead to a darkening of the soil which results in more heat being absorbed, giving a warmer soil, and by its decay it provides materials for new growth.

Environmental conditions that are determined by the physical, chemical and biological characteristics of soil are **edaphic factors**.

Soil sampling

The biologist is likely to be most interested in the effect of the soil on the ground vegetation and for this purpose a sample between the depths of 5 to 30 cm will be most useful. It is taken by means of a soil borer or auger after clearing the ground vegetation and litter. Samples should be put in separate plastic bags and labelled at once.

The **pH** of a soil may readily be determined colorimetrically or by a pH meter. In the field a reasonable result may be obtained by shaking up a portion of the sample with distilled water, allowing it to settle, decanting some of the clear liquid and adding a few drops of Universal Indicator, matching the colour from the chart. Soil samples reluctant to settle when shaken with water may be encouraged to do so by the addition of an equal amount of barium sulphate to the soil.

In the laboratory the **water content** of the sample, which of course is variable, may be determined by placing a weighed quantity in a crucible in an oven at about 105 to 120°C for some hours, cooling in a desiccator, reweighing and repeating the process until a constant weight is reached. The dry soil may be used to determine the **humus content**; the sample is heated to red heat over a bunsen burner to burn off organic matter, cooled in a desiccator and reweighed. The loss in weight representing humus is calculated as a percentage of the dry soil.

The control of populations

In very broad terms climate determines the type of soil, the type of soil is a factor in the distribution of plants which in turn influences the distribution of animals which feed on them. If some members of a species enter a new environment where there is abundant food and an absence of enemies they will flourish and reproduce, the numbers building up rapidly as shown in a normal growth curve. When the environment can support no more an equilibrium is reached between the **birth rate** and the **death rate**. This will apply to any organism capable of living in any particular environment. Various factors operate to prevent overcrowding, an obvious one is a shortage of food or water, other factors may be lack of shelter from enemies or adverse climatic conditions, disease may keep down the numbers owing to the ease with which it may spread through the population when there is overcrowding. Competition for light will result in less successful plants dying out. Some animals conserve for themselves suitable space by the establishment of **territories** which they defend against other members of the species who would be in direct competition with them. For any species in a particular environment there is an **optimum number** which the environment can support, the numbers will fluctuate about this point, when they rise above it factors will operate to reduce the number which may then fall below the optimum but soon builds up again. Suppose there is an area of grassland with rabbits, the rabbits eat the grass and the population builds up, foxes move into the area and prey on the rabbits so that the number of foxes increases but as the result of predation the number of rabbits falls. The increased number of foxes eat more rabbits so the rabbit population falls still further until the foxes cannot catch enough rabbits to feed themselves, the number of foxes then falls and the rabbits freed of some predators build up numbers again. However, even if there were no foxes in the area the number of rabbits would still be controlled but at a different level because in time there would be a shortage of grass and the numbers would fall to a level when the grass would grow again and the rabbits would increase once more. The difference is that with the foxes removed there will be an entirely new set of conditions and a new optimum level for the rabbit population.

Environmental influences that arise from the activities of living organisms as distinct from such influences as climate etc., are **biotic factors**. Man is probably one of the most important of these biotic factors.

The growth of human population

It has been estimated that in the Stone Age, man would have required about 3 to 5 km^2 of land to support himself by hunting, and that the world population at that time was under a quarter of a million. Man was then part of the natural community, the same factors would have operated to keep his numbers in check as they do for other species. 6,000 to 10,000 years ago during the Neolithic revolution when man first began to grow crops and raise stock he turned gradually from being a food gatherer to being a food producer, it then became possible for a greater number of people to be supported by the same area of land, resulting in a world population which may have reached 80 millions. However, this primitive economy would have had all the problems associated with a primitive community today; famine, malnutrition due to a restricted diet and the spread of disease which soon affects numbers of people living together under conditions with a low standard of hygiene. Thus there was from that time a slow population growth reaching, perhaps, 140 millions about the time of Christ and 500 millions in the mid 17th century. The next 200 years to 1850 saw a doubling of the world population to 1,000 millions; what records there are indicate a high birth rate and a high death rate in Britain. After this time two new factors come into operation, the gradual rise in the standard of hygiene and medical care resulting in a lowered death rate, followed by industrialization which brought prosperity and a further decline in the death rate together with a decline in the birth rate.

This pattern seems to have been followed in other industrialized countries in marked contrast to poor countries, usually called the underdeveloped countries, where the birth rate remained high. World population doubled again between 1850 and 1950 and is well on the way to doubling again by the year 2000. This rapid increase is a **population explosion.**

It will be seen that as man has gradually withdrawn from being closely associated with the natural community, his numbers have increased, each new factor setting a new level for the number the environment will support. Clearly, world population is not evenly distributed England being one of the most densely populated countries having about 330 people per km^2. England was one of the first countries to suffer a population explosion, being able as a result of scientific and industrial progress to provide food, material goods and an increasing standard of health, any population pressure being reduced by emigration to other lands with more available living space.

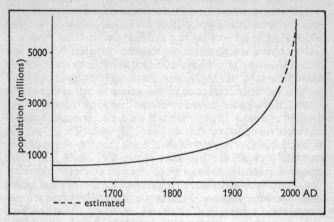

Figure 128. World population

In Britain and other countries with an advanced economy the death rate fell slowly. Underdeveloped countries now able to take advantage of new methods for the control of diseases, particularly those which are insect transmitted, have experienced a rapid fall in the death rate. In the 1950s the World Health Organisation mounted a campaign against malaria in Guyana, the malaria carrying mosquito was eliminated and in the next ten years the population of Guyana rose from 5 millions to 10 millions. The underdeveloped countries have also maintained a high birth rate while the industrialized countries are slowly recognizing the need for population control. In very general terms it seems that the present increase in population is due primarily to the falling death rate leaving a population of increasing average age.

Can education bridge the gap and bring awareness of the problems and the will to solve them voluntarily or will regulation of the population come about as the result of famine, disease and war?

The effect on the environment of increasing population

Man, the most intelligent of the animals has been very successful in exploiting the resources of the Earth for his own use, in the process he has often lost sight of the fact that he is one of a number of animal species and that in the long term his own survival depends on maintaining the stability of the environment. He cannot afford to regard himself as a superior being not subject to the natural laws which regulate other living organisms. From Neolithic times man has wrought a change in the environment, one greatly accelerated since the advent of industrialized man. While man lived in small nomadic groups, hunting, fishing, gathering fruits, nuts and birds' eggs he did little damage to the environment, but as soon as he formed more settled communities and began to change to crop growing and stock raising the attack on the environment began. It is possible to speculate what may have happened. The ground had to be cleared for crop growing which will probably have involved tree felling or clearing by means of fire. Fire would drive away dangerous animals and be an aid to capturing others for domestication, it could also contribute to soil erosion. Growth of the same few crops year after year would lead to loss of soil fertility, and the concentration of a few species of plants in an area would attract pests and enable them to spread rapidly. Stock confined to small areas would overgraze it, trampling and breaking up the ground encouraging soil erosion. The environment would cope with the relatively small amount of human waste but the collecting together of larger numbers of people would increase the risk of disease and the spread of parasites. The early agricultural practices would decrease the likelihood of starvation but may well have resulted in a less varied diet, leading perhaps to some deficiency diseases. With loss of soil fertility and soil erosion a community would move on, the small area of devastated land left behind would recover naturally in time.

The changes brought about by industrialized man are not so easily put right. They may be considered in three groups which of course are interrelated.

1. The exploitation of the environment involving the use of irreplaceable resources such as **fossil fuels** and **minerals** without regard to the future, together with the use of such materials as timber and many types of animal products, furs, hides, whale meat and oil, without adequate limits being observed to ensure **conservation of the stocks.**
2. The **destruction** of the natural environment itself to provide more living space, agricultural land and all the many facilities expected by modern man.
3. **Pollution** of the environment by industrial wastes, excess fer-

tilizers and pesticides, non-biodegradable products, or the disposal of organic wastes in quantities which exceed the natural capacity of the environment to recycle.

The use of natural resources

What will replace oil, natural gas and coal as sources of energy when they become exhausted? We are likely to be able to use atomic energy for a long period but it presents grave problems in the disposal of radioactive waste. It has just been announced in Britain (June 1978), that more money is to be available for research on alternative forms of energy. Can solar energy, or energy provided by the tides or winds ever supply the amount of energy required by industrialized man, or will industrialized man become deindustrialized man? Mineral stocks are becoming depleted, the rising cost of metals reflects to some extent the fact that increasingly inaccessible deposits are being mined. Good sources of phosphates used for fertilizer are dwindling. It is in the realms of possibility to produce a policy to conserve replaceable resources. Man has found so many uses for timber that forests are disappearing at an alarming rate, far faster than they are being regenerated or could be replaced. The oceans are being overfished with no clear policy for maintaining the stocks.

The destruction of the environment

The increasing population makes great demands on the land for dwellings and for crop growing and stock raising. As communities rise above a primitive level increasing areas of land become utilized, firstly for, perhaps, roads and markets, leading eventually to industrialized man who is found in what has been aptly described as the 'concrete jungle', consisting of housing developments with their associated shops, schools and hospitals; factories and offices; reservoirs, power stations and sewage farms; roads, railways and airports. There has been a movement away from mixed farming to specialized farming, small fields have been incorporated into larger ones as mechanization has increased, and trees and hedges have been destroyed in the process. As industrial expansion took place in Victorian England and large tracts of land disappeared with the spread of towns and the various mining activities, and slag heaps and waste tips appeared, it also gave rise to some concern for the environment expressed by the formation of the National Trust in 1895, by the demand for better housing schemes and later to the Town and Country Planning Act which placed planning under the control of central and local government. In general, public opinion although slow to find expression is ahead of government action. A

Minister for the Environment was not appointed until 1969.

Land pollution

Large acreages of land near densely populated areas have become wasteland as a result of the dumping of wastes from industrial activities. Heaps of shale and waste known as **spoil heaps** from coal mining not only deface the countryside but can be a source of danger, as was shown in 1966 when a large sodden spoil heap collapsed engulfing and killing 144 people in the village of Aberfan, South Wales. Little research appears to have been carried out on the stability of such heaps in relation to, for example, water content, ground slope and nature of the subsoil. Electricity generating plants, the majority of which use coal as a source of heat energy, produce a fine **ash** as a waste product, the total amount probably being of the order of 15 million tons a year in Britain; this ash is alkaline, having a minimum pH of 8·5 and a boron content fifteen times that of most soils, a condition highly toxic to most plants. The industry has endeavoured to dispose of this material in a responsible manner; attempts have been made to use it in agriculture with limited success although some plants, such as certain species of clover and rye, will tolerate the conditions it provides. More successful has been its use in the building industry where it has been used as a building material in road and runway construction and in filling-in unwanted pits.

The quantity of **domestic refuse** is increasing all the time and its disposal presents growing difficulties. Much of the increase is due to the rising consumption of processed and pre-packed foods and canned and bottled drinks of all kinds which leave a residue of tins, packets, and containers of plastic and glass, and to the increased use of a variety of cleaning products similarly packaged. Much domestic refuse is used for filling in pits or for depositing on marshy land as a first step in land reclamation, but it is becoming increasingly necessary to build special plant for its disposal. In some more modern plants the process is almost entirely mechanized, the refuse being burned in special self-cleaning furnaces, residue passing along a conveyor system where electromagnets remove ferrous metals, before the remainder is transported away to use for road building. The heat produced in the process may be utilized in a variety of ways to offset running costs. A large part of our refuse and litter problem comes from the non-returnable container. Glass and plastic are not only non-biodegradable, that is they are not decomposed by natural processes remaining an eyesore and a source of danger in the environment, but they also use up valuable resources. Some new refuse plants pulverize organic matter for soil improvement.

A different kind of land pollution comes from the use in agriculture and horticulture of various **pesticides, herbicides** and **fungicides**. DDT was the forerunner of modern pesticides, early results from its use were spectacular, but soon its poisonous effects on wildlife became evident and later strains of pests **resistant** to DDT began to be reported. The variety of pesticides available now is partly due to the fact that as pests evolve resistant strains so man has to change his formulations to deal with them. We now know that pesticides of the organo-chloride type, of which DDT was the first, become incorporated into food chains and because they are not metabolized they accumulate in tissues, becoming more concentrated at each stage of the food chain. In Britain in 1960 it was reported that DDT had caused the death of many small birds and it was found in the tissues of larger birds of prey and in their eggs where it affected fertility. It is known to pass through other food chains including some involving fish so that it is a danger to a wide variety of organisms and a potential danger to man. Fortunately its use is now banned in Britain and in the U.S.A.

The use of any pesticides, herbicides and fungicides upsets the balance of nature and could have far-reaching consequences. This is not surprising when it is realized that up to one million invertebrates may be found in the top soil of a square metre of land, and that they are linked nutritionally, not only with one another, but with organisms outside. More information is needed particularly about fluctuating numbers of various species to help to resolve the conflicting interests of agriculturists and conservationists. Even in soils not subjected to chemical treatments there are known to be quite wide fluctuations in the population of various invertebrates from year to year and from season to season.

Water pollution

Streams and rivers have always been regarded as a convenient way of disposing of waste on the principle of 'out of sight, out of mind'. When man began to collect together in larger communities, **sewage**, which hitherto had been broken down by soil organisms or swept harmlessly away in rivers and streams, began by reason of the quantity to give rise to problems. Industrialized man added **factory effluents** to waterways, often with a content of poisonous material as well as organic matter. In his efforts to produce more food to feed a rising population he resorted to the use of pesticides, herbicides and fungicides, some of which was washed from the soil. Even the use of water for such apparently harmless purposes as the cooling of machinery can give rise to problems.

When sewage contamination is slight bacteria and fungi in the water break it down into simple inorganic compounds, carbon dioxide, water, nitrates, sulphates and so on. All these compounds contain oxygen as part of their chemical structure, and provided the water is well aerated decomposition is complete and the river cleans itself as it flows along. With a greater degree of sewage contamination the oxygen content of the water falls rapidly to a point where if the contamination is too great, all the oxygen is used up. Decomposition of the sewage does not stop at this point but continues anaerobically with the production of unpleasant smelling gases such as ammonia and hydrogen sulphide. The lack of oxygen in the water will result in the death of most living organisms, their bodies undergoing similar anaerobic decomposition. In severe cases, banks of evil-smelling sludge accumulate along the lifeless and dirty river.

Other forms of organic matter may reach the river from such places as breweries, slaughter houses, textile factories and intensive farm units which often have too little land to enable them to make use of the manure. Even greater problems are created by industries which discharge poisonous effluent, for example, plating works where the waste may contain metal salts and acids, or tanneries where in addition to organic matter, chromium salts may be discharged, or the waste from gas works with ammonia and tar acids, as well as the variety of chemicals which may find their way into waterways from chemical works. The presence of many different chemical substances in the water means that living organisms are exposed to chemicals which may react together to produce more lethal compounds. Heavy metal salts attack the gills of fish and a concentration of one part of lead in a million is poisonous to fish, trout and salmon being particularly susceptible to heavy metal contamination. Other dangerous materials reaching waterways are mercury compounds, widely used in seed dressings, and various pesticides particularly of the organo-chloride type (see page 297).

Thermal pollution, that is the raising of the temperature of the water as occurs when water is withdrawn from the river for cooling purposes during some industrial process, is another source of difficulty. A medium sized power station will require about 50 million gallons of water per hour. Since 1939 the average temperature of the water in the lower reaches of the Thames has risen 4°C. Considering only the effects of thermal pollution, the rise in temperature of the water in any river is likely to bring about a change in the flora and fauna, and perhaps to have an effect upon physiological processes. Fish show wide differences in temperature toleration, trout eggs for example, fail to hatch if the temperature rises above about 14°C. Some species of plants and animals which normally inhabit warmer waters have established themselves near outfalls of warm water; one is *Vallisneria* a plant grown in tropical aquaria, shrimps are on the increase in some regions, and the ship worm *Teredo* which causes much damage to timbers is said to be increasing. In theory with the rise in temperature some deoxygenation should occur, in practice this has not proved to be a problem as water is returned from the power stations supersaturated with oxygen.

Once a river has become lifeless recovery is a slow and expensive process. One river which has been rehabilitated is the Thames. In the early years of last century increasing quantities of sewage poured into it while at the same time it was a source of drinking water with the result that in 1832 7,000 people died of cholera, the connection between cholera and sewage contaminated water not being appreciated until 40,000 people had lost their lives. Sewage still continued to be poured into the Thames until in Disraeli's time the smell was so bad that it drove MPs out of Parliament. Trunk sewers were constructed but raw and partly treated sewage continued to be discharged into the Thames lower down, and as industrialization spread, factory effluents added to the contamination so that by 1947 a seven mile stretch in the lower reaches of the river contained no oxygen at all. Since 1960 two costly new sewage works have been built and gradually the oxygen level in the water has risen until in 1977 it reached 94% saturation at Westminster Bridge. As the oxygen content has risen so life has returned, 41 different species of fish having been recorded in the tidal region up to 1977. In the higher reaches freshwater shrimps have returned and brought back the shoveler duck which feeds upon them. Many species of birds visit the cleaner mud in search of food and the number of mute swans has increased.

The amount of organic matter in water is determined by the **biochemical oxygen demand (BOD)**, based on a test measuring the oxygen absorbing capacity of the sample. Where the pollution is greater more oxygen will be absorbed. In a seriously contaminated river the BOD will always be high because there will be no chance of recovery before further contamination occurs. Such heavily polluted water will contain only bacteria, sewage fungus and perhaps *Tubifex* worms which will tolerate oxygen deficient conditions. The fish most resistant to pollution is the eel and the most sensitive, the trout. There is little likelihood of contamination where the trout thrives.

Excess fertilizers washed from agricultural land into lakes and waterways cause problems as they give rise to abundant growth of algae. Only the top layer of the algae receives sufficient light for photosynthesis, the remainder underneath dying and consuming large quantities of oxygen as it decays, the oxygen deficiency may then cause the death of other organisms. The increasing **nitrate** content of water is causing concern to some water authorities, it can give rise to growth of algae in reservoirs and it can cause a disease known as methaemoglobin anaemia in babies, so that one authority at least is distributing specially purified water to mothers of young babies.

After the 1939 to 1945 war the use of soapless **detergents** became widespread, the early products were not broken down in the sewage works and therefore were discharged into the river with the effluent causing banks of foam and floating masses which became known as 'swans'. Bio-degradable detergents were introduced in the mid 1960s and solved the foaming problem, but the high **phosphate** content common to both types contributes to the problem of excessive growth of algae.

Another hazard has arisen in recent years from the increased use of **oil**. In the world as a whole there is an average of almost two serious accidents to tankers each week. In 1967 the tanker Torrey Canyon was wrecked off Land's End spilling 60,000 tons of crude oil from Kuwait which polluted beaches in south-west England, Wales and France, causing the death of large numbers of sea birds and other marine and seashore organisms, and loss of amenity due to contaminated beaches. It has now been realized that the two million gallons of various detergents used to disperse the oil caused further damage to marine life. Since then there have been other minor disasters affecting the British coasts. Early in 1978 wrecking of the Amoco Cadiz off Brittany caused a spillage of 200,000 tons of oil which seriously polluted beaches in Brittany. Given different weather conditions it could well have affected British shores also. Super oil tankers mean super spillages and progress in coping with these disasters and finding more efficient ways of clearing the oil seems very slow.

Air pollution

Pollution of the air is one of the problems brought about by industrialized man. In London in 1952, pollution caused five days of 'smog', a mixture of fog, smoke and gases which drastically reduced visibility and contributed to the death of 4,000 people, mainly older men and women in poor health, but at the same time it also killed champions of the Smithfield Cattle Show presumably in prime condition. The Beaver Report on Air Pollution (1954), stated the major air pollutants to be **smoke, carbon monoxide, sulphur dioxide, grit** and **hydrochloric, sulphuric and nitric acids**. It estimated the damage caused to crops to be £10 million. New Acts, the Clean Air Act 1956 and the 1960 Act were aimed at bringing about a reduction in the level of these pollutants. 90% of the Greater London area is now covered by smoke control orders enforcing the use of smokeless fuel, this has resulted in an increase of 70% in the amount of sunshine getting through in the winter. In England and Wales as a whole smoke concentration has been reduced by about 85%. The screening of sunlight by smoky air reduces the amount of photosynthesis and the synthesis of vitamin D by the skin. Smoke, dust and acid gases aggravate respiratory diseases and the solid particles cause pathological lung conditions in man and animals. The particles contain a variety of chemical substances some of which are carcinogens; there is strong evidence to suggest that lung cancer not directly connected with smoking is very much higher in towns than in the country.

Los Angeles first reported a new kind of air pollution in 1946 which came to be known as **petrochemical smog**; it is associated with high petrol consumption, a low level of sulphur dioxide, and sunlight; it reduces visibility, produces a characteristic odour and contains chemical substances produced by the action of ultraviolet light on other pollutants which are extremely irritating to the eyes and mucous membranes. The absence of this in London, even in the summer, could well be due to the higher sulphur dioxide level.

Grit and smoke in the air cause a deposit on the leaves of plants blocking the stomata and reducing photosynthesis. Plants with rough and hairy leaves have a low survival rate as the leaves act as traps for particles, plants with smooth leathery leaves grow better as rain washes off the accumulated deposit. Sulphur dioxide in the air results in the rain being acid; if the concentration rises above about 40 ppm of sulphuric acid, it has a retarding effect on growth. The increase in the acidity of the soil interferes with bacterial activity and reduces soil fertility, in turn this results in plants with smaller

301

than average leaves, giving less surface for photosynthesis. Areas around ore-smelting plants which produce sulphur dioxide have infertile soil carrying a poor vegetation prone to soil erosion. Sulphur dioxide entering the stomata dissolves on moist surfaces and reacts to form sulphites which can poison the plant. Plants vary in their degree of resistance to sulphur dioxide, barley and alfalfa being two of the easiest to grow. Lichens very quickly disappear when the air is polluted, the slightest trace of sulphur dioxide in the air will cause some species of *Usnea* to die, other lichens being slightly more resistant. A lichen hunt in a particular area will soon give a good idea of the purity of the air.

The heavy concentration of smoke and acid fumes in air over London and elsewhere in the past, caused blackened buildings with corroded stonework. Not until the buildings were cleaned down was the extent of the damage revealed.

Pollution by radioactive materials

The long term effects of radioactive fall out products from atomic or thermonuclear explosions are unknown, as are the effects of an accident at a nuclear power station. These matters of vital concern to us all remain a matter of controversy. Britain is already the largest producer of atomic power and recently further controversy arose over the type of reactor to be used in new power stations and whether or not Britain should undertake the reprocessing of reactor fuels for other countries.

During the chain reactions of nuclear reactors or nuclear weapons the uranium atoms undergo fission, that is splitting, releasing energy and leaving radioactive fission products. These fission products include **strontium 90** which becomes incorporated into food chains. High energy nuclear particles produced by reactors or weapons can activate materials they encounter and give rise to other radioactive isotopes such as those of carbon or iron. These isotopes together with fission products are discharged over the Earth eventually coming down to ground with rain or snow as the radioactive fall out. Strontium 90 with a half-life of 28 years is a common fission product and constituent of radioactive fall-out; plants absorb it as they would calcium, and animals and man feeding on the vegetation accumulate it in bone near the bone marrow which can be readily damaged by radiation. There has been a rising concentration of strontium 90 in the bones of children since 1945, which is a cause for concern. The waste solutions from the chemical reprocessing of used reactor fuels are highly radioactive and are evaporated and stored in steel containers. Less active waste solutions are treated and discharged at sea. Radioactive solids may be packed in special containers and dumped in deep parts of the ocean.

Pollution by noise

The latest type of pollution to be recognized is that produced by noise. We live in an increasingly noisy world of machines, traffic, aircraft and radios, which can not only cause distress but has been shown to impair hearing, particularly in the higher frequency ranges. Temporary impairment of hearing has been demonstrated in children after exposure to noise such as too loud discos.

The control of disease in humans

Disease in the widest sense, that is a morbid condition of the body, may be caused by living organisms; **bacteria, protozoa, fungi, viruses,** a variety of invertebrates living as **ecto** or **endoparasites** or to **faulty diet,** hazards associated with **occupation, allergies, polluted air, radioactivity** or **genetical defects**. Those caused by living organisms may be spread in a number of ways, by **direct contact, droplet infection, contaminated food or water,** or by a **vector,** that is an animal transmitting disease-causing organisms directly from one person to another. Among diseases which can be spread directly are the sexually transmitted bacterial diseases syphilis and gonorrhoea. The common cold and influenza, both caused by viruses are spread by droplet infection, sneezing and coughing causing the projection into the air of minute droplets of moisture bearing vast numbers of virus particles which remain suspended in the air for long periods and may be breathed in by others. Cholera and typhoid are spread by water which has been polluted by faeces containing these bacteria. Typhoid and various types of food poisoning such as that caused by Salmonella bacteria may develop after eating contaminated food, usually the result of handling under unhygienic conditions or by exposure to flies which may carry all kinds of bacteria, viruses and eggs of parasitic worms. Malaria caused by the protozoan, *Plasmodium*, is transmitted by the female *Anopheles* mosquito in which it undergoes a number of stages in the life cycle. The black death, bubonic plague, caused by the bacterium *Pasteurella pestis*, also lives in black rats and is carried by rat fleas between rats, from rats to man or from man to man. Knowledge of the cause of a disease and its mode of transmission is an important step towards its control, although not always an essential one as was shown by Sammelweiss in Vienna in 1846 when he reduced the death rate from puerperal fever in his hospital, from 7% to 1% by washing his hands and rinsing them in chlorinated lime between visits to individual patients.

Some of the more important factors which bring about increasing freedom from disease are, raising the standard of **personal and domestic hygiene** and the standard of **hygiene in all places concerned with food handling**, the **control of disease carrying organisms** such as rats, mice, fleas, lice, flies, mosquitos and so on, the provision of an adequate supply of **clean water**, a proper **sewage disposal system** and **immunization** against specific diseases. Also important is the prompt treatment of disease and the taking of steps when necessary to prevent its spread among the population; for example, a person with a serious infectious disease may have to be isolated, and contacts traced and immunized.

Before 1939 malaria contributed to half the total deaths in the world as a whole, and it is still a major cause of illness and death in some parts of the world. The female *Anopheles* lays her eggs singly in still water and both the larvae and the pupae are aquatic. Effective control measures mean a massive effort over a wide area. Standing water is drained or oil sprayed on to the surface which prevents the larvae and pupae from obtaining oxygen, or insecticides may be sprayed on to the water. The minnow *Gambusia affinis* has been introduced into pools to eat the aquatic stages. Houses are sprayed and screened and the use of mosquito nets helps to protect the sleeper. A number of drugs are in use against different species of *Plasmodium*, some attacking the parasite at different stages. So far, within about ten years of the introduction of a new drug cases of resistant parasites have been reported, an example of natural selection, in this case for resistance to a particular drug. The use of DDT brought about dramatic results in the control of the malaria carrying mosquito and it was virtually cleared from a number of areas including the Mediterranean, now it is creeping back and all travellers need to make enquiries about the possible hazards from malaria and other diseases when travelling abroad, and to take appropriate action. Immunization is an effective protection against many bacterial and virus diseases (see page 145). New strains of influenza virus arise from time to time so that immunization is less effective, the disease can arise in a virulent form as in 1918 to 1919 when it caused the death of an estimated 20 million people. The effectiveness of immunization against such

diseases as smallpox, diptheria and poliomyelitis has been shown by
the fact that they have been almost eliminated in Britain.

Water supply

Britain relies solely on rainfall for a source of water, some is
pumped up from **rivers,** some collected from **run-off** into reservoirs and the remainder drawn from **bore holes** drilled down to
reach water percolated through to collect on impervious rock.
Rising population and improved standards of hygiene have increased the demand for water which now averages about 170 dm^3
per person per day. The selection of sites for reservoirs is usually
controversial, in any case it is an inefficient method of storing water
owing to the high rate of loss from evaporation. If more water is to
be pumped from rivers, a higher standard of purity in the effluent
from sewage works will have to be demanded. Britain may be
obliged eventually to construct costly **desalination** plant for the
purification of sea water.

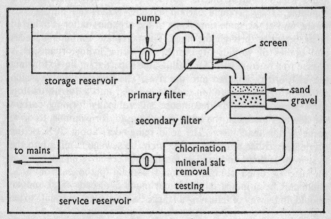

Figure 129. The layout of a waterworks

In the process of purification of water it is pumped from a **storage
reservoir** to a **primary filter** to remove larger particles, then
through a **secondary filter** consisting of sand and gravel which
removes finer particles. Next the water is **chlorinated** to kill
bacteria and if the mineral content is high it may also receive
further treatment. From the chlorination plant it is pumped to **service reservoirs** and from there to the **water mains.**

In Britain there is no doubt that crop yields could be increased by irrigation during dry periods when vigorous growth should be taking place.

Sewage treatment

Percolating filter process

Crude sewage passes through a **grit chamber** where sand settles out, and is pumped through a **screen** to break up solids before it passes to a **sedimentation tank** where solid matter collects at the bottom as **sludge.** The supernatant liquid passes on to issue from a sprinkler and percolate through a **filter** composed of stones of 4 to 6 cm diameter, which become covered by a gelatinous film of fungi, bacteria and other micro-organisms together with fine particles of sewage. Living in this material well supplied with food and oxygen are nematode worms, annelids and all stages of insect life. The living organisms form a variety of trophic relationships based on the organic food in the sewage and on the green and blue-green algae which flourish on the surface of the filter where light is available. They produce carbon dioxide, water and nitrogenous waste, and at the same time some of the organic matter is oxidized in its progress through the filter. The percolate containing faeces and bodies of various organisms, and some living organisms is passed to a **humus tank** for settling, the supernatant liquid forming the **effluent** discharged into the river. The primary sludge which settles in the sedimentation tank is pumped into a **fermentation tank** where the solids decompose anaerobically forming carbon dioxide and methane, the latter may be used, for example, to drive some of the machinery. The solid remainder, about 30% of the original, is either returned to mix with the sewage coming into the system or is dried and used as fertilizer. There are some dangers in the use of dried sludge, it could contain pathogens or toxic chemicals from industrial waste but much is already used and we should find a way of returning all these essential plant nutrients to the soil.

Activated sludge process

The activated sludge process was first introduced in Manchester in 1914 and is now in use in most of the large towns in the country. It takes up less space than the percolating filter process and avoids the fly problem associated with the exposed filters. The two processes are similar at the beginning, the sewage passes through a grit chamber and a screen to a sedimentation tank. In the activated sludge process it stands for six hours before passing to an **aeration**

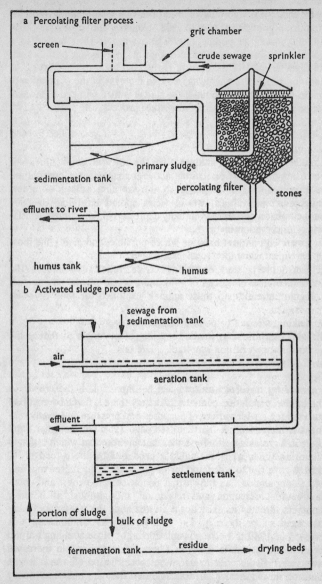

Figure 130. Two processes for the disposal of sewage

tank where it is vigorously stirred or has air blown into it. With the rich supply of food and oxygen, bacteria and protozoa thrive building up large populations. The sewage is then passed to a **settlement tank** where micro-organisms and sewage particles settle together, part of the **sludge** is then fed back to the start of the aeration process to encourage a rapid increase in the population of micro-organisms. The bulk of the sludge is then pumped to fermentation tanks as in the percolating filter process.

Conservation

Conservation means maintaining the natural environment, if necessary by means of sensible active management. Conservation in Britain arose in response to the warning voices of a few enlightened individuals, whose views spread until they became public opinion and were eventually expressed in government legislation. Conservation involves,

1. Preserving natural habitats where possible, and giving the most careful consideration to all uses of land.
2. Formulating and observing strict policies to ensure the maintenance of stocks of wild animals and plants, paying particular attention to those animals exploited for food or other products.
3. Taking care not to pollute land, water or air.
4. Directing attention to the recycling of materials to reduce the consumption of non-renewable materials.
5. Controlling the growth of human population.

Preserving natural habitats will be impossible if the growth in the human population continues. Already there is fierce competition for land for a wide variety of purposes and pressure on the environment is increasing all the time (see page 295). On the other hand there is a growing desire for a pleasant environment which began in Victorian times when the squalor produced by the spread of industry gave rise to a demand for better housing. Increased mobility of the population has shown that people seek the coast and countryside for recreation and relaxation and although their sheer numbers threaten its existence it affords hope that they may be encouraged to preserve it. The National Parks Commission was created in 1949 to be responsible for areas of outstanding natural beauty and scientific interest. There is on the whole increased awareness of the need to carry out construction of, for example, housing developments and roads so that they are not aesthetically displeasing.

Man has been responsible for the **extinction** of many animals and plants, and many more have been brought to within danger of extinction. Millions of bison once roamed the plains of North America and in less than twenty years in the last century they were reduced to very low numbers. The American passenger pigeon which once existed in huge numbers is now extinct. The koala bear was hunted almost to extinction, over one million pelts being exported from Australia in one year alone. The orang-utan is one of the many animals in danger. These animals have not been killed principally for food, but for sport and human vanity. With care and knowledge of the biology of a species, natural animal populations may be cropped; in Scotland about 14% of the red deer population is culled each year and about a third of the deer in Forestry Commission land in England. Whaling has resulted in the severe **depletion of stocks** of the humpback whale, blue whale, fin whale and other species. The International Whaling Commission was established in 1964 to control whaling and prevent extinction of the species, quotas were recommended but commercial interests made agreement difficult. The seas around Britain and elsewhere are being **overfished**, this is shown by the reduction in the catch and by the age and size of the individual fish within it. Some international agreement has been reached for some fish but it does not include the herring, the catch of this fish has declined drastically since 1965. Agreement between nations is urgently needed to prevent over exploitation of the productivity of the sea, which is likely to become an increasingly important source of food if the population continues to rise.

There have been encouraging signs of concern for our wildlife. The Protection of Birds Act (1954), makes it an offence to interfere with wild birds or to collect their eggs. Nature reserves have been established, for example, Havergate Island off Orfordness in Suffolk where the rare avocets breed, Monk's Wood in Huntingdonshire which has a very fine insect fauna, the Gower coast in Glamorgan with rare limestone plants and breeding sea birds. When an animal population falls below a certain critical level it becomes doomed to extinction as the individuals are too spread out to meet to breed, under these conditions man can try to conserve the species by capturing a few animals and transferring them to a zoo to breed in captivity. The Arabian oryx was saved in this way by being bred in captivity in Arizona which has a similar climate to its native environment.

The problem of **pollution** has been mentioned (see pages 296 to

303). With the rising consumption of material goods of all kinds and the increase in the use of disposable packaging (i.e. non-disposable in the biological sense for they are not decomposed), it should not be beyond the ingenuity of man to **recycle** the materials to prevent litter and conserve valuable natural resources.

The single most important factor in conservation is the **control of population growth**. Thomas Malthus in his essay on population in 1798 pointed out that population would outstrip food production. So far this has been offset by man moving into less populated areas, and by increased crop yields due to specially bred varieties of plants, use of fertilizers and pesticides, and increased mechanization in agriculture. However, the increased food production encourages population growth, an example of positive feedback, and sooner or later a balance must be reached. At present the highly developed nations tend to overeat while the underdeveloped countries suffer large numbers of people dying from starvation and malnutrition, a problem which will not be solved by food distribution. In the animal world natural laws operate to control numbers and to space out members of a species: fighting is normally a ritual, little physical damage being sustained. Little is known about the behaviour of people when forced into more and more crowded communities. Even war has had little effect on population size, but future wars with their appalling prospect of nuclear and biological warfare would be likely to do so. Population control by voluntary means instead of war is a practical possibility, as has been shown by Japan since 1945. Legislation in 1948 permitted sterilization and abortion, contraceptive practice is well established and there is a fall in population.

In Britain an average of 2·2 children per family will maintain a stable population in a country already overcrowded; at present it has not fallen to this figure. The Royal Commission on Population (1949) thought a large population increase to be undesirable but that there were good economic reasons for encouraging a higher birth rate. This resulted in a scheme of family allowances for all children after the first. While larger families have financial assistance in this and other forms, any attempt to popularize population control are likely to be offset. The National Health Service (Family Planning) Act (1967) was aimed at encouraging local authorities to provide advice on contraception, and the Abortion Act was introduced in the same year. Two years later Regional Hospital Boards were asked to give advice on family planning, and in 1974 free supplies of contraceptives became available under the

National Health Service. There is as yet insufficient awareness of the problem of increasing population and perhaps of the family planning services available. Television commercials relating to family planning were banned until 1970.

Key terms

Biochemical oxygen demand (BOD) A measure of the oxygen absorbing capacity of a sample of water indicating the degree of pollution.

Biotic factors Environmental influences that arise by the activities of living organisms.

Conservation Maintenance of the natural environment, if necessary by sensible active management.

Edaphic factors Environmental conditions determined by the physical, chemical and biological characteristics of soil.

Leaching The washing out of mineral salts from soil by rain.

Soil profile The superimposed layers of soil visible in a vertical section.

Vector An animal, most frequently an insect, transmitting disease organisms from one animal to another or one plant to another.

Questions

1. Insects are a highly successful group biologically. Discuss the reasons for this success.
2. Write an essay on the economic importance of fungi.
3. Assign the following organisms to their correct systematic position and discuss the ecological relationship between any three of them; earthworm, garden snail, clover plant, thrush, honey bee, *Rhizobium*.
4. What are the factors influencing the rate of enzyme reactions? Describe an experiment to investigate the effect of one of these factors in a named enzyme reaction.
5. Write a simple account of the chemistry of carbohydrates. What is their importance to living organisms?
6. Draw a diagram of a simple animal cell. In what ways do the following cells differ from it, a) a sensory neurone b) a red blood cell c) an unstriated muscle cell d) a bone cell e) a sperm cell?
7. Write an illustrated account of cell organelles.
8. What are the characteristic features of parasites? Illustrate your answer by reference to one *named* animal parasite and one *named* plant parasite.
9. What is the importance of iron, calcium, iodine and phosphorus in the diet of a mammal?
10. Survey the range of feeding mechanisms in the invertebrates.
11. Describe in general terms the process of photosynthesis. In what other ways are plants influenced by light?
12. Briefly describe the successive stages in the aerobic respiration of green plants.
13. In terms of the amount of energy obtained aerobic respiration is much more efficient than anaerobic. How would you account for this?
14. Discuss the role of haemoglobin in the blood of a mammal. In what way is it affected by an increasing concentration of carbon dioxide?
15. Describe the structure of xylem and phloem in a flowering plant. What evidence is there that these tissues form the major transport system of the plant?
16. Distinguish between excretion and osmoregulation. Describe how these processes are carried out in a mammal.
17. Account for the differences in composition of the blood in the renal artery and renal vein of a mammal.

18. Describe the structure and function of a mammalian kidney tubule. Kidney tubules with a long loop of Henlé are found in desert mammals. How may this be related to their way of life?

19. What is homeostasis? Give an account of three homeostatic mechanisms in man.

20. Describe the organisation of the nervous system in a mammal. In what ways are the nervous system and the endocrine system complementary?

21. Compare and contrast the structure and function of xylem and phloem in a herbaceous dicotyledon.

22. Discuss the role of auxins in flowering plants. Distinguish between tropisms and nastic movements, kinesis and taxis.

23. Write an essay on the importance of water to living organisms.

24. What problems were faced by living organisms when they left water to colonize the land? How were these problems overcome?

25. A mammal eats a protein food containing an amino acid labelled with a radioactive isotope of nitrogen. Trace the progress of this radioactive isotope in the body until it appears in the urine.

26. What are the major differences between mitosis and meiosis? What is the significance of these differences? When does meiosis occur in the life cycle of a liverwort, a flowering plant and a mammal?

27. What are the differences between asexual and sexual reporduction. What are the advantages and disadvantages of each?

28. What are the factors influencing the rate of growth of an organism? In what ways does the growth of a mammal differ from a) an insect b) a seaweed?

29. Describe the pollination mechanism in a *named* flowering plant. Trace the development of the pollen grain and embryo sac up to the time of fertilization.

30. What conditions are necessary for seed germination? What processes take place when a seed germinates? A large batch of seeds were allowed to germinate and an equal number removed daily for fourteen days and their dry mass determined. Draw a diagram to illustrate the graph you might expect to obtain by plotting dry mass against time.

31. Discuss the role of nucleic acids in the synthesis of proteins in a living cell.

32. What is meant by a) a multiple allele b) a lethal gene c) sex linkage d) polyploidy e) continuous variation?

33. In what ways could our knowledge of the inheritance of blood groups be used to help to decide a case where paternity is disputed?

34. In Leghorn poultry pea comb (P) is dominant over single comb (p) and white plumage (W) over coloured (w). Four birds, two male and two female all with pea comb and white plumage, are interbred. Male A with female C produces offspring with pea comb and white plumage. Male A with female D produces offspring with pea comb and white plumage. Male B with female C produces offspring with pea comb, some with white plumage and some with coloured. Male B with female D produces offspring with white plumage, some with pea comb and some with single. What is the genotype of each parent bird?

35. What is the importance of variation, natural selection and mutation in the evolution of new species?

36. What evidence is there in addition to fossil evidence, that evolution has taken place?

37. What new evidence for evolution has come to light since the time of Charles Darwin?

38. Give an account of the methods you have used in an ecological study of a *named* area.

39. Comment on the distribution of any *named* organism you have studied in the field. What factors have been found to influence its distribution?

40. Name a disease of man caused by a) a bacterium b) a virus c) a fungus d) a protozoan. What general measures are important in the prevention of the spread of disease? Discuss one measure in detail.

41. How are the properties of soil related to the particle size? What are the constituents of good agricultural soil? Discuss the importance of each.

42. A completely new island arises in the ocean as a result of volcanic activity. Discuss how it might become colonized by living organisms.

43. Write an essay on the importance of physical and chemical methods in biology.

44. How would you carry out a simple analysis of a sample of soil for water and humus content, pH and presence of carbonates?

45. Explain why a knowledge of the life cycle of a disease-causing organism is important for the effective control of the disease.

46. In what ways has biological knowledge been of assistance in increasing food production?

47. Write an essay on the importance to human society of the study of biology.

Index

Other study aids in the **keyfacts** series

KEY FACTS CARDS

Latin	English History (1815–1914)
Julius Caesar	English History (1914–1946)
New Testament	Chemistry
German	Physics
Macbeth	Biology
Geography Regional	Geometry
English Comprehension	Geography
English Language	French
Economics	Arithmetic & Trigonometry
Elementary Mathematics	General Science
Algebra	Additional Mathematics
Modern Mathematics	Technical Drawing

KEY FACTS COURSE COMPANIONS

Economics	Geography
Modern Mathematics	French
Algebra	Physics
Geometry	Chemistry
Arithmetic &	English
Trigonometry	Biology
Additional Mathematics	

KEY FACTS A-LEVEL BOOKS

Chemistry	Pure Mathematics
Biology	Physics

KEY FACTS O-LEVEL PASSBOOKS

Modern Mathematics	Physics
English History	Geography
(1815–1939)	French
Biology	English
Chemistry	Economics

KEY FACTS O-LEVEL MODEL ANSWERS

Modern Mathematics	Physics
English History	Geography
(1815–1939)	French
Biology	English
Chemistry	

KEY FACTS REFERENCE LIBRARY

O-Level Trad. & Mod. Mathematics	O-Level Biology
O-Level History (1815–1914)	O-Level Physics
O-Level Geography	O-Level Chemistry

KEY FACTS A-LEVEL PASSBOOKS

Physics	Chemistry
Biology	Pure Mathematics
Geography	Pure & Applied Mathematics
Economics	Applied Mathematics